D1462544

STRESS-RUPTURE PARAMETERS: ORIGIN, CALCULATION AND USE

STRESS-RUPTURE PARAMETERS: ORIGIN, CALCULATION AND USE

by J. B. CONWAY

Nuclear Systems Programs
Missile and Space Division
General Electric Company, Cincinnati, Ohio

GORDON AND BREACH, SCIENCE PUBLISHERS
New York London Paris

150 Fifth Avenue, New York, N.Y. 10011

Library of Congress Catalog Card Number: 68-8276

Editorial office for Great Britain:
Gordon and Breach, Science Publishers Ltd.
8 Bloomsbury Way
London W.C.1

Editorial office for France:
Gordon & Breach
7-9 rue Emile Dubois
Paris 14e

Distributed in Canada by:
The Ryerson Press
299 Queen Street West
Toronto 2B, Ontario

(0186)

Printed in the United States of America

PREFACE

Much has been written on the subject of stress-rupture parameters. These writings began in 1952 which can be considered as the year in which a new concept was introduced into the analysis and correlation of stress-rupture data. Initially, of course, all the attention was focused on the identification and development of these functional relationships. As this was accomplished, and various different parameters were conceived and proven to have merit in defining general relationships between stress, temperature and rupture life (and at times minimum or steady state creep rate), appropriate emphasis was given to the analysis of numerous sets of experimental data in terms of these parameters. Then, some consideration was given to parameter mathematics particularly in regard to the establishment of suitable approaches to the calculation of parametric constants and functional relationships between parameter values and stress. Almost simultaneously with the above many studies were devoted to the use of these parametric approaches in the interpretation and extrapolation of experimental data. Along with these studies numerous comparisons were made to assess the effectiveness of the various parameters, not only in terms of their ability to represent stress-rupture data over a series of temperatures but also, and perhaps more importantly, in terms of how accurately these functional quantities allow extrapolation of existing data.

Admittedly, the above attempt to be chronological is idealized. It was undertaken only to show that some sequence does exist in the development of this subject. As a matter of fact, it is probably true that no single element within the sequence stated above can be considered completely established or in such a state of development that no modifications or improvements are needed. To say, for example, that the parameters now known are to be the only ones ever employed is pure speculation. So is any statement that the approaches now in use are possessed of an effectiveness that cannot be surpassed. It seems almost certain, therefore, that parameter studies will continue to be made and it seems just as certain that improvements in every aspect of parameter technology will evolve.

A careful study of the existing literature dealing with parameter development, evaluation and use suggested that a textbook on this subject was definitely warranted. In preparing the present text, it was felt it should accomplish at least the following:

1. Consider those parameters which are in common use along with some others whose usefulness has not as yet been completely established.
2. Discuss in at least some depth the origin of, or the thinking which led to, the development of the more widely used parameters; in doing this, perhaps the path leading to another parametric approach might be suggested.
3. Explain how stress-rupture parameters function to provide a correlation of stress-rupture data.
4. Outline in complete detail the mathematical approach to the calculation of parameter constants and the establishment of parameter plots.
5. Consider the use of stress-rupture parameters in the interpolation and extrapolation of experimental data.
6. Provide some comparison of the effectiveness of the more widely used parameters in terms of how accurately existing data are correlated within the range of experimental results and extrapolated into the range where no data exist.
7. Provide a representative listing of the articles which have appeared in the published literature dealing with stress-rupture parameters.

In addition, it was felt that the value and usefulness of this text would be enhanced by the inclusion of certain other features. In this respect:

1. Some data which have appeared in the literature and which were felt to be improperly analyzed were subjected to further study using the analytical techniques in existence at GE-NSP. These results were then compared with the existing literature results.
2. Mention is made, and illustrations given, of several approximate methods for use in calculating parameter constants when only a preliminary analysis of the data is in order.
3. An explanation is given of how the strength of several materials may be compared when the same parameter plot is used; this involves both equal and unequal values of the parameter constants.
4. In connection with (3) a special type of graph paper is introduced for use with parameter plots; the incorporation of a nomograph at the top of the paper allows convenient conversion of parameter values into temperatures and rupture times.
5. Full-page individual nomographs are included to allow convenient conversion of parameter values into corresponding rupture times and temperatures.
6. Some relationships between rupture time, stress and temperature which evolve from certain parameter studies are presented.
7. A section has been devoted to a discussion of the fundamental con-

siderations of least squares as applied to the analysis of stress-rupture data. Both linear and non-linear regression analyses are described.

Throughout an attempt has been made to be fairly thorough so that at least the more commonly employed parameters would be treated in considerable depth. An attempt was also made to stress the practical side of parameter technology in the hope that this text would provide the reader with a correct appreciation of the usefulness of stress-rupture parameters. Some thought was also given to those persons not completely familiar with the use of parametric approaches. In this regard, an attempt was made to provide a logical development of the subject so that new students desiring to develop a fairly comprehensive understanding in this area could achieve this objective.

In the preparation of this text much information has been taken from the published journal articles and technical reports of many other investigators. Were it not for the existence of this type of information, the assemblage of the present text would not have been possible. For this reason, the author is especially indebted to those who have contributed such excellent work to the existing literature on this subject. Special acknowledgment is given to all those whose work has been referenced in this book, and readers are referred to the enclosed bibliography, for really, this list embraces what I consider to be the collaborating authors of this text. Particular acknowledgment is made of the work of S. S. Manson and his associates of NASA, Lewis Research Center, Cleveland, Ohio, for their contributions to the field of parametric analyses have been extensive and extremely valuable. Special acknowledgment is also given to those investigators whose pioneering work has, like that of S. S. Manson, led to the currently employed parametric formulations. Included in this listing are F. R. Larson, J. Miller, J. H. Hollomon, L. D. Jaffee, R. L. Orr, O. D. Sherby, J. E. Dorn, A. M. Haferd (with S. S. Manson), P. Brozzo, G. Murry, G. Succop, W. F. Brown, Jr., C. Zener, F. F. A. Walles, A. Graham, A. Chitty and D. Duval. Also to be mentioned in a special way are those investigators who have contributed significantly to the mathematical analysis of parameters and/or to the evaluation of parameter effectiveness. These include A. Mendelson, E. Roberts, Jr., R. M. Goldhoff, F. J. Clauss, H. Conrad, E. C. Larke, N. P. Inglis, F. Garofalo, C. Richmond, W. F. Domis, F. von Gemmingen, A. W. Mullendore, J. M. Dhosi, R. Widmer, N. J. Grant, D. S. Wood and J. B. Wade. A special indebtedness is due also to Messrs. Jules Simmons and A. Van Echo of the U.S.A.E.C., Fuels and Materials Branch, Division of Reactor Development and Technology, for the financial support of the program from which the present manuscript has evolved. Also to be acknowledged are: Lars H. Sjodahl, for devising most of the computer programs employed in the analyses discussed herein; Robert Schneithorst, for preparing most of the figures and tables used in this text; and Miss Carolyn Thall, for her capable assistance in manuscript typing.

Joseph B. Conway

June 1968

CONTENTS

CHAPTER 1

INTRODUCTION

One of the most familiar and useful measurements of the mechanical strength of a material is that involving the stress-rupture characteristics. In this evaluation, a specimen having a well-defined geometry is heated to a certain temperature and a load is applied. Measurement of the time required for the specimen to rupture identifies the rupture strength for the particular conditions involved. Other measurements involving different temperatures and stresses lead to a complete evaluation of the stress-rupture behavior over a fairly wide range of test conditions. Such data lead to the familiar stress-rupture plot shown in Figure 1-1. Ordinarily logarithmic coordinates are employed inasmuch as this type of plot usually leads to linear isotherms. Of course, it is typical of these plots that the slopes are negative since at a given temperature decreasing the stress leads to increased rupture times. Another pattern to be noted in these plots is that the isotherms are shifted upward and to the right as the temperature decreases.

In many cases, creep-rupture rather than stress-rupture measurements are made. These measurements, although somewhat more complicated and involved, do yield much more information than obtained in the stress-rupture evaluation. Instead of just measuring the time to rupture measurements of the creep-rupture characteristics emphasize the determination of strain as a function of time throughout the course of the rupture test. Hence, in addition to measuring the time to rupture, a fairly detailed evaluation of the strain-time behavior results. Such data lead to the familiar creep curve shown in Figure 1-2. In general, an instantaneous elongation, OA, follows immediately upon loading and is composed of an elastic and a plastic extension. At point A, when the load is fully applied, the rate of plastic deformation or creep is fairly large but gradually decreases with time. Such behavior defines a region along the creep curve characterized by transient behavior insofar as the creep rate is time dependent. This region, AB, is commonly referred to as the first stage of creep. Eventually the rate of plastic deformation reaches an essentially constant or steady state value which is independent of time giving rise to a linear strain versus time relation. This region, BC, has been termed the second stage of creep. As deformation proceeds further, the creep rate eventually begins to increase in a manner which is usually exponential with time. This region, CD, is preliminary to rupture and is generally referred to as the third stage of creep.

While the shape of the creep curve shown in Figure 1-2 is considered typical it is by no means the behavior to be expected in every

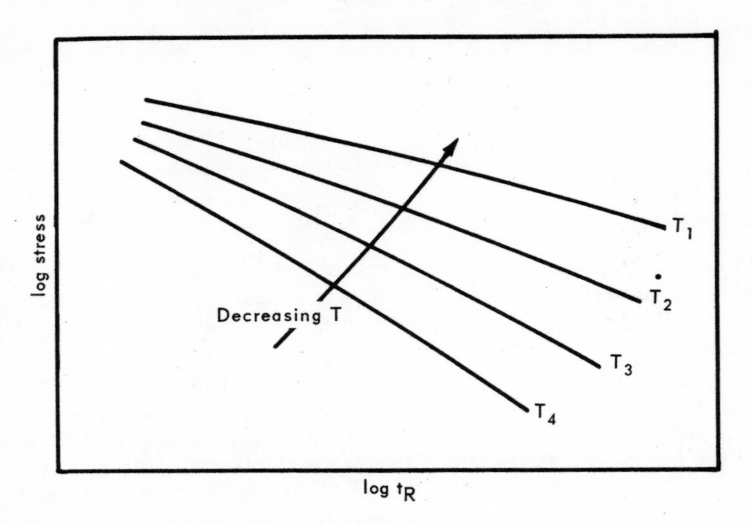

Figure 1-1 – Typical stress-rupture plot.

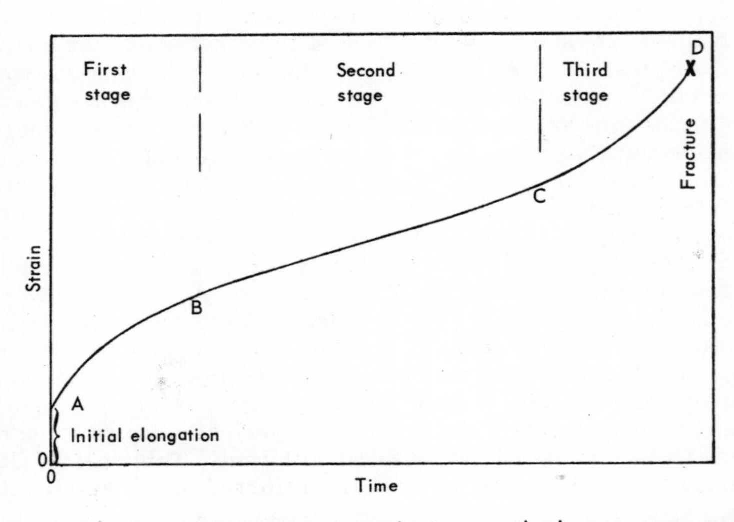

Figure 1-2 – Typical creep curve obtained in constant load creep-rupture test.

instance. Nor should it be assumed that all the stages of creep illustrated in Figure 1-2 are necessarily observed in every creep evaluation. Material characteristics, as well as the test conditions, exert the major influence in determining the actual shape of the curve describing strain-time behavior. For example, certain combinations of stress and temperature lead to creep curves which exhibit only transient type creep and hence the second and third stage portions of the creep curve are not observed. Also the shape of the creep curve is determined by whether the test is performed at constant stress or at constant load (the latter being the usual condition for stress-rupture and creep-rupture evaluations). A creep curve corresponding to a constant stress test is typically one which exhibits a creep rate which decreases gradually almost to the rupture point. If obtained at all, rupture, in such tests, occurs at times much greater than those observed in the constant load tests even though the initial stresses are identical.

It will be observed from Figure 1-2 that a creep-rupture evaluation allows various material characteristics to be identified. Of course, as already mentioned the time to rupture or fracture is obtained. However, it also becomes possible to identify the following information:

1. The initial elongation on loading (usually a very difficult measurement however);
2. The strain or time corresponding to the end of first stage creep;
3. The strain or time corresponding to the end of second stage creep;
4. The time spent in second stage creep;
5. The time spent in third stage creep;
6. The instantaneous creep rate as a function of strain or time in first stage creep;
7. The secondary or linear creep rate;
8. The time to yield a certain value of strain at temperature and under load (times to yield 1, 2 and 5 percent strain are good examples of design information);
9. Data sufficient to allow for the development of a mathematical equation describing either various portions of or the entire creep curve.

Since rupture represents the terminal point on a creep curve and hence must be considered as one of the component parts of the overall creep process, it is not too illogical to consider that the rupture point must be related to various preceding portions or characteristics of the creep curve. As a result much thought has been given to the identification of just such relationships. One of the most common of these relationships involves an inverse proportionality between the rupture time and the minimum creep rate. Referring to the typical creep curve shown in Figure 1-3 the second stage creep rate can be expressed as:

$$\epsilon_s = \frac{\epsilon_3 - \epsilon_1'}{t_R} \qquad (1\text{-}1)$$

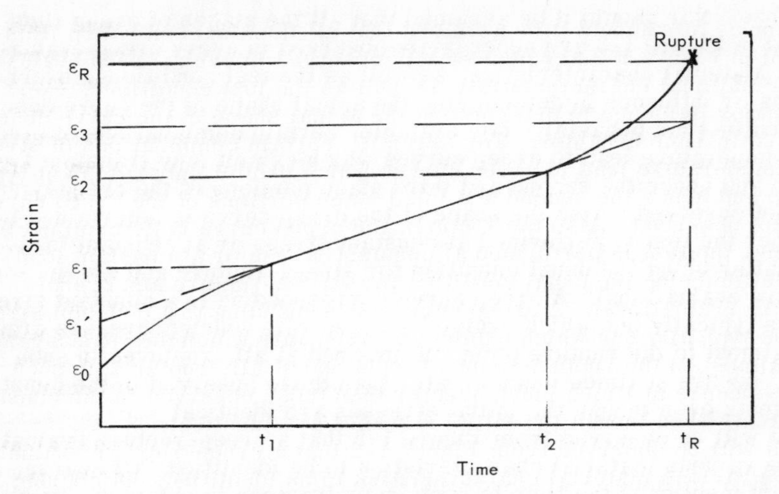

Figure 1-3 – Typical creep curve.

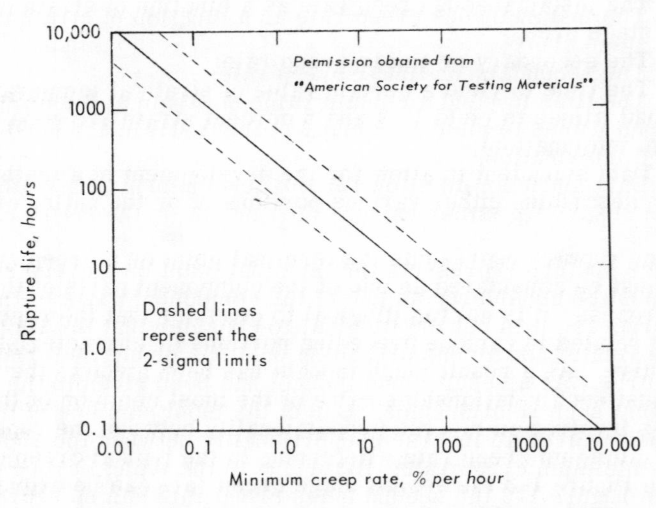

Figure 1-4 – Plot of log t_R versus log ($\dot{\varepsilon}_s$) for aluminum[25] between 500°F and 1100°F.

and hence if the quantity $\epsilon_3 - \epsilon_1'$ remains reasonably constant with stress for a given temperature then the rupture time, t_R, is seen to be inversely proportional to the steady state creep rate, $\dot{\epsilon}_s$. A plot then of $\dot{\epsilon}_s$ versus t_R on logarithmic coordinates will be linear with a slope equal to minus one. If the quantity, $\epsilon_3 - \epsilon_1'$, is also relatively independent of temperature then the logarithmic plot just mentioned will be applicable for any stress-temperature combination. Hence once the creep curve exhibits a linear portion, a good estimate of the rupture life can be obtained once the plot of $\log \dot{\epsilon}_s$ versus $\log t_R$ has been prepared.

In a recent discussion of the relationship in equation (1-1), Garofalo[22] mentioned that the first observation of the fact that $\epsilon_3 - \epsilon_1'$ was approximately constant was attributed to H. J. French by Tapsell.[23] Some studies by Tapsell confirmed this behavior for iron and several types of steel and even more recent studies by Servi, et al.,[24] Monkman and Grant,[25] Feltham[26] and Garofalo, et al.,[27] have shown an inverse proportionality between t_R and $\dot{\epsilon}_s$. A typical illustration of this relationship is presented in Figure 1-4 based on the data of Monkman and Grant.[25] In addition, some recent data for arc-cast molybdenum[6] at 2000°C are shown in Figure 1-5 to indicate an extremely linear $\log t_R$ versus $\log \dot{\epsilon}_s$ plot. Unfortunately the type of correlation shown in Figures 1-4 and 1-5 is not obtained in every case and hence the inverse proportionality between t_R and $\dot{\epsilon}_s$ cannot be considered as being completely substantiated. This is particularly true with regard to temperature dependence for there appears to be some evidence to indicate that different linear relations between $\log t_R$ and $\log \dot{\epsilon}_s$ are obtained as temperature is varied. In other words, the quantity (ϵ_3 $\dot{\epsilon}_1$) is not always completely independent of temperature and stress and the ideal relation, of the type shown in Figure 1-5, is not always obtained. At the moment, therefore, the proportionality mentioned above should be considered as being only approximate.

In some studies dealing with austenitic stainless steel, Garafalo, et al.,[27] identified a relationship between the rupture life and the duration of the second stage of creep as follows:

$$t_R = A\,(t_2 - t_1)^b \qquad (1\text{-}2)$$

Another relationship between rupture life and the time corresponding to the initiation of the third stage of creep was also identified as:

$$t_R = B\,(t_2)^c \qquad (1\text{-}3)$$

Typical plots of these relationships are shown in Figures 1-6 and 1-7. Slope and intercept calculations using these linear logarithmic plots lead obviously to b or c and A or B values, respectively. Values for A and B have been found to be temperature dependent while the b and c values are independent of temperature and very close to unity. These characteristics are obvious from the logarithmic plots.

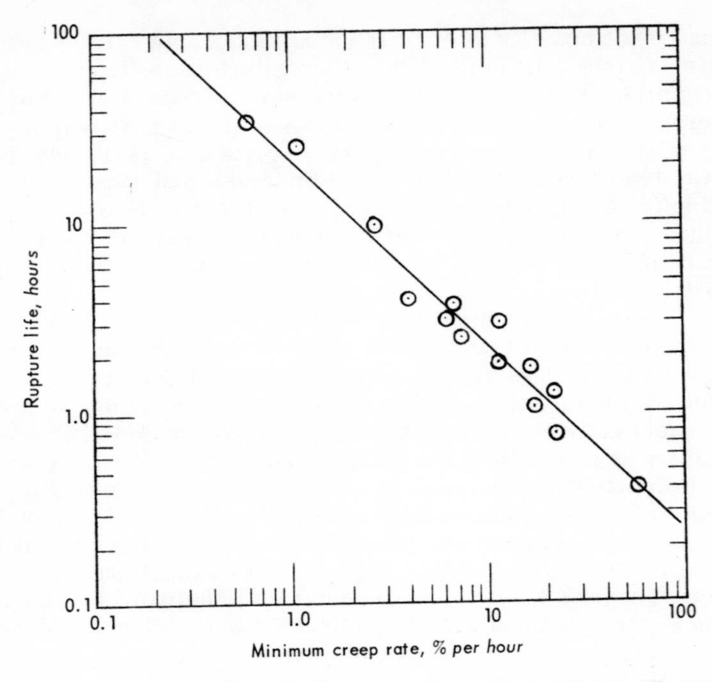

Figure 1-5 – Plot of log t_R versus log $\dot{\varepsilon}_s$ for molybdenum(6) at 2000°C.

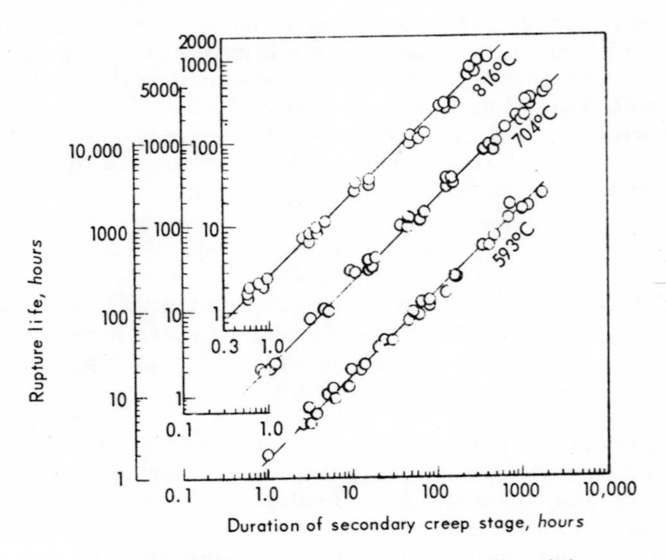

Figure 1-6 – Relationship between rupture life and the duration of secondary creep(27).

In discussing equations (1-2) and (1-3) Garofalo, et al., pointed out (refer to Figure 1-3) that since:

$$\dot{\epsilon}_s = \frac{\epsilon_2 - \epsilon_1}{t_2 - t_1} = \frac{\epsilon_2 - \epsilon_1'}{t_2} \tag{1-4}$$

substitution in equations (1-2) and (1-3) and considering b and c to be unity leads to:

$$t_R = \frac{A(\epsilon_2 - \epsilon_1)}{\dot{\epsilon}_s} = \frac{B(\epsilon_2 - \epsilon_1')}{\dot{\epsilon}_s} \tag{1-5}$$

which again reveals the inverse proportionality between t_R and $\dot{\epsilon}_s$ as long as $(\epsilon_2 - \epsilon_1')$ is constant with stress. Obviously, since A and B in equations (1-2) and (1-3) were identified as functions of temperature, the presence of these quantities in equation (1-5) requires the conclusion that while plots of log t_R versus log $\dot{\epsilon}_s$ may be linear at a given temperature a different linear relationship would be obtained as the temperature was changed. These would be parallel according to equation (1-5) since variation of the constant B merely requires different intercepts. Only when the quantity $B(\epsilon_2 - \epsilon_1')$ is independent of temperature would a single linear log t_R versus log $\dot{\epsilon}_s$ plot obtain to represent various temperatures.

Other suggested methods used to represent stress-rupture data are presented in Table 1-1. Of these, (1) and (2) are by far the most common. Whether stress or log stress is plotted as the ordinate is usually left to individual preference, although in general the plot which results in linearity is the one usually employed. When such linearity is obtained in a given isotherm, a simple relationship between stress and rupture life can be developed and then some thought can be given to the dependence of these equation constants on temperature. Ideally, a single relationship could result to describe the stress-rupture behavior of a given material over a finite range of test conditions.

One of the most striking illustrations of the similarity between stress-rupture and creep behavior is offered by the type of plot shown in Figure 1-8. In many cases it has been found that the slope of the linear log stress versus log minimum creep rate plot is equal numerically but opposite in sign to the slope of the linear stress-rupture plot. Such is the case shown in Figure 1-8 where the slopes are 0.225 and -0.225, respectively. Obviously, this behavior describes an exact proportionality between rupture life and minimum creep rate and follows directly when equation (1-1) is applicable.

A very important conclusion to be drawn from the behavior observed in Figure 1-8 and in equation (1-1) involves the representation of stress-rupture data by means of the familiar creep equation forms. For example, if rupture life and minimum creep rate are inversely related in the form:

$$t_R = \frac{\text{constant}}{\dot{\epsilon}_s} \tag{1-6}$$

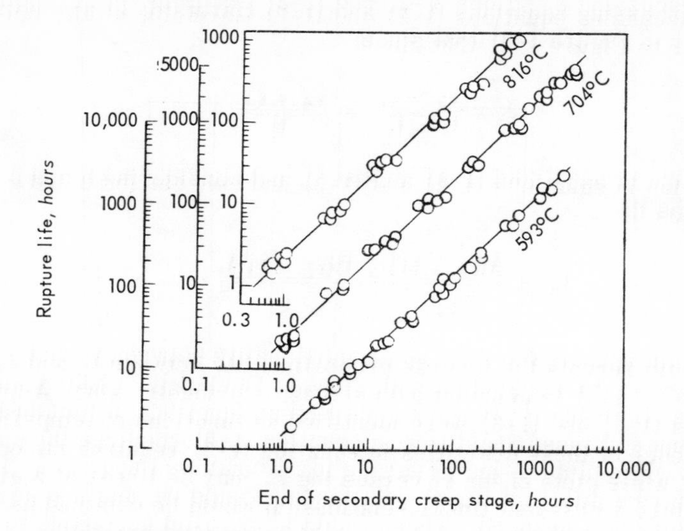

Figure 1-7 – Relationship between rupture life and the time at initiation of tertiary creep(27).

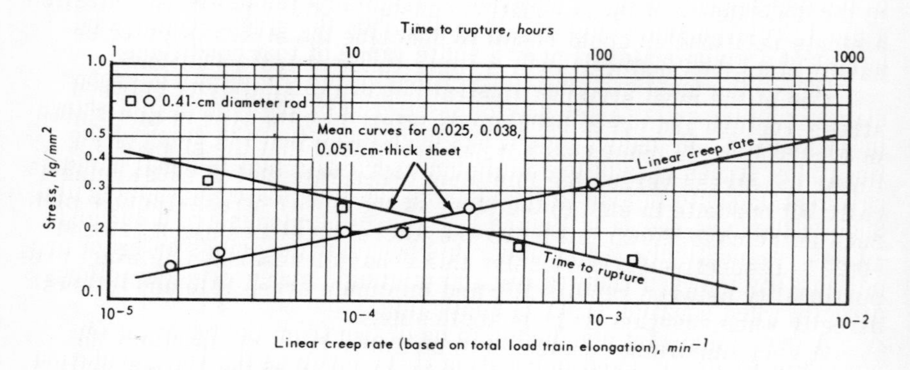

Figure 1-8 – Stress-rupture and minimum creep rate for arc-cast tungsten at 2200°C(15).

Table 1-1. Some Common Methods Used in Presenting Creep-Rupture Data

	Ordinate	Abscissa	Remarks
1.	Log stress	Log rupture time	at constant temperature
2.	Stress	Log rupture time	at constant temperature
3.	Log stress	Log elongation at rupture	at constant temperature
4.	Elongation at rupture	Log rupture time	at constant temperature or at constant stress
5.	Log stress	Log minimum creep rate	at constant temperature
6.	Log stress	Log average creep rate (rupture elongation/ rupture time)	at constant temperature
7.	Log rupture time	Log average creep rate	at constant temperature; very similar to equation (1-1)
8.	Temperature	Log rupture time	at constant stress; should be linear
9.	Stress	Temperature	Isochronal plot with rupture time as a parameter
10.	Log rupture time	Reciprocal of absolute temperature	at constant stress

then a mere substitution in one of the commonly employed steady state creep equations[22,29] leads to a similar expression in terms of rupture life. Based on the stress-rupture behavior presented in Figure 1-8 and a very widely used creep equation employing a power stress law[29] the following expression obtains:

$$t_R = \text{constant}\ \sigma^{-n}\ e^{\frac{\Delta H}{RT}} \tag{1-7}$$

where σ is the stress, T the temperature, ΔH the activation energy for creep, R the gas constant and n an empirical constant. Clearly, slope and intercept calculations, based on the type of plot shown in Figure 1-8, lead to values for n and the (constant $e^{\Delta H/RT}$) product. Other tests at constant stress would then allow a plot to be made of log rupture life versus the reciprocal of the absolute temperature. This plot should be linear if both n and ΔH are independent of temperature. Slope and intercept calculations would then yield values for ΔH and the constant to completely identify all the unknown terms in equation (1-7).

An important stress dependency was identified recently by Garofalo[33] in an analysis of the minimum creep rate data for several

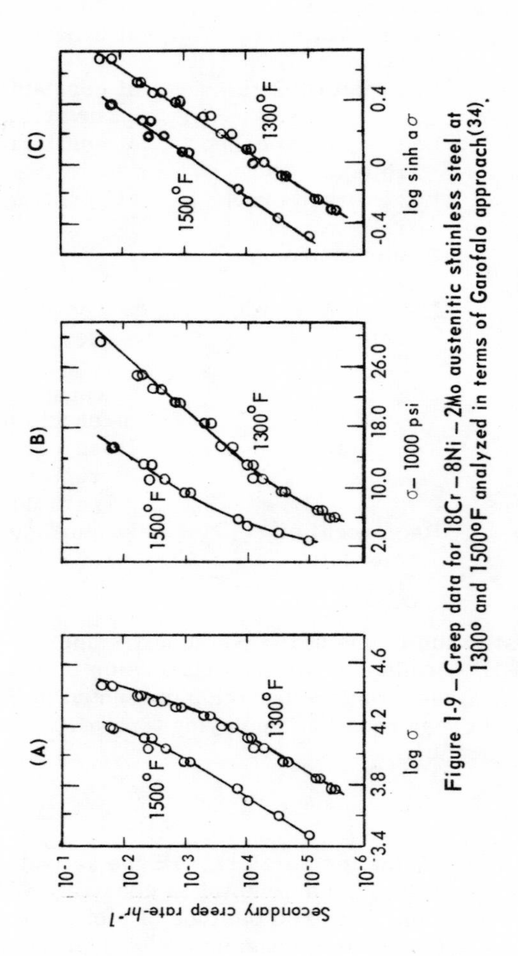

Figure 1-9 – Creep data for 18Cr – 8Ni – 2Mo austenitic stainless steel at 1300° and 1500°F analyzed in terms of Garofalo approach(34).

metals. At low stress levels the steady state (minimum) creep rate, $\dot{\epsilon}_s$, was related to stress as follows:

$$\dot{\epsilon}_s = A\sigma^n \tag{1-8}$$

A plot, therefore, of $\dot{\epsilon}_s$ versus σ on logarithmic coordinates was approximately linear but definite curvature was detected at the higher stress levels (see Figure 1-9A). In the region of higher stresses a plot of $\dot{\epsilon}_s$ versus stress on semi-logarithmic coordinates was found to be linear (see Figure 1-9B) indicating the following relationship:

$$\dot{\epsilon}_s = A' \; e^{B\sigma} \tag{1-9}$$

For the entire stress range Garofalo found that:

$$\dot{\epsilon}_s = A'' \; (\sinh a\sigma)^n \tag{1-10}$$

which yielded a linear relation between log $\dot{\epsilon}_s$ and (log sinh $a\sigma$) over the entire stress range. This behavior is shown in Figure 1-9C. In this plot the slope is equal to n and the intercept yields the value for A''.

At low values of $a\sigma$ (i.e., at low stresses) equation (1-10) reduces to:

$$\dot{\epsilon}_s = A'' \, a^n \sigma^n \tag{1-11}$$

and the behavior expressed by equation (1-8) is obtained. Furthermore, at high values of $a\sigma$ equation (1-10) approaches:

$$\dot{\epsilon}_s = \frac{A'' \, e^{an\sigma}}{2^n} \tag{1-12}$$

and the behavior described by equation (1-9) is indicated. Hence, the hyperbolic sine approach can describe the stress dependency noted at both the low and high stress levels.

Before the plot in Figure 1-9C can be made a value for "a" must be known. While a non-linear regression analysis using a least squares approach (see Chapter 10) can yield such a value it is also possible to make a fairly accurate determination of this constant from the type of plot shown in Figure 1-9. From (A) the slope yields the value for n and from (B) the slope, being equal to "an," allows the value of "a" to be calculated directly.

It was pointed out by Garofalo[33] that due to the inverse relationship between $\dot{\epsilon}_s$ and t_R it is possible to use equation (1-10) in the form:

$$t_R = B(\sinh a\sigma)^{-n} \tag{1-13}$$

for use in the correlation of rupture data.

Functional representations of the type given by equations (1-8) and

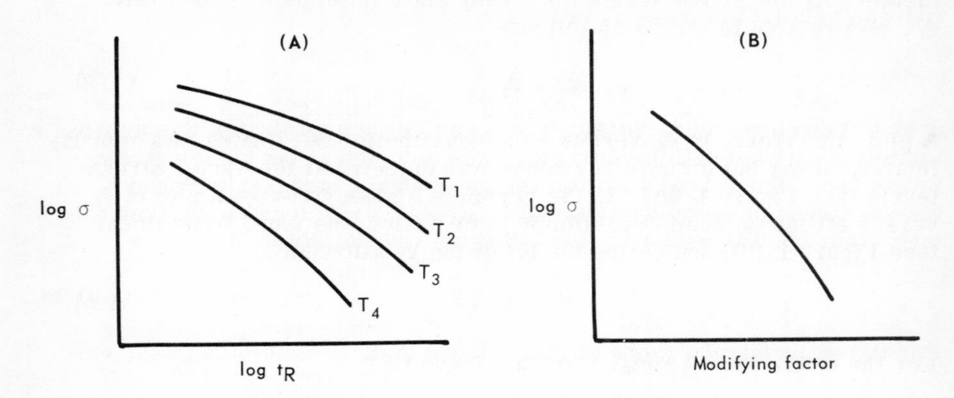

Figure 1-10 – Schematic representation of stress-rupture isotherms and correlation plot.

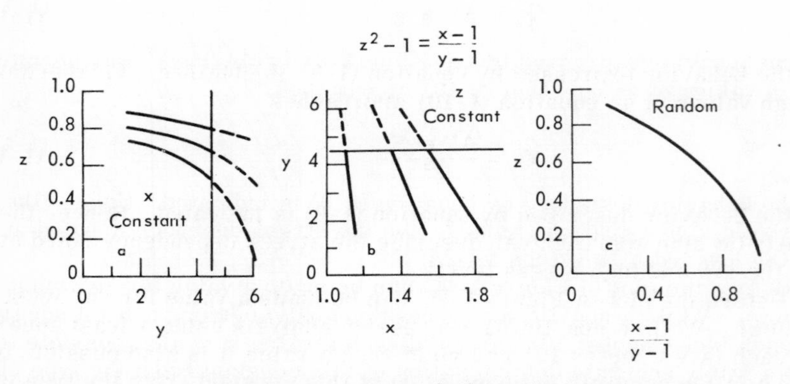

Figure 1-11 – Graphical representation of relationship between x, y and z variables[56].

(1-13) are termed "two-variable" correlations. If now the constants A and B can be expressed as a function of temperature, a three-variable correlation results and the relationship between time, temperature and stress will be identified. A typical example of this is given by equation (1-7) which yields an explicit relationship once the equation constants are identified. An analytical expression relating time, temperature and stress is thereby obtained.

Actually the fact that an explicit formulation does not evolve does not lessen the value of three-variable correlations. It is of considerable usefulness to merely identify the fact that some time-temperature combination (commonly called parameter) is constant at a given stress level and a plot of this combination or parameter versus stress yields a single curve or line. For example, in studies of the effect of temperature on the tensile strength, S, of copper, a correlation in terms of strain rate, $\dot{\epsilon}$, was employed by Zener and Hollomon[60] in the form:

$$S = f(\dot{\epsilon}\, e^{\frac{\Delta H}{RT}}) \tag{1-14}$$

where ΔH was identified as a heat of activation. Mention was made of the use of parameters in data analysis and this function is now commonly referred to as the Zener-Hollomon parameter. Many studies have applied this concept to creep behavior in relating the minimum creep rate to temperature and stress. One typical study is that of Orr, Sherby and Dorn.[32]

Once developed, three-variable correlations can be useful in the interpolation and extrapolation of stress-rupture information. For example, if stress-rupture data are available at 1000°, 1200° and 1400°F and at stresses ranging from 5,000 to 50,000 psi, one might ask what the 1,000-hour rupture stress is at 1100°F. Now obviously this information could be obtained from a stress-rupture plot using a simple interpolation between the 1000° and 1200°F isotherms. This procedure is not without its inaccuracies and something more reliable is desired. Besides interpolation, it is hoped that some degree of extrapolative effectiveness would result from a stress-rupture correlation. In this instance, if rupture data in the 1,000-hour range were available, a proper correlation would allow the prediction of 10,000-hour results. If successful this approach would result in the saving of many thousands of test hours. Extrapolation can, of course, be made graphically by a mere extension of the isotherms in the type of plot shown in Figure 1-1 but a more convenient and reliable approach is afforded by parameter correlations. Mention should also be made here of mathematical extrapolation procedures which will be discussed in Chapter 9.

Basically, a successful stress-rupture correlation would convert the series of isotherms shown in Figure 1-10 to a single curve or line as shown in this same figure. To accomplish this it is obvious that some modified time scale must be employed to reposition each isotherm so that a single curve or line is obtained. Just what type of

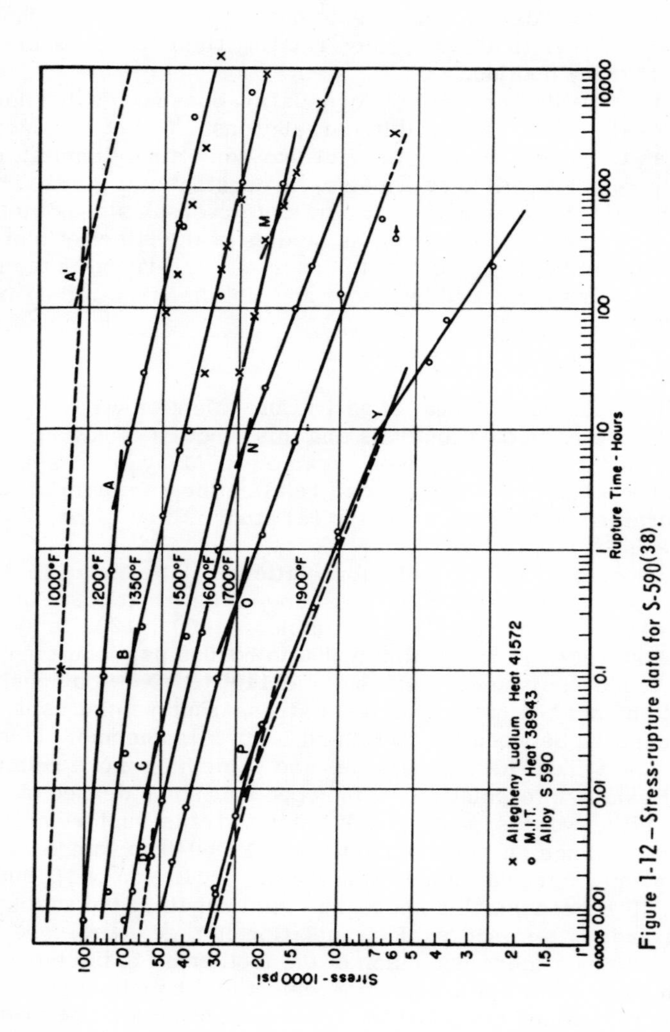

Figure 1-12 – Stress-rupture data for S-590(38).

modifying factor is needed is not easy to identify. But nevertheless the degree of success achieved in identifying a proper modification factor will determine how effective the eventual correlation will prove to be. Certainly in the correlation plot of Figure 1-10 an excellent representation is indicated and one which can:

1. be used to construct the isotherms in Figure 1-10A to allow a comparison with the experimental points;
2. be used to position any isotherm between T_1 and T_4 for which no experimental data are available;
3. be used to position any isotherm outside the T_1 to T_4 temperature range and for which no experimental data are available (extrapolation);
4. allow calculation of the rupture strength corresponding to a certain rupture life for any temperature either between T_1 and T_4 (interpolation) or outside the T_1 to T_4 range (extrapolation);
5. predict long-term rupture behavior based on available short-term rupture data (extrapolation).

Obviously, when extrapolation is involved some caution should be exercised. However, for temperatures within a few hundred degrees of the data range no serious error should result. Also, if extrapolations are confined to no more than one to two log cycles on the time scale, experience has shown that no serious error should be encountered provided the parameter being employed yields an effective correlation of the data.

Time-scale modification factors have been termed "parameters" in general or "stress-rupture parameters" when used with rupture data. Usually these quantities contain only rupture life and temperature and are devoid of all reference to stress. Ideally, then, a proper stress-rupture parameter should so modify the time scale that all the stress-rupture isotherms become coincident and a plot of log stress versus the parameter yields a smooth curve or line. If the isotherms are linear the parameter plot will also be linear; and, of course, curved isotherms lead to a curved parameter plot.

A very interesting introduction to parameter type correlation was described by Manson.[56] A three-variable correlation was considered relating the general variables x, y and z in the form:

$$z^2 - 1 = \frac{x - 1}{y - 1} \qquad (1\text{-}15)$$

It was assumed that while this expression accurately described the interrelationship between x, y and z this exact relation was unknown to the experimenter interested in studying the x-y-z variation. An experimental program might then be established to study the effect of y on z with the x variable held constant. Data of this type would then lead to the plot shown in Figure 1-11(a). Of course, a certain amount of data scatter would always be present and, hence, some mean or average curve would have to be drawn. Such curves are shown solid in

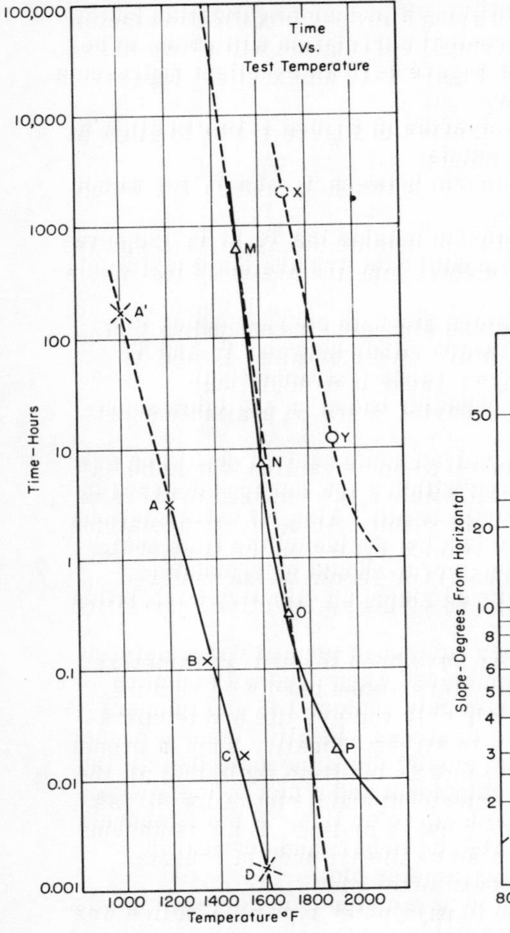

Figure 1-13 – Plot of instability points of Figure 1-12[38]

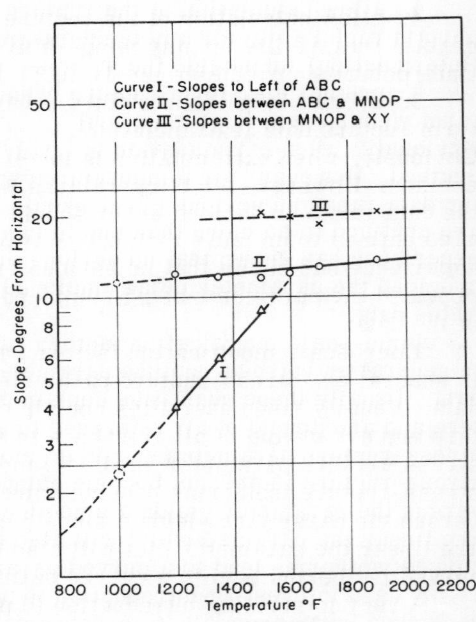

Fig. 1-14 – Slopes of straight line portions of Figure 1-12[38].

this figure. If these curves had to be extrapolated beyond the data range, some difficulty would be encountered if agreement with the exact functional relationship (shown dashed) were to be obtained. As a matter of fact, a graphical extrapolation of the lower curve would in all probability lead to fairly serious error. It is unlikely that, having positioned the solid curves and not knowing the form of the function, a graphical extrapolation to y values beyond 5.0 would yield acceptable results.

Another experimental program might choose to hold z constant and measure the effect of x on y. This program would then yield the linear relation indicated in Figure 1-11(b). In this instance, extrapolation to higher values of y (dashed lines) would probably lead to more accurate results than obtainable through Figure 1-11(a). Furthermore, the linearity in Figure 1-11(b) might serve to suggest the actual functional relationship which exists between x and y and perhaps even between the three variables. Such reasoning can also identify that the proper plot is that between z and the quantity $(x - 1)/(y - 1)$. If this is attempted the results shown in Figure 1-11(c) obtain to define a single curve which relates the parameter $(x - 1)/(y - 1)$ and z. With this plot, extrapolation to obtain a value of y corresponding to x and z values is greatly simplified. In contrast to Figure 1-11(b) the master plot in Figure 1-11(c) provides for a continuous variation in terms of z.

In an analysis of the type of data presented in Figure 1-1 Grant and Bucklin[38] described an approach for use in the interpolation and extrapolation of existing stress-rupture isotherms. While this approach did not involve a parameter approach it is pertinent to the general discussion of parametric analysis of stress-rupture data. Considering the data shown in Figure 1-12 various breaks (slope changes) in the isotherms were attributed to changes taking place either in the material or in the deformation process. An analysis of the instability points ABC and MNOP yielded the results shown in Figure 1-13 where extrapolation to 1000° and 1900°F has been effected. As a next step, the slopes of the various straight line portions of each isotherm in Figure 1-12 were plotted as a function of test temperature as shown in Figure 1-14. Extrapolation of these data led to slope values for each straight line portion at 1000° and 1900°F. Then the 10,000-hour rupture life was read from Figure 1-12 using the slopes just calculated and a plot of these data versus temperature is given in Figure 1-15. These plots allow the construction of the rupture curves at 1000° and 1900°F as shown dashed in Figure 1-12.

In Figure 1-12 the instability point corresponding to P was predicted from Figures 1-14 and 1-15 because the MNOP curve in Figure 1-13 was expected to curve away from a straight line toward the melting point of S-590. Hence since only two of Figures 1-13, 1-14 and 1-15 are necessary to predict the curve at another temperature, the third figure acts as a check on the accepted values.

At 1000°F the only check on the predicted curve is a short-time tensile value. Good agreement is seen to exist.

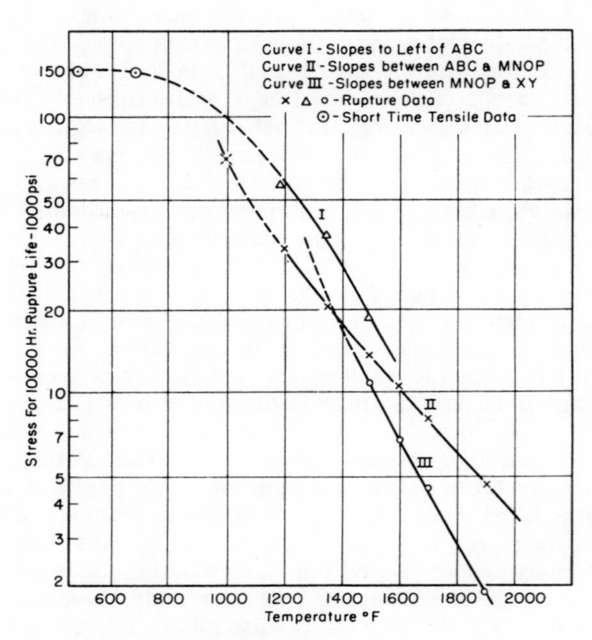

Fig. 1-15 – Plot of 10,000-hour rupture data for S-590[38].

Based on Figure 1-13 it is possible to predict that no instability of the MNOP type will occur in less than 1 x 10^6 hours at 1200°F; at 1350°F it will not occur in less than 100,000 hours. Hence linear extrapolation of these isotherms appears safe within these limits.

Point Y at 1900°F presented only one point for use in instability predictions at other temperatures. At 1700°F (see Figure 1-12) the instability is not indicated within 500 hours. It was felt that even this one value at point Y led to some measure of assurance in estimating the minimum time at which deviations from straight line behavior could be expected at lower temperatures. In Figure 1-13 the line, XY, was expected to have a slope parallel to or less steep than the MNOP line. If, as in this analysis, some range of stress can be identified within which the isotherm slope remains unchanged then obviously extrapolation within this range can be easily made and accurate results can be expected.

In an empirical approach Servi and Grant[55] proposed a three-variable correlation in the form:

$$\log r = a + \left(\frac{b}{T} - c\right)(\log \sigma - d) \tag{1-16}$$

where r is the minimum creep-rate, σ is the stress, T is the absolute temperature and a, b, c and d are constants depending on the material and the structure. If creep rate and rupture time are inversely related then equation (1-16) becomes:

$$-\log t_R = a' + \left(\frac{b}{T} - c\right)(\log \sigma - d) \tag{1-17}$$

A simple rearrangement yields:

$$(a' + \log t_R) = \left(\frac{b - cT}{T}\right)(d - \log \sigma) \tag{1-18}$$

and

$$T(a' + \log t_R) = (b - cT)(d - \log \sigma) \tag{1-19}$$

where the quantity on the left represents the Larson-Miller parameter. That this approach is not identical to that of Larson and Miller follows from the temperature-dependent term given by (b - cT). As will be seen in Chapter 2 the Larson-Miller parameter is considered to be a function of stress alone.

Another modification of equation (1-17) yields:

$$\frac{a' + \log t_R}{b - cT} = \frac{d - \log \sigma}{T} \tag{1-20}$$

which is quite similar to the Manson-Haferd parameter approach (see Chapter 4). One additional modification at constant stress yields:

$$-\log t_R = a' + \frac{b''}{T} - c'' \tag{1-21}$$

and

$$\log t_R + \frac{b''}{T} = \text{constant at constant stress} \quad (1\text{-}22)$$

This will be seen to be exactly the Dorn parameter approach (see Chapter 3).

Throughout the remainder of this text various stress-rupture parameters will be considered. Special calculation procedures will be described pertinent to the evaluation of the constant or constants associated with each parameter. Also some discussion will be devoted to the use of these parameters with particular reference being made to the effectiveness of these quantities in providing a satisfactory correlation of stress-rupture data. While not all the parameters ever considered will be mentioned, due emphasis will be placed on the ones which have enjoyed the widest acceptance.

Proper mention should be made at this point that parameters are used primarily, and perhaps even exclusively, for purposes of data correlation, interpolation and extrapolation. No claim has ever been made that these quantities can be used in identifying the actual mechanism or mechanisms associated with creep or rupture phenomena. As a matter of fact, the opposite sequence seems to be the case. In subsequent sections it will be seen that certain parameter forms (Larson-Miller and Dorn parameters, for example) have evolved from a rearrangement of expressions which have been proposed to represent creep behavior.

CHAPTER 2

LARSON-MILLER PARAMETER

In 1952 the Larson-Miller[1] parameter was introduced, and with it a very effective method for use in rationalizing the time-temperature (and even rate-temperature) effects observed in stress-rupture and creep testing, was identified. Since its introduction, this parameter has been used quite extensively and even today is without doubt one of the most well-known of all the parametric approaches now in existence in this field.

It is noteworthy that the Larson-Miller parameter had its origin in the tempering studies of Hollomon and Jaffe.[2] These investigators noted that certain material properties (notably hardness) varied with time during a tempering (i.e., isothermal soaking) treatment. Some consideration was given, therefore, to the question of whether certain combinations of time and temperature would lead to the same value of a given material property (hardness). Tempering at a high temperature for a short time might, for example, yield the same result (hardness) as a long term tempering at a lower temperature. In this type of correlation, it was felt by Hollomon and Jaffe that diffusion processes were involved in tempering operations and hence the attained material property (i.e., hardness) should be related to time and temperature in a form similar to a diffusion equation. Thus:

$$H = f(t\ e^{-Q/RT}) \qquad (2\text{-}1)$$

where H is the material hardness observed after sintering at temperature T (absolute) for time, t; Q is a constant depending on the material and R is the universal gas constant. An obvious similarity between equation (2-1) and the standard diffusion equation is readily recognized.

Little success was achieved by Hollomon and Jaffe in the application of equation (2-1) to the tempering data for various steels. Using time-temperature combinations which yielded the same hardness, equation (2-1) was employed to obtain values for the constant, Q. Applying this expression to two time-temperature pairs which yield the same hardness leads to:

$$t_1\ e^{-Q/RT_1} = t_2\ e^{-Q/RT_2} \qquad (2\text{-}2)$$

from which

$$Q = \frac{R \ln\left(\frac{t_2}{t_1}\right)}{\left(\frac{1}{T_2} - \frac{1}{T_1}\right)} \qquad (2\text{-}3)$$

It was found that Q was not really a constant but rather varied with the hardness value from Q = 50,000 cal/mole at Rockwell C-20 to about 12,000 cal/mole at Rockwell C-65. Moreover, it was observed that when a time-temperature combination was substituted into equation (2-1), along with the Q value corresponding to a given hardness, the parameter described by equation (2-1) did not vary smoothly with hardness but rather was constant. It was necessary, therefore, to consider a different time-temperature functional relationship. Such a relation was developed based on the observations associated with the use of equation (2-1). From what was said above:

$$Q = f_1 (H) \tag{2-4}$$

and

$$t\, e^{-Q/RT} = t_0 \tag{2-5}$$

where t_0 is a constant. Now taking logarithms of equation (2-5) and equating the value of Q to the value of Q in equation (2-4) yields:

$$Q = RT (\ln t - \ln t_0) = f_1 (H) \tag{2-6}$$

which can be expressed as:

$$H = f_2 [T (\ln t - \ln t_0)] \tag{2-7}$$

which can also be written as:

$$H = f_3 [T(C + \log t)] \tag{2-8}$$

Hence for a constant value of hardness:

$$T_1 (C + \log t_1) = T_2 (C + \log t_2) \tag{2-9}$$

Obviously, the value of "C" is obtained from two time-temperature pairs using the rearrangement of equation (2-9) in the form:

$$-C = \frac{T_1 \log t_1 - T_2 \log t_2}{T_1 - T_2} \tag{2-10}$$

Fairly interesting results were obtained with the tempering parameter given by equation (2-8). A typical illustration of the Hollomon and Jaffe study is presented in Figure 2-1 based on tempering data for a fully quenched 0.96 percent carbon steel. As will be noted, the value of C is equal to 9.7 with the time given in seconds and the temperature in °K. A given hardness value can be achieved by any time-temperature combination which is consistent with the parameter value read from the parameter plot at the hardness value in question. For example, if a Rockwell C value of 40 is considered, the parameter value from Figure

2-1 is seen to be about 10,000. Hence the desired hardness can be achieved by either a tempering at 645°C for 10 seconds or one of 90 seconds at 560°C.

It is worth noting that the method of calculating "C" given by equation (2-10), indicates that the actual value of "C" is not affected by the temperature scale (Kelvin or Rankine) employed. Either one can be used just as conveniently with the same value of "C" being employed. Of course, the choice of one temperature scale over another will affect the type of plot shown in Figure 2-1 insofar as the abscissa is concerned. However, it will be readily observed that the use of one temperature scale instead of the other merely causes a horizontal shifting of the parameter plot. In other words, it is very easy to convert the parameter plot of Figure 2-1 to one based on degrees Rankine simply by multiplying all data points and abscissa values by 1.8.

In the case of the "C" value, a similar situtation does not prevail in terms of time for the actual magnitude of this constant is dependent on the units of time employed. Once again, though, equation (2-1) clearly identifies this relationship. Notice that if $C = 10$ for time in minutes, then the value of "C" for time in seconds will be $10 + \log 60$. For time in seconds, then, $C = 11.78$. Obviously, a complete replotting of the parameter relationship is required if the units of time are changed. Of course, if the change in units happens to be from seconds to minutes, then the C value will decrease since the new "C" value then would be (assuming $C = 10$ for time in seconds) $10 - \log 60$ or 8.22.

Master tempering curves, similar to the one shown in Figure 2-1, were constructed by Nehrenberg[3] for several stainless steels. One such plot for a Type 410 stainless steel is shown in Figure 2-2 for time in hours and T in °R. Several values of C were employed to illustrate that fairly good correlations result even though the value of C varies quite markedly. However, a value of $C = 20$ seems to be the optimum value for these data since the data scatter is at a minimum when this value is employed. It was suggested that perhaps a value of $C = 20$ could be employed for the tempering data of all steels in view of the results shown in Figure 2-2. Such usage would allow a direct comparison of the tempering characteristics of all steels to be made on a single plot. Since C is not the same for all materials, a direct comparison (see later section) on a single master tempering plot is not possible.

Some slight inconvenience may be attributed to the use of the parameter shown in master tempering plots for neither temperature nor time can be read directly. This small difficulty is overcome, however, by the incorporation of the conversion coordinates described by Nehrenberg.[3] As seen in Figure 2-2, the graphical solution afforded by the network at the top of the plot allows for convenient conversion of a parameter value to a time-temperature combination. Note, though, that these conversion coordinates correspond to a given value

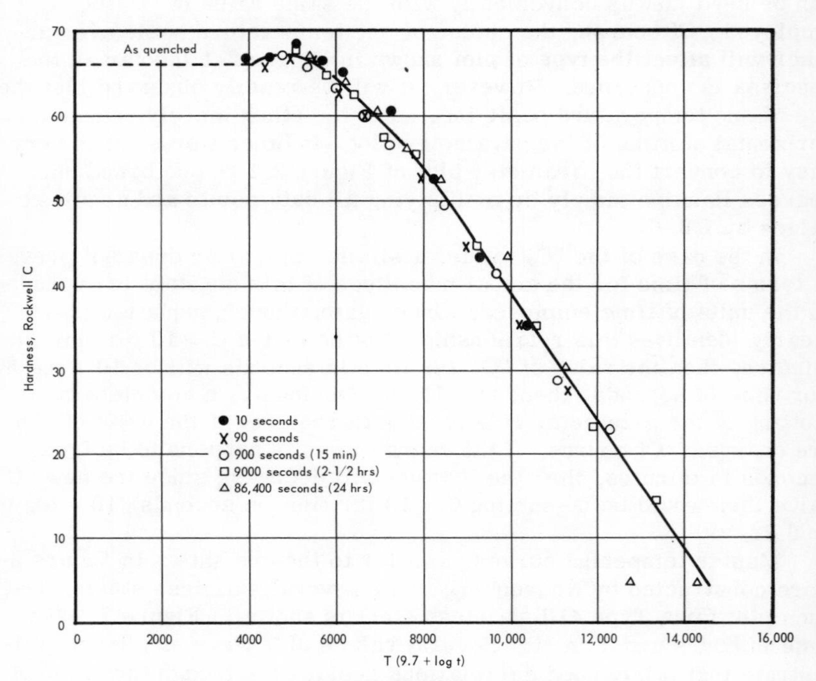

Figure 2-1 – Hardness versus tempering parameter for fully quenched 0.96 percent carbon steel(2).

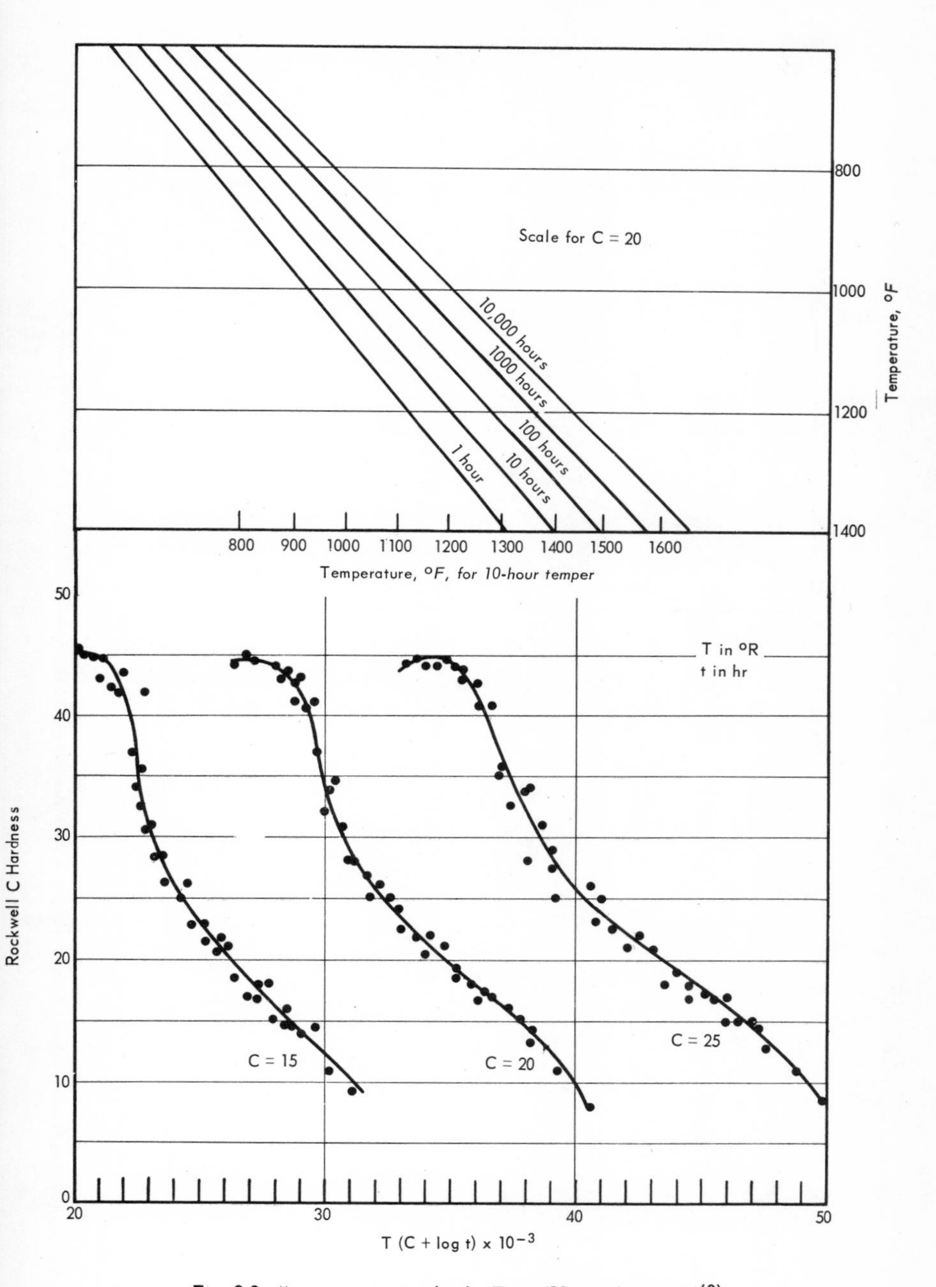

Fig. 2-2 – Master tempering plot for Type 410 stainless steel[3].

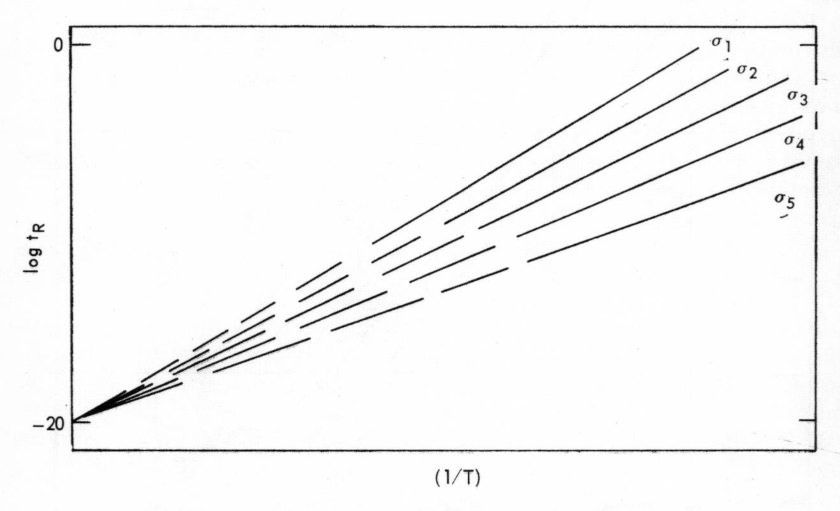

Figure 2-3 – Plot of log t_R versus (1/T) for various stresses.

of C and must be adjusted for each change in the value of this constant. It will also be noted that for a given C value it is possible to select one or several test times and construct a temperature scale, corresponding to this behavior, across the top of the master plot. Such a scale is shown in Figure 2-2 for 10-hour behavior and represents a common usage in this type of data presentation.

Recognizing that the creep behavior of metals had some similarity with tempering phenomena, Larson and Miller[1] reasoned that the time-temperature relations of creep and rupture might correlate using the same approach as used by Hollomon and Jaffe.[2] This reasoning proved quite sound and what is now known as the Larson-Miller parameter was introduced. Paralleling equation (2-8) it was proposed that the relation between time to rupture, t_R, and temperature, T, at a given constant stress could be described* as:

$$T\,(C + \log t_R) = \text{constant} \qquad (2\text{-}11)$$

where the left-hand side defines the Larson-Miller parameter, C is the Larson-Miller constant which is material dependent and T is in degrees absolute. At a constant stress, then, rupture occurs at any given time-temperature combination which is consistent with the parameter value. Also, if rupture at a given stress is known to occur at a given combination of time, t_{R_1}, and temperature, T_1, then from equation (2-11):

---

*In a subsequent discussion [4] the creep rate, r, was expressed in the familiar form:

$$r = A\,e^{-Q/RT}$$

where Q is the activation energy for creep and A is a constant for a given material and stress level. Assuming that the time for rupture to occur varies inversely with the creep rate, it is possible to replace r by the reciprocal of the rupture time. Making this substitution and then taking logarithms leads, on rearranging, to:

$$T(C + \log t_R) = Q/2.3R = \text{constant}$$

This is obviously identical to equation (2-11).

Some mention should be made of the expression developed by Machlin and Nowick[45] based on rate theory. This equation had the form:

$$\log t_R = \frac{A + BT - D\sigma}{T}$$

where A and B are constants and D is a function of temperature. Simple rearrangement yields:

$$T\,(\log t_R - B) = A - D\sigma$$

which is very similar to the Larson-Miller parameter. However, the fact that D is temperature dependent causes this approach to differ from that described in equation (2-11). Little success has been achieved by this Machlin-Nowick approach and its application and usefulness are at the moment very limited.

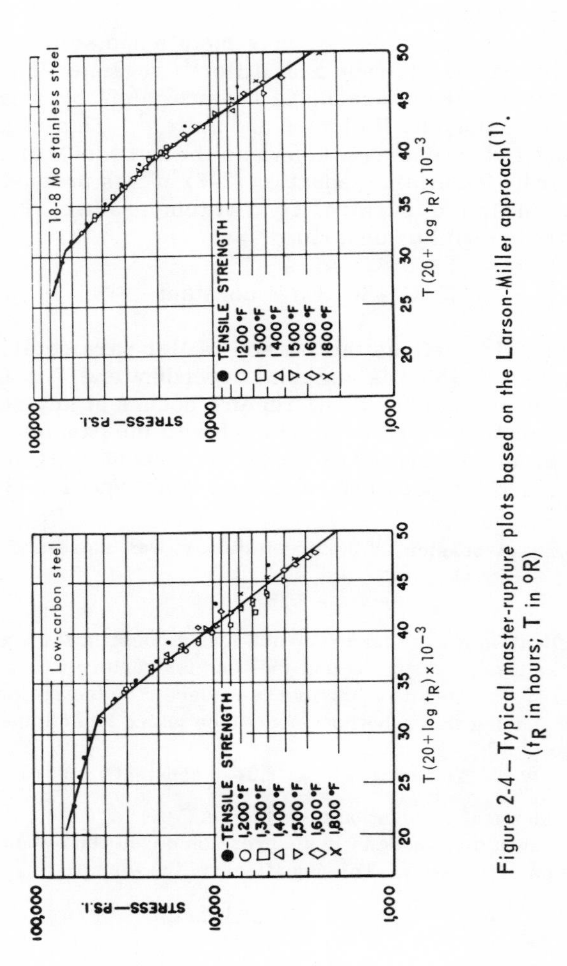

Figure 2-4 – Typical master-rupture plots based on the Larson-Miller approach[1]. (t_R in hours; T in °R)

$$T_1 \; (C + \log t_{R_1}) = T_2 \; (C + \log t_{R_2}) \tag{2-12}$$

and the temperature, T_2, corresponding to rupture in a certain time, t_{R_2}, can be calculated directly. Of course, due to the identical nature of equations (2-12) and (2-9) the Larson-Miller constant, C, can be calculated from equation (2-10) once any two pairs of time-temperature values are known.

Values for C can also be obtained graphically. A slight rearrangement of equation (2-11) leads to:

$$\log t_R = -C + \frac{\text{constant}}{T} \tag{2-13}$$

hence, a plot of $\log t_R$ versus $(1/T)$ will be linear and the intercept of this plot at $(1/T) = 0$ will yield the value of -C. Such a plot for other stresses should yield similar straight lines with a common intercept as shown in Figure 2-3. This calculation of the Larson-Miller constant is clearly influenced by all the time-temperature combinations available for a given material and is preferable and certainly more representative than a value based on only two time-temperature pairs (a least squares approach to the calculation of the Larson-Miller constant will be described below).

Once the value of C has been identified, the Larson-Miller parameter values can be calculated and a master-rupture plot prepared. Several of these plots are shown in Figure 2-4 where a value of C = 20 has been employed. (It is extremely interesting that the C value of 20 which Larson and Miller found to apply adequately to so many sets of rupture data is identical to the value found by Nehrenberg to represent the tempering data of so many metals and alloys.)

Ordinarily master-rupture plots are constructed from relatively short-term rupture data. Once such a plot is available, a prediction of longer term rupture behavior is made possible. Such plots are also helpful in providing a comparison of the stress-rupture (or creep-rupture) characteristics of several materials (see Figure 2-5). In this type of comparison, though, the same value of the Larson-Miller constant must apply to all materials if a direct comparison is to be made.

A thorough familiarity with the type of plot shown in Figure 2-5 is recommended in order to enable accurate comparisons to be made of the stress-rupture behavior of different materials. It is well to note, for example, that if materials A and B have the same C value and if the parametric curve for material A is coincident with that for material B then identical stress-rupture behavior is indicated. Such a situation is shown schematically in Figure 2-6I where $C_A = C_B = 20$. Obviously, stress-rupture isotherms reconstructed from this plot would be identical for both materials. In Figure 2-6II, all materials (A, B, and D) are assumed to have a C value of 20. However, material D is stronger than material B and material B in turn is stronger than material A. In other words, if all the materials being compared have the same value of C, then, no matter what this value of C is (i.e., it need not be 20),

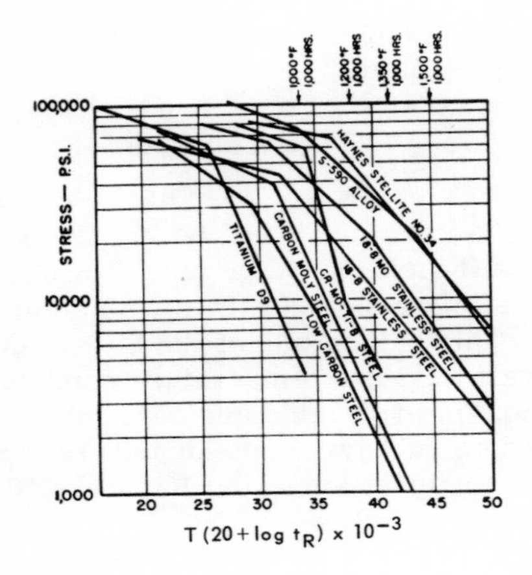

Figure 2-5 – Comparison of rupture characteristics of various materials(1).

the material with the parameter curve which is farthest to the left will be the weaker material. Conversely, the strongest material will have a parameter curve which is positioned nearest the right-hand side of the parameter plot. It should be noted that the fact that the lines in Figure 2-6II are drawn parallel will cause the isotherms of all three materials to be parallel. In other words, the rupture life for all three materials will exhibit the same stress dependency even though the relative strengths of the three materials are quite different. Different stress dependencies are illustrated in Figure 2-6III. Material B is shown to be stronger than material A; but a given change in stress will cause a greater change in the rupture life of material B than it will for material A. Of course, it also follows that on the familiar log stress versus log t_R plot a given isotherm will be steeper in the case of material A. A different situation is shown in Figure 2-6IV where the stronger material (i.e., B) has the smaller stress dependency. Although not shown in Figure 2-6, it should be clear that parameter lines can cross to represent different relative strengths in different stress ranges. From the examples given in Figure 2-6, it should be clear that if the parameter plot is linear then the log stress-log rupture time isotherms will also be linear. Naturally, if the parameter plot is curved then the log stress-log rupture time isotherms must also be curved. Regarding the question of curvature of the parameter plot, it seems safe to say categorically that any curvature will be concave downward. While it might not be completely accurate to say that no parameter plot can be concave upward, this type of behavior is extremely rare.

It is definitely in order to consider the type of comparison plots shown in Figures 2-5 and 2-6 for those cases involving different values of the Larson-Miller constant, C. In the first place, as already has been stated, when different C values are encountered a direct comparison of the relative strengths of the materials being considered is not possible. Some generalizations can however be made. For example, in Figure 2-6V materials A and B are shown to have the same parameter plot. But since $C_B > C_A$ it can be deduced that material A is stronger than material B. This follows from the fact that at a given stress each material has the same parameter value which is only brought about at the same temperature by having the rupture time for material A greater than that for material B. In other words, at the same temperature and stress, material A exhibits a rupture time greater than that of material B and, hence, the former is stronger. It is also correct to generalize by saying that any material with a Larson-Miller constant greater than C_B, and with a parameter line or curve, positioned to the left of the material B line or curve will be weaker than material B. No generalization, however, can be made regarding materials with C values less than C_B and with parameter curves to the left of the material B parameter curve. A similar obstacle to generalization involves materials with C values greater than C_B and with parameter curves positioned to the right of the curve for material B. It

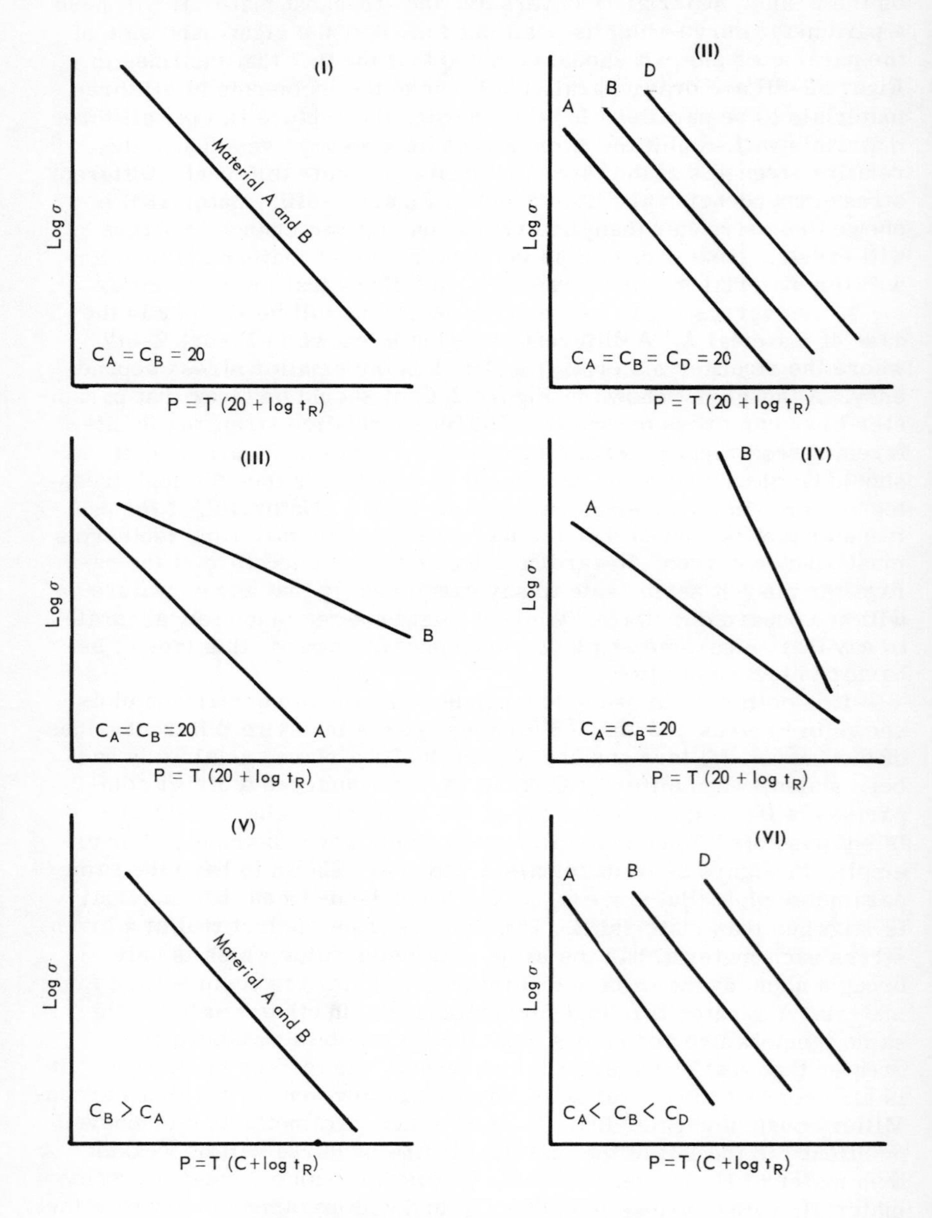

Figure 2-6 – Typical Larson-Miller parameter plots.

is easy to show that material A with $C_A < C_B$ could have a strength identical with that of material B and still have a parameter curve to the left of that of material B. By the same token, a material D with $C_D > C_B$ could have a parameter curve positioned to the right of the curve for material B and still have a strength similar to the strength of material B. This situation is illustrated in Figure 2-6VI. Observe that it is quite possible for material A to have the greater strength of these three materials. It is also possible for material D to be stronger than material B and for material A to be stronger than material B. It is important, therefore, to recognize the important effect of the C value in comparing stress-rupture behavior on this type of parameter plot.

From what has just been said it can be recognized that if the materials involved have different C values then the type of comparison plot shown in Figure 2-5 will not lend itself to a direct comparison of strength. In other words, it is not possible to view the type of plot shown in Figure 2-6VI and make a direct comparison of the stress-rupture behavior of various materials. A brief assessment, however, of the relative magnitudes of the C values will make a fairly accurate comparison possible. It can be noted in Figure 2-6VI, for example, that even for equal strength the parameter curve for material D must fall to the right of material B just due to the higher value of C. Hence, the higher parameter values for material D when compared at the same stress level are due to this single factor. As a matter of fact, for equal strengths of materials B and D, the parameter curve for D will be displaced a distance to the right of the B curve equal approximately to the ratio of C_D/C_B. Therefore, if $C_D = 22$ and $C_B = 20$, then at a given stress value the parameter ratio, P_D/P_B, should be approximately equal to the ratio C_D/C_B. In such a case, the materials would have equal strengths. Actually, the parameter ratio will be slightly less than the ratio of C values due to the effect of the log t_R term. For example, employing $C_D = 22$ and $C_B = 20$ equal strengths will be indicated for a rupture time of 1 hour when the parameter ratio is 1.1 (i.e., same as C ratio); for $t_R = 10$ hours, the parameter ratio corresponding to equal strengths would be 1.09; and for 100-hour rupture, the parameter ratio would be 1.086. Hence, for an approximate comparison of the relative strengths of various materials having different C values, the ratio of C values provides a convenient criterion. If the ratio of the parameter values at a given stress is equal to the C-value ratio, then approximately equal strength is indicated; if the parameter ratio is greater than the C-value ratio, then higher strength is indicated; then if the parameter ratio is less than the C-value ratio, lower strength is suggested. Based on these remarks, a few simple calculations (made mentally for approximate results) will enable a comparison of relative material strengths to be made when different C values are involved in the type of plot shown in Figure 2-5.

A comparison more accurate than that just described is made possible by the use of a graphical aid similar to that shown in Figure 2-2.

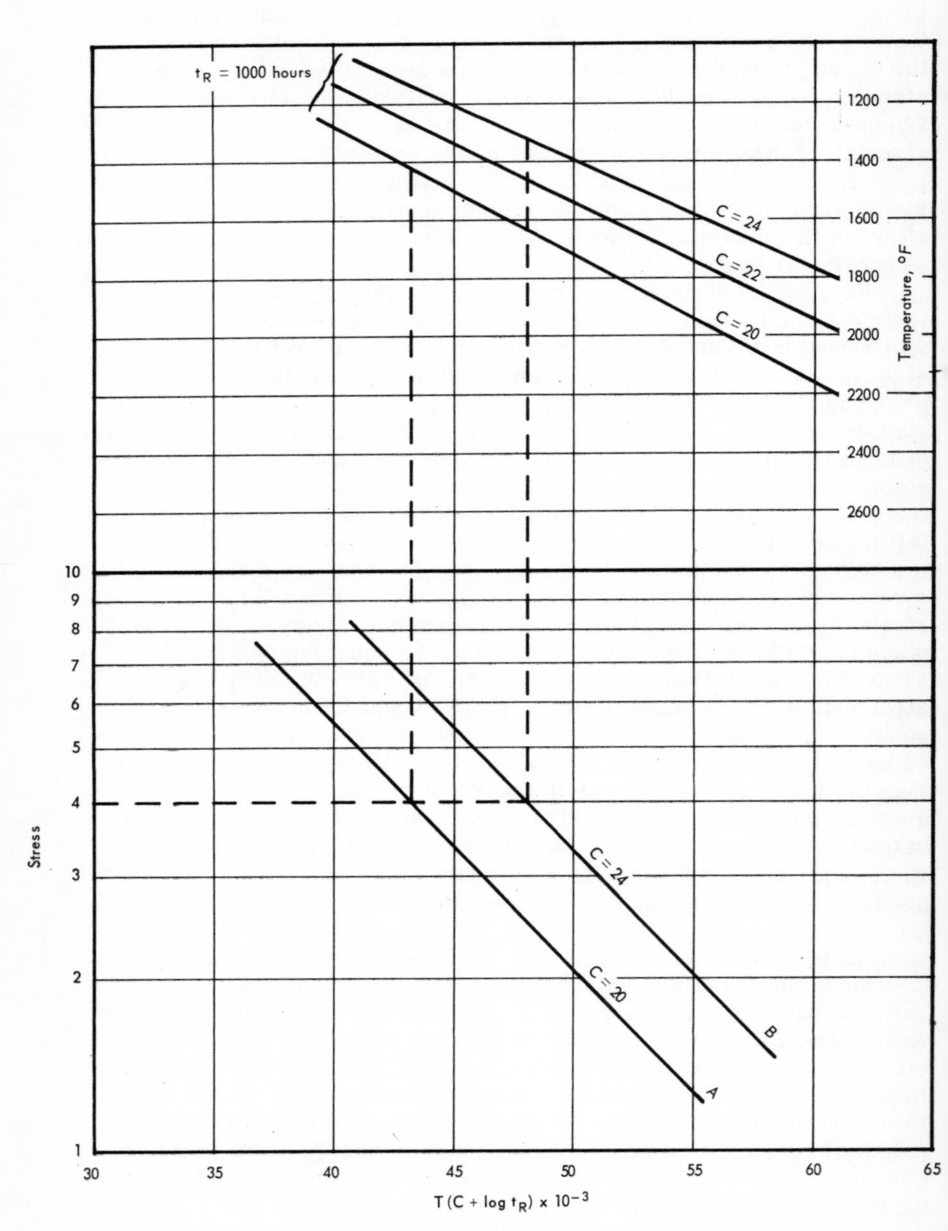

Figure 2-7 – Graphical aid used in conjunction with comparison plot of rupture behavior.

Instead of lines of various rupture times, lines of various C values are employed. Such a construction must correspond to a given rupture time so that a rupture life in the intended use range should be chosen. An illustration is presented in Figure 2-7 in which the lines representing the various C values are based on t_R = 1000 hours. Then for the two materials represented (C_B = 24 and C_A = 20) a line of constant stress is chosen and the parameter values, P_A and P_B, are located. Proceeding vertically to intersect the appropriate C-value line identifies the temperature corresponding to 1000-hour rupture life for each material. In the example shown, material A is the stronger of the two since 1000-hour life is achieved at a higher temperature. A disadvantage associated with this type of plot is that the comparison is based on only one rupture time. At the expense of a little more complexity, another set of C-value lines could be employed, for perhaps 10-hour rupture life, which allows results to be obtained over a fairly extensive range of rupture times.

A more useful plot has been developed[40] to allow a convenient comparison of the relative rupture strengths of materials in terms of the Larson-Miller parameter when different C values are involved. Special graph paper has been developed as shown in Figure 2-8. If such a plot is used to present the parametric results of several different materials then whether these materials have the same or different C values, a rather simple graphical solution enables a rapid evaluation of the relative strengths of the materials under consideration. As illustrated in Figure 2-8, a comparison begins by drawing a line of constant stress to locate P_A and P_B. Projecting these points vertically locates two points on the P scale at the top of the graph. A straight edge is then used to connect these points in turn with the same temperature value and the intersection of these two lines with the α scale is located. Then lines drawn from the corresponding C values (on the C scale) through the corresponding points of intersection on the α scale locate the rupture times on the t_R scale. In this way, all the information necessary to the comparison of the relative strengths is obtainable. This simple procedure can then be repeated for other stress levels at the same temperature to establish the isotherms for the two materials. In this way, a fairly accurate comparison is provided in a relatively short time.

It will be noted that the graphical aid used in Figure 2-8 is a nomograph to solve:

$$P = T(C + \log t_R)$$

A large version of this nomograph is given in Appendix A.

Returning now to the general discussion of the Larson-Miller parameter, it is well known that it is also possible to apply this concept to secondary (linear) creep rate data. In this instance though the parameter has the form:

$$P = T(C - \log \dot{\epsilon}_s) \qquad (2\text{-}14)$$

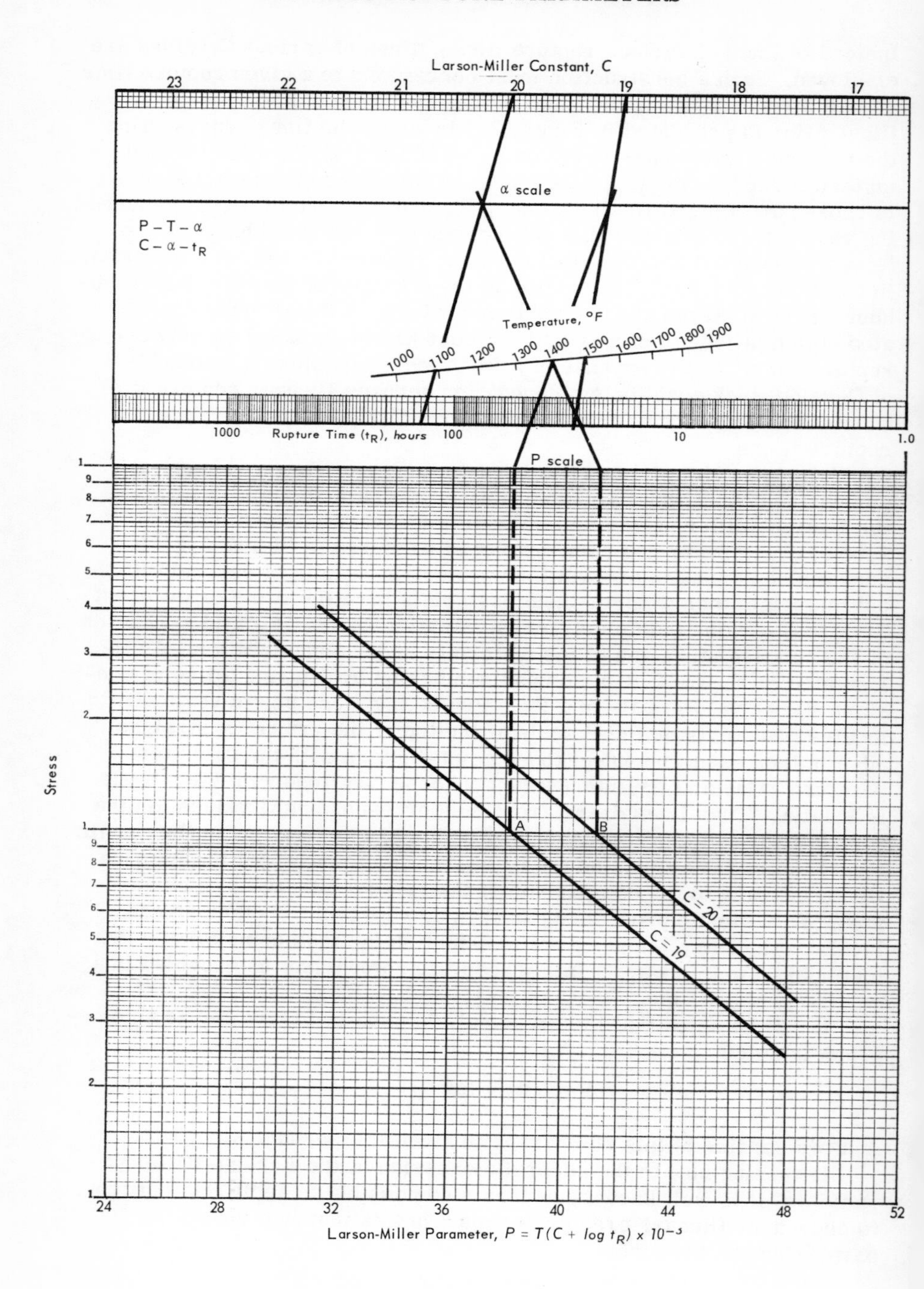

Figure 2-8 – Special graph paper[40] for Larson-Miller parameter plots.

where $\dot{\epsilon}_s$ is the secondary stage creep rate. Master-rupture type plots based on linear creep rates are identical in form (see Figure 2-9) to those obtained with rupture data. Of course, the minus sign in equation (2-14) represents a slight difference compared to equation (2-11) and, hence, the equation for calculating C will differ accordingly but this modification is easily made. It was also pointed out by Larson-Miller that a parametric approach to the correlation of strain data is possible. In this case the time term in equation (2-11) would represent the time corresponding to a given elongation (1 percent, for example). Other plots could then be made to represent data for various other elongations. Naturally, if the C value were the same for all elongations, this comparison could be made on a single plot. Unfortunately, this situation does not usually exist. Different values of C are usually necessary as the strain values change and, hence, single-plot comparisons of strain data are not possible. Actually, the Larson-Miller parameter approach (or any other parameter approach for that matter) has not been employed too extensively in the analysis of strain behavior. Why this is so is not known at this time but it might be due to the fact that the parameter approach is not as sound for use with strain data. For example, it is easy to see that the Larson-Miller approach does not make any allowances for ϵ_0 (instantaneous elongation on loading) values. Since these values, even for a constant stress, are a function of temperature, it is not unexpected that some difficulty would be encountered in an attempt to construct parameter plots for strain data. This failure to account for ϵ_0 values would be particularly noticeable in the region of small strain values and would probably lead to excessive scatter in the parameter versus stress plot. Perhaps only at high strains, where the effect of different ϵ_0 values is not too significant or when ϵ_0 is essentially zero, wou d the strain correlation be possible.

For a given value of C, it is possible to employ equation (2-12) and calculate equivalent conditions for rupture at a given stress. Employing a C value of 20, Larson and Miller have shown the following rupture conditions to be equivalent:

	Operating Conditions		Test Conditions
1	10,000 hours at 1000°F	=	13 hours at 1200°F
2	1,000 hours at 1200°F	=	12 hours at 1350°F
3	1,000 hours at 1350°F	=	17 hours at 1500°F
4	1,000 hours at 300°F	=	1.1 hours at 400°F

Rupture stresses for these conditions have been prepared[1] and are listed in Tables 2-1 through 2-4. It can be seen that the agreement between long- and short-term rupture data is excellent. Also, the agreement, in Table 2-4, between long- and short-term strain behavior is quite impressive.

In the Larson-Miller study, data for some 40 materials were evaluated and it was found that the Larson-Miller constant was very

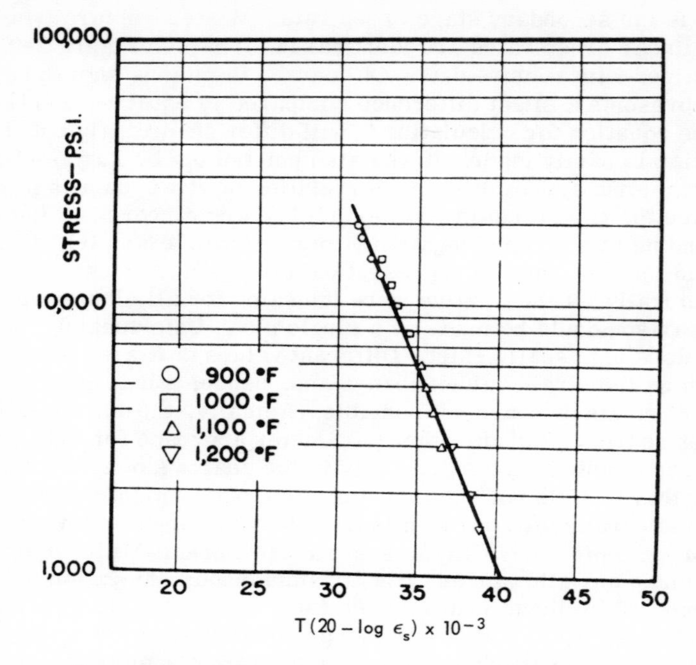

Figure 2-9 – Master creep rate plot for carbon-moly steel[1].

TABLE 2-1

COMPARISON OF 10,000-HR RUPTURE STRENGTH AT 1000°F WITH 13-HR RUPTURE STRENGTH AT 1200°F FOR LOW-ALLOY STEELS[1]

Steel	Stress for rupture in 10,000 hr at 1000 F psi	Stress for rupture in 13 hr at 1200 F, psi
C-Steel	7000	8000
C-Mo	12000	12000
Sicromo-5S	13000	12000
Sicromo-3	15000	13000
Sicromo-2	15000	14000
2 Cr-Mo	15000	14000
5 Cr-Mo	17000	13000
2¼ Cr-1 Mo	19000	17000
DM-2	22000	18000
DM	23000	17000

TABLE 2-2

COMPARISON OF 1000-HR RUPTURE STRENGTH AT 1350°F WITH 17-HR RUPTURE STRENGTH AT 1500°F FOR HIGH-TEMPERATURE ALLOYS(1)

Alloy	Stress for rupture in 1000 hr at 1350 F, psi	Stress for rupture in 17 hr at 1500 F, psi
Inconel	8000	9000
Timken	19000	20000
Hastelloy B	19000	22000
N-155	24000	25000
S-590	25000	26000
H.S.-34	29000	28000
H.S.-88	30000	30000
S-816	30000	30000
X-40	34000	32000
Inconel X	41000	39000

TABLE 2-3

COMPARISON OF 1000-HR RUPTURE STRENGTH AT 300°F WITH 1.1-HR RUPTURE STRENGTH AT 400°F FOR ALUMINUM ALLOYS(1)

Alloy	Stress for rupture in 1000 hr at 300 F, psi	Stress for rupture in 1.1 hr at 400 F, psi
99.6% Al-H12	6000	6000
99.6% Al-H18	6000	8000
2S-H12	6000	7000
3S-H12	11500	10000
3S-H18	13500	12000
52S-H38	12500	17000
61S-T6	28000	27000
24S-T3	40000	43000

TABLE 2-4

COMPARISON OF 1000-HR CREEP STRENGTH AT 1200°F WITH 12-HR CREEP STRENGTH AT 1350°F FOR STAINLESS SHEET ALLOYS(1)

Type	Stress for 1 per cent creep in 1000 hr at 1200 F	Stress for 1 per cent creep in 12 hr at 1350 F
321-CR[a]	3000	3600
Inconel-A[b]	9000	10000
347-CR	10500	11500
321-A	13000	15500
Inconel-CR	17000	19000
347-A	18000	17500
316-A	19000	16000
Timken-CR	26000	28500
316-CR	29000	27500
Inconel-X	52000	56000

[a] CR = cold-rolled.
[b] A = annealed.

Table 2-5. Value of C in Parameter $T(C + \log t_R)$ for Several Alloys[1]

Alloy	Value of C (for t_R in hours, and T in deg R)
Low-carbon steel	18
Carbon-moly steel	19
2-1/4 Cr - 1 Mo steel	23
Cr-Mo-Ti-B steel	22
18-8 stainless steel	18
18-8-Mo stainless steel	17
25-20 stainless steel	15
S-590 alloy	20
Haynes Stellite No. 34	20
Titanium D9	20

close to 20 for all materials. A partial listing of Larson-Miller constants is presented in Table 2-5. Values ranging from 17 to 23 are noted. This observation that the C value is close to 20 has led to some general acceptance that the Larson-Miller constant is the same for all materials. As a matter of fact, graph paper is available commercially based on the use of C = 20. However, for best results, each set of data should be evaluated individually and the appropriate or what might be called the "optimum" C value determined. In later discussions some values for C will be noted which deviate quite markedly from the value which Larson and Miller found to apply to essentially all the materials studied.

LEAST SQUARES APPROACH TO PARAMETER ANALYSIS

While the analytical expression given by equation (2-10) and the graphical solution of Figure 2-3 can both be used to obtain the value of the Larson-Miller constant, certain disadvantages are involved. In one, too few data are employed and the C value obtained might not be representative. In the other case, all available data are used but some arbitrary judgment must be introduced to locate the common intercept. These disadvantages are removed and a unique solution obtained using a least squares approach. Because of the simplicity of equation (2-13), a very basic least squares calculation would lead to values for the slope and intercept (C) values for a given stress. Written in usual least squares notation (see Chapter 10) the following relations apply at a given stress level:

$$\sum \log t_R = -n\,C + b \sum (1/T) \tag{2-15}$$

$$\sum \frac{\log t_R}{T} = -C \sum (1/T) + b \sum (1/T)^2 \tag{2-16}$$

where C is the Larson-Miller constant, b is a constant (actually the slope of the line in Figure 2-3) and n represents the number of data points at a given stress. Direct solution is possible and it is clear that a definite value for C is obtained. Such an approach, however, will lead to slightly different C values for each stress and while these would not differ very much some question would arise concerning which value of C should be selected to represent the given material. In a specially developed least squares approach, Manson and Mendelson[5] proposed a procedure to allow stress-rupture data for all stress levels to be analyzed simultaneously in obtaining a single least squares value for C. A simple substitution in equation (2-13) gives:

$$y = a + bL \tag{2-17}$$

where:

$y = \log t_R$

$L = (1/T)$

$a = -C$

and $b = \text{constant}$

For the first, second and jth constant stress lines in Figure 2-3

$$y_I = a + b_I L_I \tag{2-18}$$

$$y_{II} = a + b_{II} L_{II} \tag{2-19}$$

and

$$y_j = a + b_j L_j \tag{2-20}$$

Since these lines have a common intercept the principle of least squares may now be employed to calculate this intercept value along with the least squares value of b corresponding to each stress level. In this approach the sum of the squares of the residuals, S, will be given by:

$$S = \sum (R)^2 = \sum_{i=1}^{N_I} (y - a - b_I L)_I^2 + \sum_{i=1}^{N_{II}} (y - a - b_{II} L)_{II}^2 + \ldots$$

$$+ \sum_{i=1}^{N_P} (y - a - b_P L)_P^2 \tag{2-21}$$

where:
P is the number of stress levels being analyzed and N_I, N_{II}, etc. are the number of experimental points at stress levels I, II, etc. Following the usual least squares approach to minimize the sum of the squares of the residuals, equation (2-21) is differentiated with respect to a, b_I, b_{II}, etc. to b_P. Then these deriatives are set equal to zero to define the minimum. These derivatives yield:

for a

$$N_T a + b_I \sum_{i=1}^{N_I} L_I + b_{II} \sum_{i=1}^{N_{II}} L_{II} + \ldots + b_p \sum_{i=1}^{N_P} L_p = \sum_{i=1}^{N_T} y \tag{2-22}$$

where N_T is the sum of N_I, N_{II}, etc. to N_P. Then for b_I:

$$a \sum_{i=1}^{N_I} L_I + b_I \sum_{i=1}^{N_I} (L)_I^2 = \sum_{i=1}^{N_I} (y\ L)_I \tag{2-23}$$

for b_{II}

$$a \sum_{i=1}^{N_{II}} L_{II} + b_{II} \sum_{i=1}^{N_{II}} (L)_{II}^2 = \sum_{i=1}^{N_{II}} (y\ L)_{II} \tag{2-24}$$

and for b_P

$$a \sum_{i=1}^{N_P} L_P + b_P \sum_{i=1}^{N_P} (L)_P^2 = \sum_{i=1}^{N_P} (y\ L)_P \tag{2-25}$$

Now equation (2-23) can be written as:

$$a A_I + b_I B_I = C_I \tag{2-26}$$

or in general for the jth stress level:

$$a A_j + b_j B_j = C_j \tag{2-27}$$

where:

$$A_j = \sum_{i=1}^{N_j} L_j \tag{2-28}$$

$$B_j = \sum_{i=1}^{N_j} (L)_j^2 \tag{2-29}$$

$$C_j = \sum_{i=1}^{N_j} (y\ L)_j \tag{2-30}$$

Solution of equation (2-27) reveals:

$$b_j = \frac{C_j - a A_j}{B_j} \tag{2-31}$$

Also, equation (2-22) can now be written as:

$$N_T a + \sum_{j=1}^{P} b_j A_j = \sum_{i=1}^{N_T} y \tag{2-32}$$

Substitution of equation (2-31) into equation (2-32) and solving yields:

$$a = \frac{\sum_{i=1}^{N_T} y - \sum_{j=1}^{P} \frac{A_j C_j}{B_j}}{N_T - \sum_{j=1}^{P} \frac{A_j^2}{B_j}} \qquad (2\text{-}33)$$

All the necessary summation terms in this equation can be evaluated from a given set of stress-rupture data involving various stress levels to enable the value of "a" (actually -C) to be obtained. Then with "a" calculated, equation (2-31) is employed to yield the value of b for each stress level. This value need be calculated only if the constant stress lines in Figure 2-3 are to be positioned. Otherwise, this calculation is unnecessary.

An illustration of the evaluation of equation (2-33) is presented in Table 2-6 for a set of data involving 6, 7, and 8 data points at stress levels, I, II, and III, respectively.

In most cases, stress-rupture data are obtained at constant temperature to yield the familiar stress-rupture isotherms on log stress (or stress) versus log rupture time plots. Such plots can, of course, be used to obtain the constant stress data to be employed in the data analysis just described. However, this conversion of constant temperature data into data at constant stress is not necessary for Manson and Mendelson[5] have proposed a least squares technique which is applicable directly to the isothermal data. In this approach the data are analyzed in terms of the Larson-Miller parameter, P, and an expression between P and log stress evolves: In general, the relation between P and log stress is of the form:

$$(y + C)T = a_0 + a_1 x + a_2 x^2 + \ldots + a_m x^m \qquad (2\text{-}34)$$

where $x = \log \sigma$ and, as before, $y = \log t_R$. Once the Larson-Miller constant, C, is identified along with a_0, $a_1 \ldots a_m$ then the master-rupture curve can be constructed. Usually a satisfactory analysis is obtained with no more than a second or third degree polynomial in equation (2-34) although many instances of a form linear in log stress (i.e., first degree) have been identified.

Rearranging equation (2-34) leads to:

$$y = -C + a_0 L + a_1 Lx + a_2 Lx^2 + \ldots + a_m Lx^m \qquad (2\text{-}35)$$

where, as before, $L = (1/T)$. Then the sum of the squares of the residuals is given by:

$$S = \sum_{i=1}^{N} (y + C - a_0 L - a_1 Lx - a_2 Lx^2 - \ldots - a_m Lx^m)^2 \qquad (2\text{-}36)$$

Table 2-6. Evaluation of Summation Terms for Use in Equation (2-33)

	$y = \log t_R$	$L = (\frac{1}{T})$	$L^2 = (\frac{1}{T})^2$	$y\,L = \frac{\log t_R}{T}$	
σ_I, $N_I = 6$	⋮	⋮	⋮	⋮	
	Σ_I	$\Sigma = A_I$	$\Sigma = B_I$	$\Sigma = C_I$	$\frac{A_I C_I}{B_I}$ and $\frac{A_I^2}{B_I}$
σ_{II}, $N_{II} = 7$	⋮	⋮	⋮	⋮	
	Σ_{II}	$\Sigma = A_{II}$	$\Sigma = B_{II}$	$\Sigma = C_{II}$	$\frac{A_{II} C_{II}}{B_{II}}$ and $\frac{A_{II}^2}{B_{II}}$
σ_{III}, $N_{III} = 8$	⋮	⋮	⋮	⋮	
	Σ_{III}	$\Sigma = A_{III}$	$\Sigma = B_{III}$	$\Sigma = C_{III}$	$\frac{A_{III} C_{III}}{B_{III}}$ and $\frac{A_{III}^2}{B_{III}}$

$$\sum_{i=1}^{N_T} y = \Sigma_I + \Sigma_{II} + \Sigma_{III}$$

$$N_T = 21$$

$$\sum_{j=1}^{P} \frac{A_j C_j}{B_j} \text{ and } \sum_{j=1}^{P} \frac{A_j^2}{B_j}$$

Minimizing the sum of the squares of the residuals by differentiating equation (2-36) with respect to C, a_0, a_1, etc. leads to:

$$\sum_{i=1}^{N} y = -NC + a_0 \sum_{i=1}^{N} L + a_1 \sum_{i=1}^{N} Lx + a_2 \sum_{i=1}^{N} Lx^2 + \ldots + a_m \sum_{i=1}^{N} Lx^m \qquad (2\text{-}37)$$

$$\sum_{i=1}^{N} Ly = -C \sum_{i=1}^{N} L + a_0 \sum_{i=1}^{N} L^2 + a_1 \sum_{i=1}^{N} L^2 x + a_2 \sum_{i=1}^{N} L^2 x^2 + \ldots + a_m \sum_{i=1}^{N} L^2 x^m \qquad (2\text{-}38)$$

$$\sum_{i=1}^{N} L x y = -C \sum_{i=1}^{N} Lx + a_0 \sum_{i=1}^{N} L^2 x + a_1 \sum_{i=1}^{N} L^2 x^2 + a_2 \sum_{i=1}^{N} L^2 x^3 + + \ldots + a_m \sum_{i=1}^{N} L^2 x^{m+1} \qquad (2\text{-}39)$$

etc. to:

$$\sum_{i=1}^{N} Lx^m y = -C \sum_{i=1}^{N} Lx^m + a_0 \sum_{i=1}^{N} L^2 x^m + a_1 \sum_{i=1}^{N} L^2 x^{m+1} + + a_2 \sum_{i=1}^{N} L^2 x^{m+2} + \ldots + a_m \sum_{i=1}^{N} L^2 x^{2m} \qquad (2\text{-}40)$$

In these equations the summation terms are easily evaluated once the degree of the polynomial is selected and then simultaneous solution leads to the constants C, a_0, a_1, etc., to a_m. Obviously, the number of unknown constants is equal to the degree of the polynomial plus two which is also the number of equations which must be solved simultaneously. This type of solution, therefore, not only yields a value for the Larson-Miller constant, C, but it also allows an exact positioning of the master-rupture curve through the calculated values of a_0, a_1, etc. Aunique solution is thus obtained using all the experimental data without any need for adjusting to the constant stress case.

An illustration of the above solution procedure is given in Figure 2-10. This master-rupture plot for molybdenum was formed using the least squares approach applied to stress-rupture data from several investigators covering the temperature range from 870° to 2400°C.

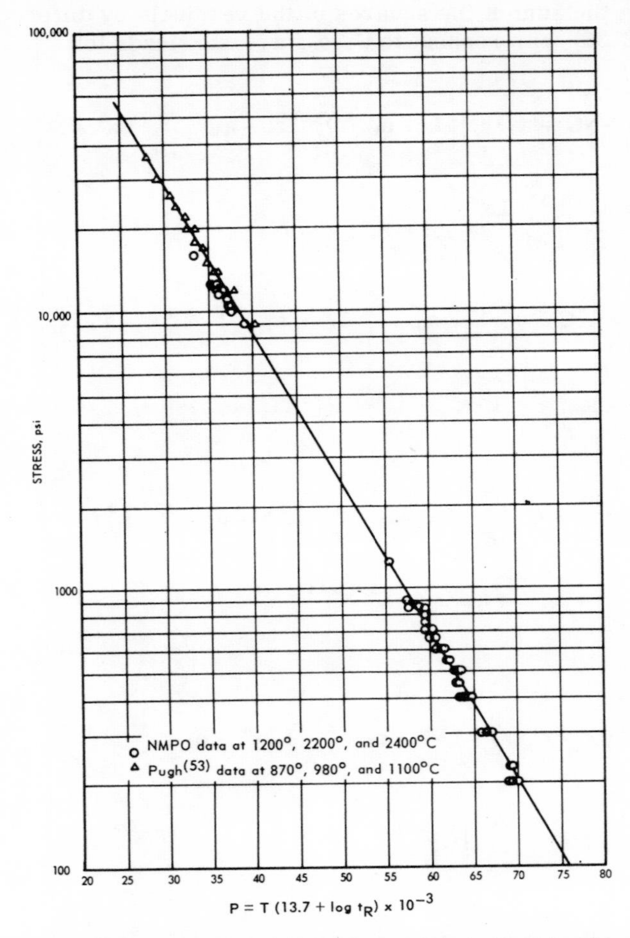

Figure 2-10 – Master-rupture plot for molybdenum based on least squares calculation procedure.

Using a first degree polynomial a value for C = 13.7 was obtained along with a_0 = 112,800 and a_1 = -18,500. A fairly definite linearity in P versus log σ is noted.

Similar analyses for arc-cast tungsten and molybdenum data[6] in the temperature range from 1200° to 3000°C are presented in Figure 2-11A. Fairly linear relationships are defined for both the tungsten and molybdenum data. Using the solid curves in the figure, the stress-rupture isotherms were constructed as shown in Figure 2-11B. As will be noted, the agreement with the experimental points is quite excellent.

Paralleling the use of the hyperbolic sine approach as discussed in Figure 3-6 of Chapter 3 a similar analysis[41] in terms of the Larson-Miller parameter led to the results presented in Figure 2-12. A striking linearity is seen to exist.

SOME RELATIONS WHICH EVOLVE FROM THE LARSON-MILLER APPROACH[21]

In many instances, the relationship between the Larson-Miller parameter, P, and log stress is found to be fairly linear in which case an equation can be fitted which has the following form:

$$P = T(C + \log t_R) = a - b \log \sigma \qquad (2\text{-}41)$$

in which "a" and "b" are constants. Rearranging gives:

$$C + \log t_R = \frac{a}{T} - \frac{b}{T} \log \sigma \qquad (2\text{-}42)$$

and

$$\log \sigma = \frac{T}{b}\left(\frac{a}{T} - C\right) - \frac{T}{b} \log t_R \qquad (2\text{-}43)$$

For a given material (constant C) at a given temperature, the first term on the right-hand side of equation (2-43) is a constant and the equation defines a straight line when log stress is plotted as a function of log rupture time. This is recognized as the standard form usually employed in this type of data presentation. The conclusion from this relationship is that stress-rupture data, which yield a straight line on a log-log plot of stress versus rupture time, suggest the linear form of the Larson-Miller parameter versus log stress shown in equation (2-41). Or saying it another way, the linear parametric relationship of equation (2-41) results only when the stress-rupture data are linear on a log-log plot of stress versus rupture time. The very fact that equation (2-42) applies makes it necessary that the log-log stress-rupture plot be linear.

Another interesting observation can be made in regard to equations (2-41) and (2-42). Note that the slope of the log-log stress-rupture plot, as given in equation (2-43), which is equal to T/b, enables a direct calculation of the constant "b" in equation (2-41). In other words, the slope

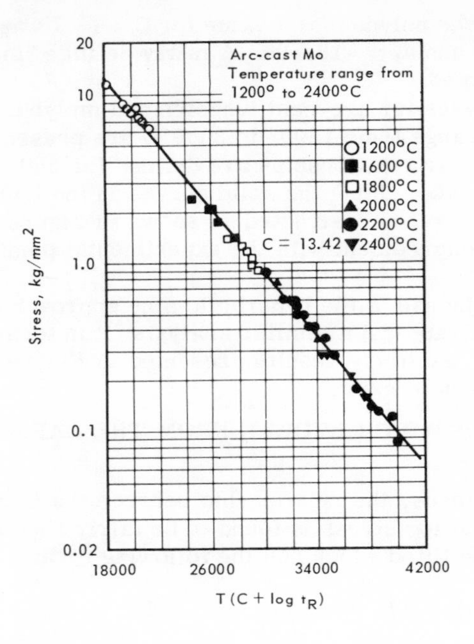

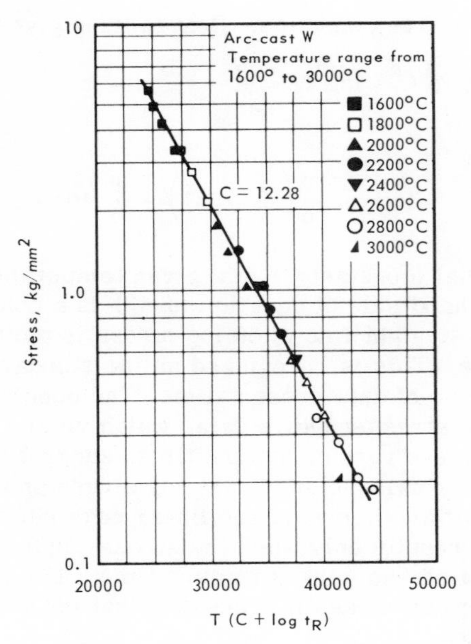

Figure 2-11A – Larson-Miller plots for arc-cast tungsten and molybdenum[6].

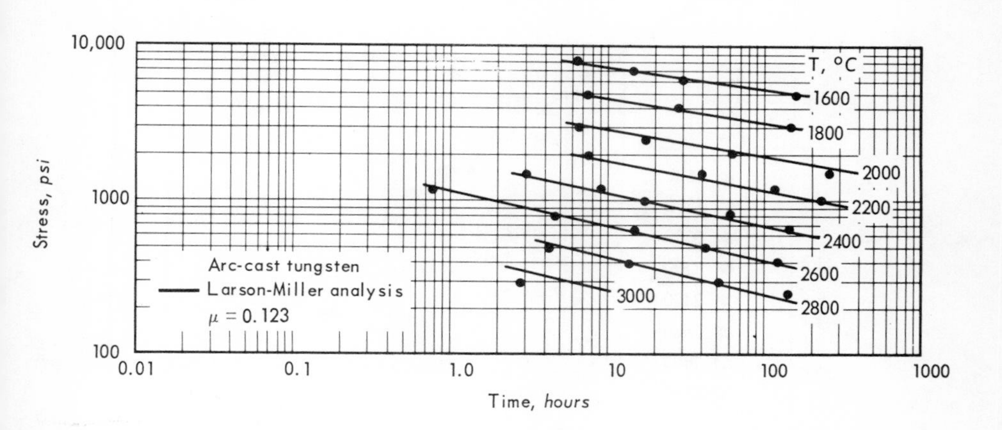

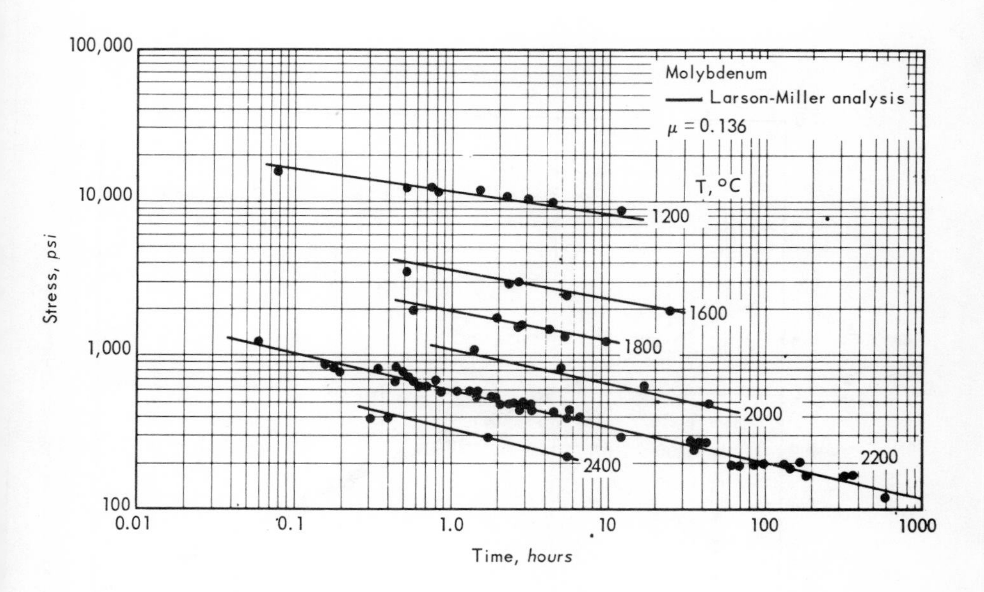

Figure 2-11B – Stress-rupture isotherms constructed from Figure 2-11A.

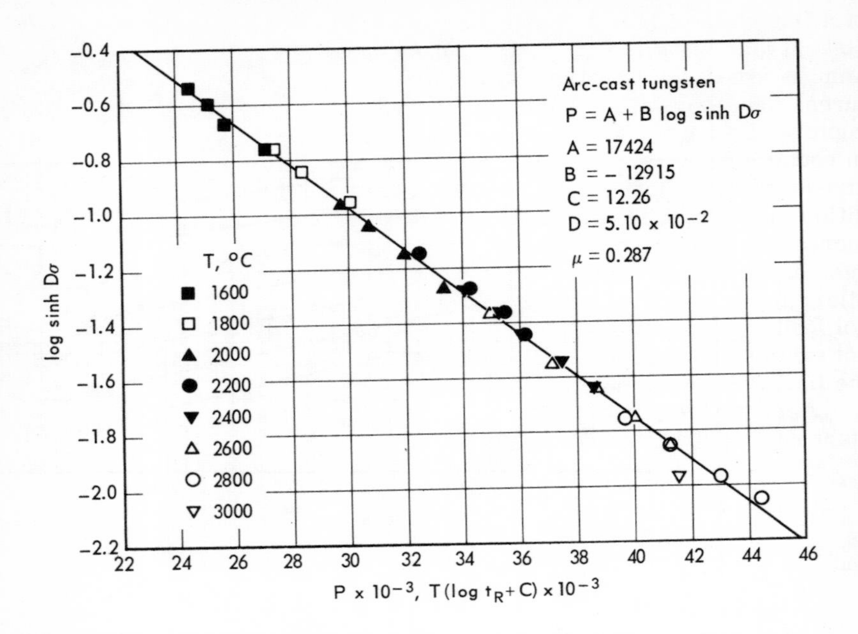

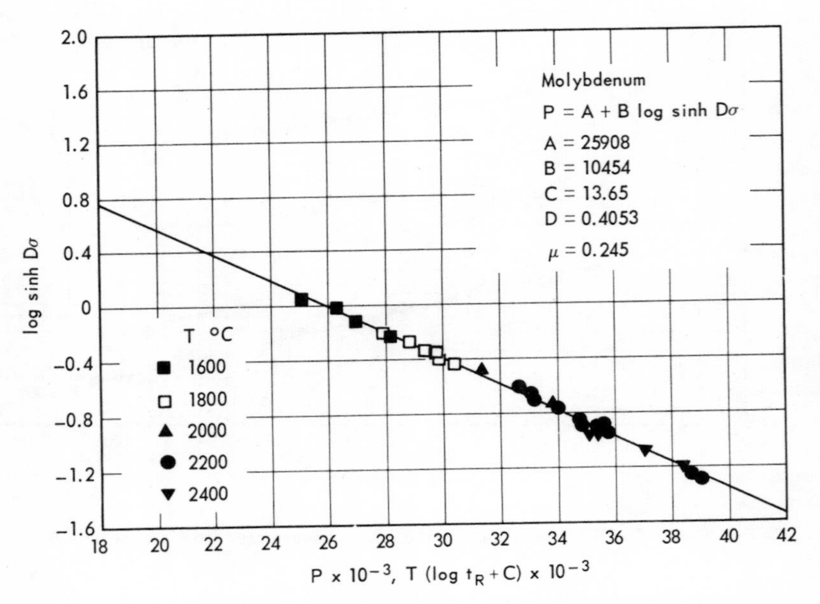

Figure 2-12 – Plot of Larson-Miller parameter as a function of a hyperbolic sine function of stress.

of a line on the common log-log stress-rupture plot leads directly to "b" It also follows that, since in the case of the assumed relationship in equation (2-41) the value of "b" is constant for all temperatures, the slopes of the various isotherms on the log-log stress-rupture plot cannot be the same. Indeed the existence of the relationship in equation (2-41) precludes a system of parallel lines on this common stress-rupture plot. As a matter of fact, it further specifies that in addition to non-parallelism these isotherms must become steeper with increasing temperature. Such a condition is indeed found to exist in the case of the stress-rupture data reported for molybdenum[7]. As a corollary to the above, it may be stated that stress-rupture data which do not lead to a linear log-log stress-rupture plot or whose isotherms do not exhibit a steeper slope as the temperature increases will not yield the linear relationship of equation (2-41).

Applying equation (2-43) to two different temperatures at a constant rupture time results in:

$$\log \sigma_1 = \frac{T_1}{b}\left(\frac{a}{T_1} - C\right) - \frac{T_1}{b} \log t_R \qquad (2\text{-}44)$$

and

$$\log \sigma_2 = \frac{T_2}{b}\left(\frac{a}{T_2} - C\right) - \frac{T_2}{b} \log t_R \qquad (2\text{-}45)$$

Subtracting and rearranging gives:

$$b \log \frac{\sigma_1}{\sigma_2} = C(T_2 - T_1) + \log t_R\,(T_2 - T_1) \qquad (2\text{-}46)$$

and finally:

$$C = \frac{b}{(T_2 - T_1)} \log \frac{\sigma_1}{\sigma_2} - \log t_R \qquad (2\text{-}47)$$

Equation (2-47) affords a rapid and simple method for calculating the Larson-Miller constant from the log-log stress-rupture plot. The slope of a given linear isotherm is measured (this measurement can be made with a ruler if the lengths of the log cycle on ordinate and abscissa are identical) and the value of "b" calculated based on equation (2-43) as:

$$\text{slope} = \frac{-T}{b} \qquad (2\text{-}48)$$

Then at an abscissa (rupture time) value of 1.0 hour (making $\log t_R$ in equation (2-47) equal to zero) read the stress corresponding to rupture for two different temperatures. Substitution in (2-47) yields:

$$C = \frac{b}{(T_2 - T_1)} \log \frac{\sigma_1}{\sigma_2} \qquad (2\text{-}49)$$

Thus, in a matter of a few minutes a value of the Larson-Miller constant can be calculated from a few simple mathematical procedures

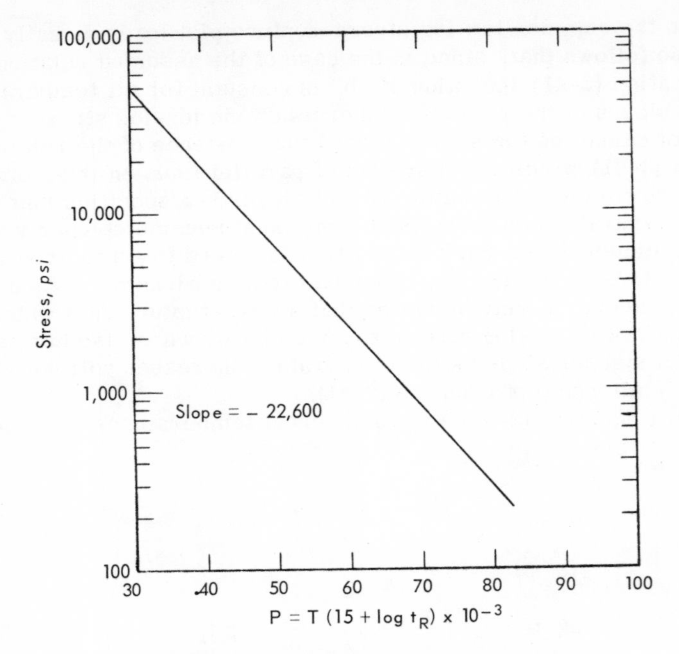

Figure 2-13 – Typical P versus log stress plot.

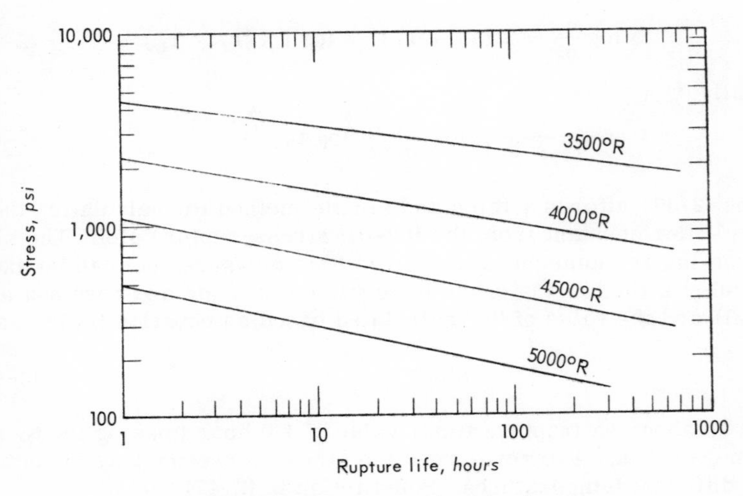

Figure 2-14 – Stress-rupture plot formed using Figure 2-13.

employing data read directly from the log-log plot of stress-rupture data. Of course, it is not to be overlooked that the above reasoning has been based on the linear relationship of equation (2-41) being applicable. However, if as mentioned above, the log-log plot is linear for the various isotherms and if these lines exhibit slopes which become more negative with increasing temperature, then, this is ample justification for proceeding with the above approximate calculation.

Another comment concerning equation (2-41) follows from a simple rearrangement to give:

$$\log \sigma = \frac{-T(C + \log t_R)}{b} + \frac{a}{b} \qquad (2\text{-}50)$$

Differentiation at constant t_R yields:

$$\left(\frac{\partial \log \sigma}{\partial T}\right)_{t_R} = \frac{C + \log t_R}{-b} \qquad (2\text{-}51)$$

This result is significant for it identifies a method by which stress-rupture data of this type (i.e., linear P versus log stress plot) may be interpolated or extrapolated without resorting to the calculation of Larson-Miller constants or parameters. It is noted that since C and b are both constants, the derivative (actually the slope of a log σ versus T plot) given in equation (2-51) will be a constant at a specific value of the rupture time. Hence, a plot of log stress versus the temperature at a constant rupture time will be linear and can be used for convenient interpolation or extrapolation of data. Assuming a typical P versus log stress relationship as shown in Figure 2-13, with C = 15, leads to the stress-rupture data shown in Figure 2-14. When these data are presented in the isochronal plot shown in Figure 2-15, distinct linearity is noted for all three selected values for t_R. Note that although the data for the three rupture times yield a linear relationship the lines are not parallel. This is consistent with equation (2-51) which indicates that for a given material (constant C and b) the slopes of these lines should become more negative as the rupture time increases. In any case, the data presented in the form of Figure 2-15 would allow the positioning of other isotherms in Figure 2-14.

The above considerations have been applied[21] to the existing stress-rupture data for several of the refractory metals; and while the data for these materials are somewhat limited, the basic relationships seem to be substantiated. The stress-rupture data from Green, Smith and Olson[7] for sintered molybdenum in the temperature range from 1650° to 2500°C are plotted in Figure (2-16) for the 1- and 10-hour rupture life. Both lines appear linear in accord with equation (2-51); and in addition, the slope of the 10-hour line is slightly more negative than that of the 1-hour line as suggested by eqaution (2-51). This method of data presentation would indicate that the data at about 4100°F are not consistent and may be in error. Another interesting aspect of this plot is that the calculated slope of the 1-hour line is -6.6×10^{-4} which compares quite favorably with the predicted value based on

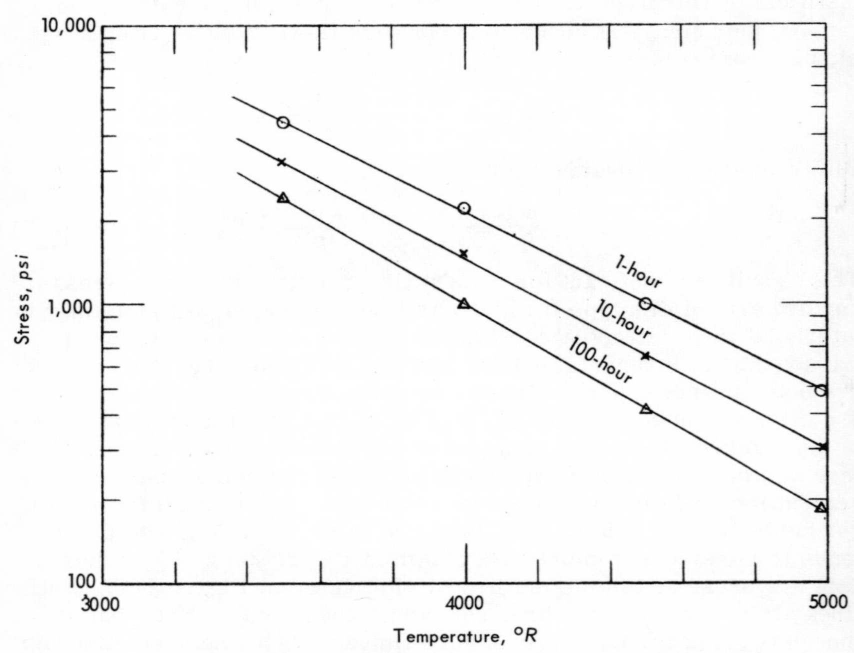

Figure 2-15 – Isochronal stress-rupture plot using data from Figure 2-14.

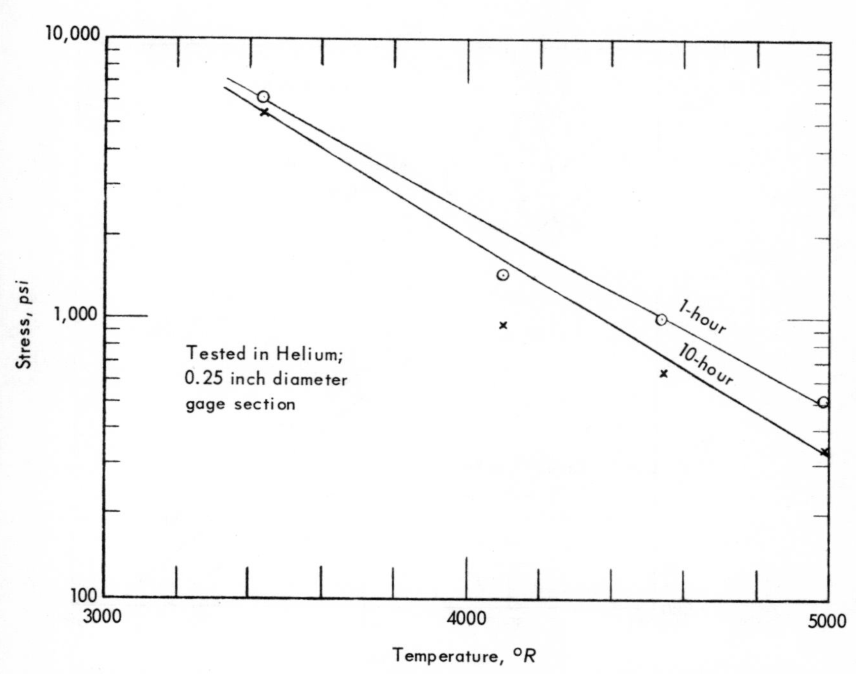

Figure 2-16 – Isochronal plot of rupture data for sintered molybdenum[7].

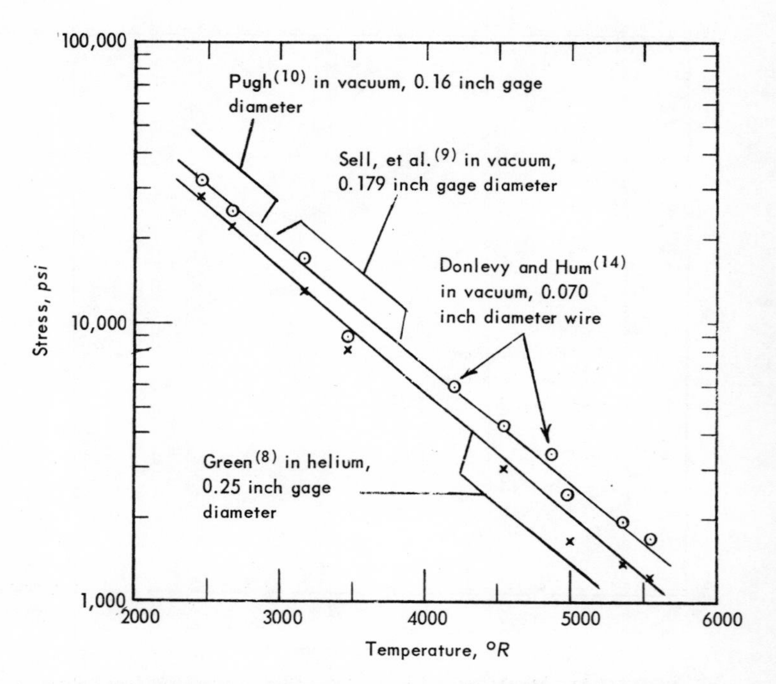

Figure 2-17 – Isochronal stress-rupture plot for tungsten data.

equation (2-51). The Larson-Miller constant reported for these data was 15.8 and the slope of the P versus log stress plot (i.e., the -b value) was -24,000. Combining these values in equation (2-51) for rupture in 1-hour gives:

$$\frac{15.8 + \log 1.0}{-24,000} = -6.6 \times 10^{-4}$$

which is in excellent agreement with the measured slope.

The data for sintered tungsten published by Green[8] are presented in Figure 2-17 along with some data from several other investigations. A linear relation exists over a rather large temperature range and all the data seem to be in fairly good agreement. The exceptions are the 5000°R data of Green[8] and the 3440°R data of Sell, et al.[9] It should be pointed out, however, that two lower temperature points from Pugh[10] were not included since they fell somewhat below the line in this figure. These isochronal data for tungsten show again the linearity of this type of plot and the steeper slope as the rupture time is increased. The fact that some of these data were obtained in vacuum while others were obtained in helium is quite noteworthy in view of the agreement exhibited in this plot.

An isochronal plot based on the stress-rupture data for tantalum is shown in Figure 2-18. Once again the data conform reasonably well to the relationship given by equation (2-51). In this plot the data[11] at one temperature (1200°F) for sintered tantalum sheet seem to be in good agreement with the data[12] for the electron beam melted sheet tested in vacuum. Also, the single point for arc-cast sheet material (0.030 inch) tested in argon[13] is consistent with these data. While the temperature range in this comparison is somewhat limited the linearity is quite definite and based on the previously discussed results of other materials it would be expected to persist at higher temperatures.

Some data for the Ta-10% W alloy are presented in Figure 2-19. In terms of 1-hour rupture life excellent agreement is found between the data for arc-melted material obtained in hydrogen[15] and the Donlevy and Hum[14] data obtained in vacuum with electron beam melted material. The NRC data[13] obtained with 30 mil arc-melted sheet in argon also are in excellent agreement. The data point at about 4860°R from Donlevy and Hum[14] seems slightly high and a point[14] at 5260°R was omitted because it appeared too low; but otherwise all the data presented seem reasonably consistent. Recent data for Ta-10W[15] represent the only available stress-rupture values for 10-hour life and these data points appear to define a fairly linear relationship. Based on only these three values it would be difficult to state that the slope of this 10-hour line is steeper than that for the 1-hour line. For this reason, more Ta-10W data will be required before the slope variation predicted by equation (2-51) can be evaluated.

The 1-hour stress-rupture data for the materials discussed

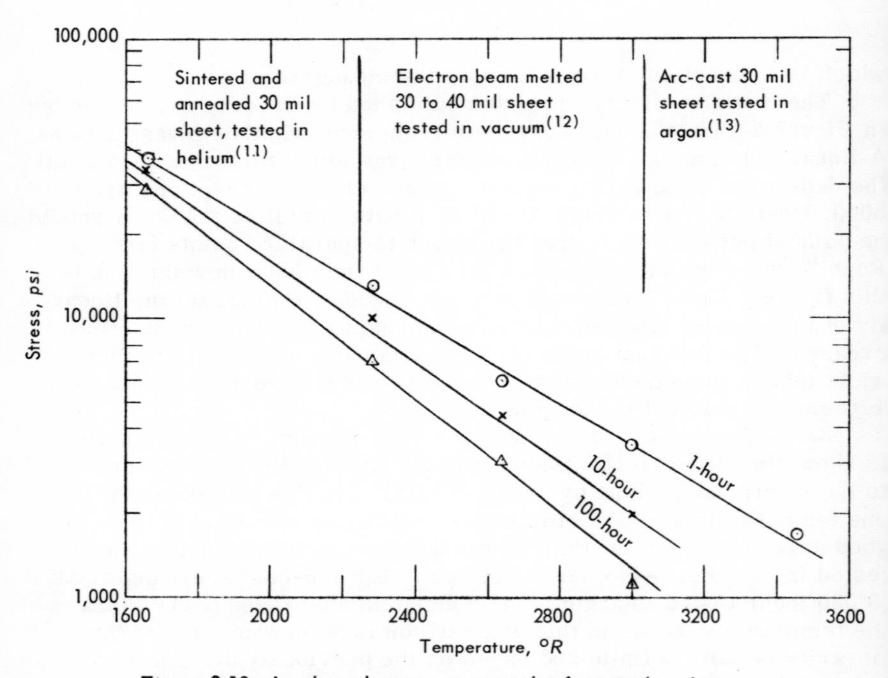

Figure 2-18 – Isochronal stress-rupture plot for tantalum data.

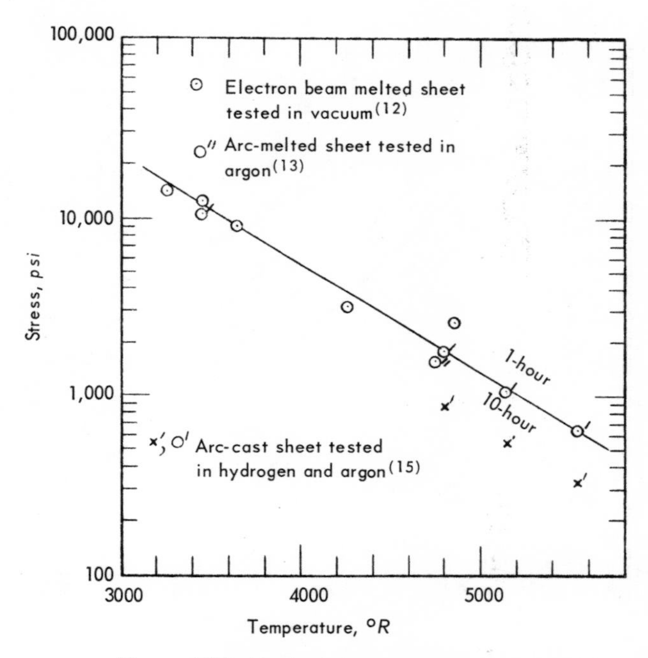

Figure 2-19 – Isochronal stress-rupture plot for Ta – 10W data.

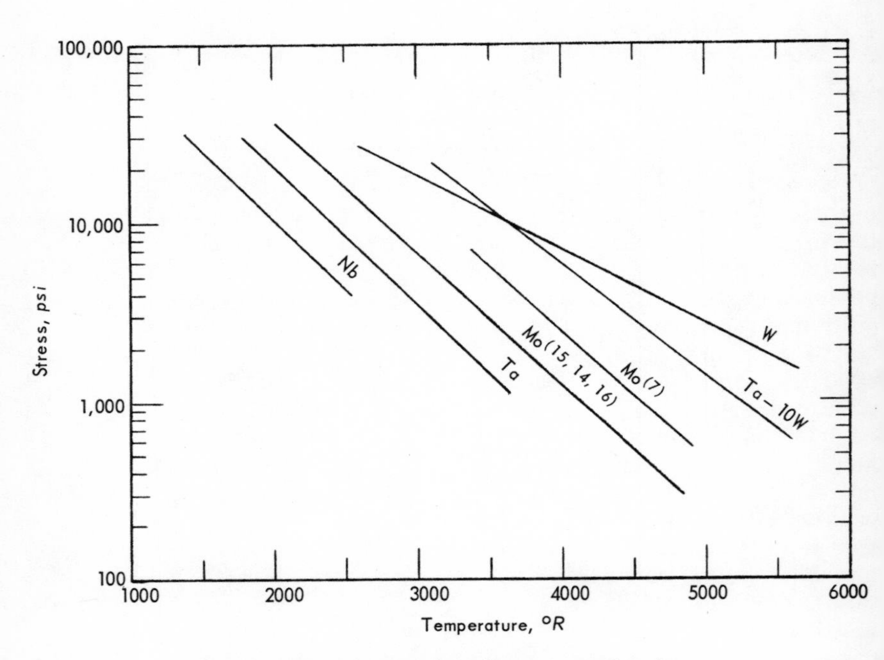

Figure 2-20 – Summary of one-hour rupture data for several refractory metals.

Table 2-7. Comparison of Slope of Lines in Figure 2-20 With Calculated -C/b Values

Material	Slope of Line in Figure 2-20	c	-b	-c/b
W	-4.1×10^{-4}	12.2	-30,000	-4.1×10^{-4}
Ta-10W	-6.25×10^{-4}	10.8	-17,800	-6.1×10^{-4}
Mo[7]	-7.3×10^{-4}	15.8	-24,000	-6.6×10^{-4}
Mo[15,14,16]	-7.4×10^{-4}	13.5	-17,500	-7.7×10^{-4}

previously and for niobium are summarized in Figure 2-20. Based on equation (2-51) and in view of the 1-hour data ($\log t_R = 0$) the slope of these lines is equal to -C/b. Measured slopes of the lines in Figure 2-20 are listed in Table 2-7 along with -C/b values calculated from reported stress-rupture data for several materials. The agreement is quite excellent.

It is obvious from Figure 2-20 that in the temperature range below 4000°R, molybdenum is stronger than tantalum even though melting point considerations would predict an opposite relationship. It is also obvious that for the Group VI-A metals, tungsten and molybdenum, the slope, -C/b value, increases as the melting point increases. Furthermore, the lines for tantalum, niobium and molybdenum which appear parallel should have the same C/b value although in view of the limited data on tantalum and niobium this observation might be somewhat premature. This is especially true in view of the statement just made for the Group VI-A metals regarding the slope increase with increasing melting temperature, for, if this were to apply to the Group V-A metals as well, the slope of the tantalum line should be greater than that of the niobium line.

The usefulness of equation (2-51) is not confined to interpolation and extrapolation operations for it also suggests a method for correlating stress-rupture data in terms of homologous temperatures, T_H (test temperature divided by the absolute melting temperature). Multiplying both sides of equation (2-51) by the melting temperature, T_M, this equation becomes:

$$\left(\frac{d \log \sigma}{d T_H}\right)_{t_R} = \frac{T_M (C + \log t_R)}{-b} \qquad (2\text{-}52)$$

This equation specifies a linear relationship when the log of the stress to produce rupture in a certain time period is plotted against the homologous temperature. Such a plot is shown in Figure 2-21 for 1-hour data for molybdenum, tungsten and chromium. Most of the data points fall along a straight line. The 10-hour data, in light of equation (2-52), would yield a similar plot with a slightly steeper slope. The few points in Figure 2-21 which fall somewhat below the line may be the result of

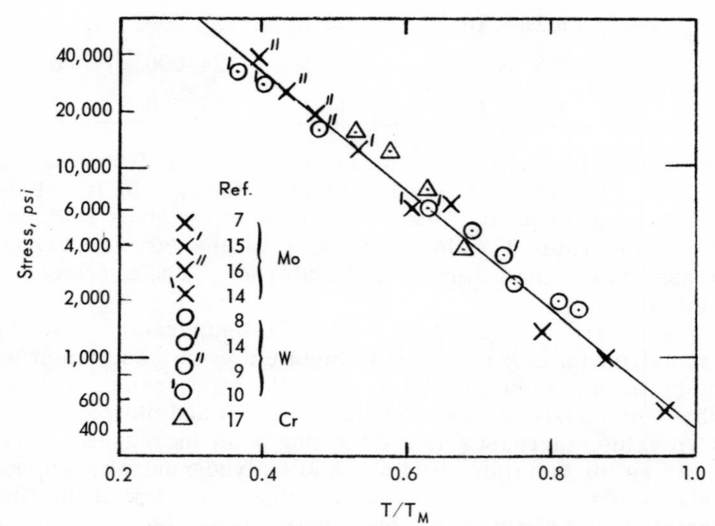

Figure 2-21 – Homologous temperature plot for one-hour rupture data for W, Mo and Cr.

Table 2-8. Comparison of $\left(\frac{CT_M}{-b}\right)$ Values for W, Mo and Cr

Material	Reference	T_M, °R	C	-b	$\frac{CT_M}{-b}$
Mo	7	5190	15.8	-24,000	-3.4
Cr	17	3910	16.0	-18,390	-3.4
W	8	6630	12.2	-30,000	-2.7

the different types of materials (i.e., arc-cast and powder metallurgy) involved or to slight differences in impurity levels. Schmidt, et al.,[18] emphasized this point when the homologous temperature concept was employed in a plot of stress (rather than log stress) to produce rupture in 100 hours for various refractory metals.

Data for the Group V-A metals (tantalum, niobium and vanadium) describe a completely different line in Figure 2-21 for 1-hour life. This line is definitely lower than that for the Group VI-A metals but an accurate identification of the slope must await more high temperature data at homologous temperature values between 0.6 and 0.9. This difference between the Group VI-A and Group V-A metals has been discussed previously[19] when homologous temperatures were plotted against stress to rupture in 1 and 100 hours. However, this plot which employed stress rather than log stress resulted in definite curvature and it is felt that the method of plotting employed in Figure 2-21 is much to be desired.

A final observation pertaining to eqaution (2-52) is noteworthy. Since the slope of the line in Figure 2-21 is common to the Group VI-A metals and since 1-hour data have been employed ($\log t_R = 0$) it follows that for these metals the ratio $T_M C/-b$ must be a constant. This value obtained from the slope of the line in Figure 2-21 is found to be -3.1. The calculation of this grouping for the Group VI-A metals is illustrated in Table 2-8 to allow a comparison with this value of -3.1. The agreement is seen to be quite good. Recalling the statement made earlier that the -C/b value for the Group VI-A metals increases as the temperature increases it now can be said that the product of the absolute metling temperature and the -C/b value is constant for these materials. A corollary to this, of course, is that -C/b values, for the Group VI-A metals, plotted against the reciprocal of the absolute melting point yield a linear relationship.

THE CLAUSS[20] EVALUATION

Mathematically the relationship between temperature, log stress and the log of the rupture time can be written as:

$$\log t_R = f(\log \sigma, T) \qquad (2\text{-}53)$$

Unfortunately, the exact functional relationship is not easy to identify

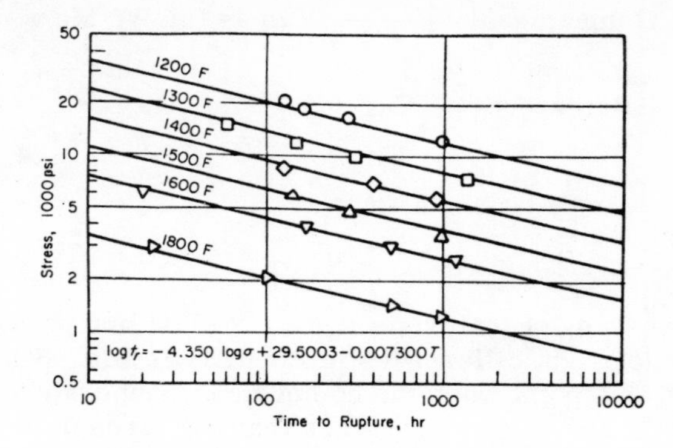

Figure 2-22 – Stress-rupture plot for Timken 35-15 stainless steel[20].

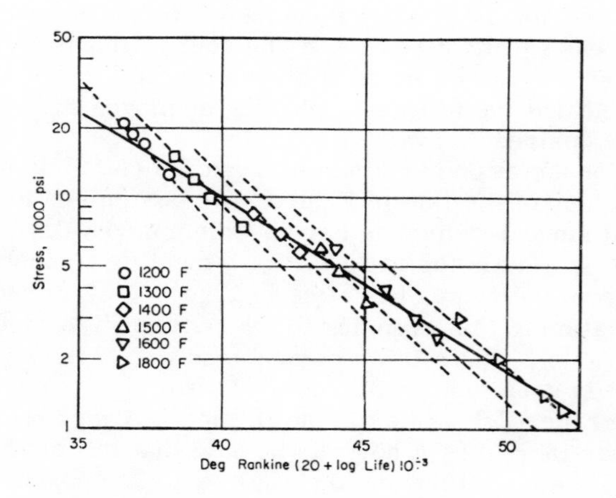

Figure 2-23 – Larson-Miller plot for Timken 35-15 stainless steel[20].

and certainly no general form can be expected. Usually, however, it is possible to employ a set of experimental data to develop a sufficiently accurate formulation of this functional relationship. To the extent that this is successful, an acceptable correlating parameter will be identified.

Employing the relationship given by equation (2-53), Clauss[20] studied several types of stress-rupture behavior as determined by the relative shape and position of the stress-rupture isotherms. An attempt was made to evaluate the relative merits of various correlating parameters in terms of how effectively the actual experimental data could be described by a given parameter expression. In the type of behavior termed Class I, the stress-rupture isotherms consisted of a family of straight and parallel lines on a log stress versus log rupture time plot. An example of this type of behavior was given by the data for Timken 35-15 stainless steel as presented in Figure 2-22. For this case, equation (2-53) becomes:

$$\log t_R = a \log \sigma + b(T) \qquad (2\text{-}54)$$

where "a" is the slope of the isotherms, and which is independent of both stress and temperature, and b(T) represents the intercept of each isotherm. Of course, the latter is a function of temperature only and has been evaluated to yield:

$$\log t_R = -4.35 \log \sigma + 29.5003 - 0.0073T \qquad (2\text{-}55)$$

where T is in °F. Using this expression, the lines in Figure 2-22 were positioned to indicate excellent agreement with the experimental data.

When these same data were correlated[20] in terms of the Larson-Miller parameter, using C = 20, the results shown in Figure 2-23 were obtained. Average behavior is indicated by the solid line and a high degree of scatter is noted. As a matter of fact, it must be said that this correlation is rather unsatisfactory. Dashed lines defined by equation (2-55) are shown to demonstrate that the data for each temperature seem to describe a separate line; and hence, it is hard to accept that the Larson-Miller approach affords any measure of correlation in this case. In other words, a single line or curve is not obtained to represent the data at all the various temperatures involved. Also of importance is the fact that the points representing the shorter rupture times are positioned above the average line in Figure 2-23 while the lower rupture time points are located below the line. Hence, any attempt to predict long-term behavior from available short-term data, using the average line of this parametric approach, will involve considerable error. For example, Clauss has shown that the error involved in extrapolating the short-time life at 1600°F to predict the long-term behavior at 1400°F results in a predicted life at 6000 psi which is some 400 percent longer than the material would actually survive.

Before proceeding further with the Clauss analysis it should be

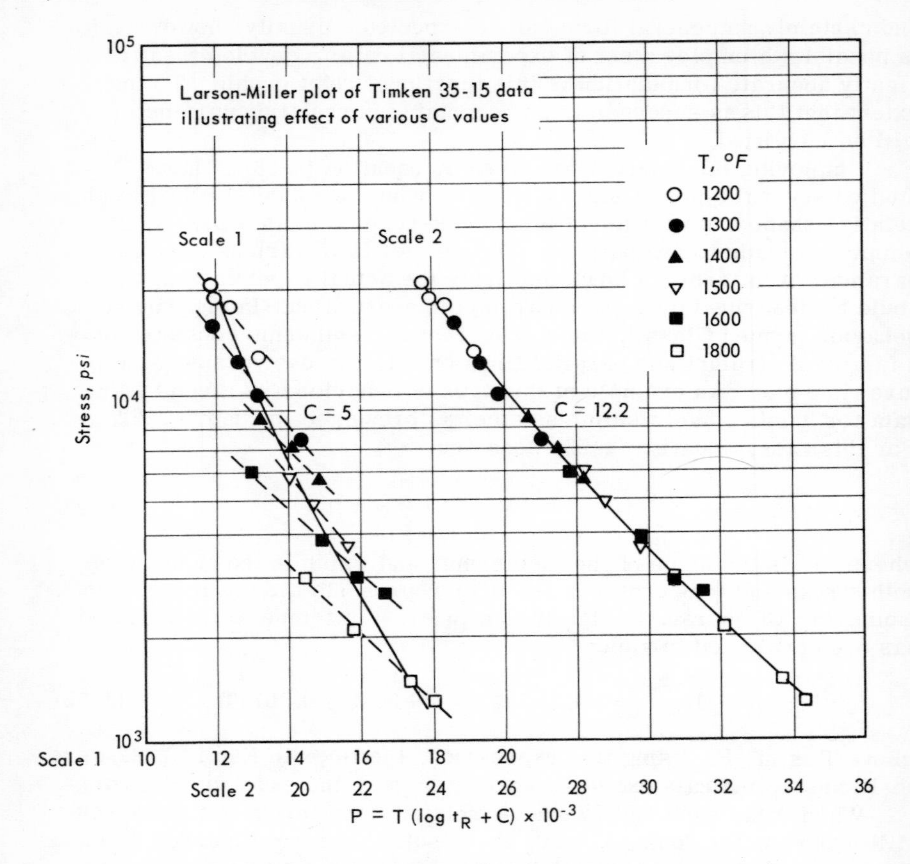

Figure 2-24 – Data for Timken 35-15 steel reanalyzed in terms of different C values(41).

mentioned that a recent evaluation[41] has shown that the poor correlation shown in Figure 2-23 results from an improper choice of the C value. Using the least squares approach outlined in a previous section, the optimum C value was found to be 12.2. As shown in Figure 2-24, this leads to an excellent correlation of these data. In an extension of this analysis a value of C = 5 was selected just to determine the effect of this change on the parameter results. This effect is also presented in Figure 2-24 where the lower value of C has led to another poor correlation of the Timken 35-15 data. Particularly noteworthy is that once again the data at the various temperatures describe individual and separate lines just as was noted in Figure 2-23. At the higher C value though these lines have steeper slopes with respect to the average curve than the corresponding isotherms in Figure 2-24. It is apparent that, as the C value is lowered in this case, a certain value is reached at which all the isotherms seem to be colinear and a good parameter correlation results.

Taking the differential of $\log t_R$ in equation (2-53) Clauss[20] wrote:

$$d \log t_R = \left(\frac{\partial \log t_R}{\partial \log \sigma} \right)_T d \log \sigma + \left(\frac{\partial \log t_R}{\partial T} \right)_\sigma dT \qquad (2\text{-}56)$$

where the first partial derivative represents the change of the log of the rupture time with respect to the log of the stress at constant temperature; and hence, it is seen to be the actual slope of a stress-rupture isotherm. Also, the second partial derivative will be recognized as the change in the log of the rupture time with respect to temperature at constant stress. This can be identified as a measure of the separation between isotherms on the log-log stress-rupture plot. Both these partial derivatives can be functions of stress, temperature, or both; to the extent that they are the stress-rupture behavior is more complex. In Figure 2-22, both derivatives are seen to be independent of both temperature and stress.

At constant stress equation (2-56) becomes:

$$d \log t_R = \left(\frac{\partial \log t_R}{\partial T} \right)_\sigma dT \qquad (2\text{-}57)$$

Integrating at constant stress between a fixed reference temperature and any temperature T the following result is obtained:

$$\log t_R - \int^T \left(\frac{\partial \log t_R}{\partial T} \right)_\sigma dT = \text{constant} \qquad (2\text{-}58)$$

which Clauss observed to have the general form of a correlating parameter. Before equation (2-58) can be integrated, though, the partial derivative term must be evaluated. In general, this quantity is a function of both temperature and stress but can be evaluated from experimental stress-rupture data. For the type of data shown in Figure 2-22, if the

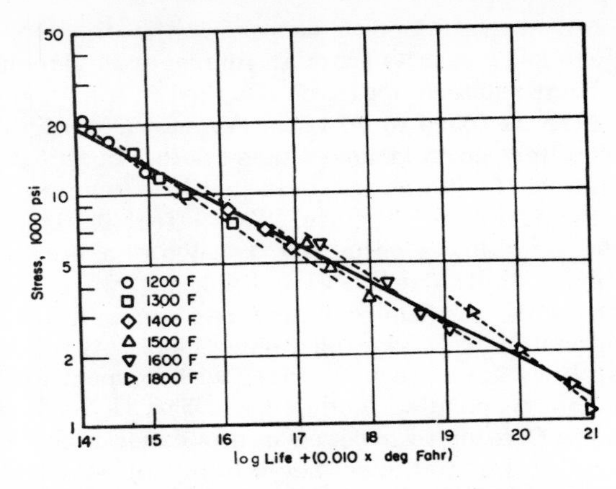

Figure 2-25 – Master-rupture plot for Timken 35-15 stainless steel based on an approximate correlating parameter.

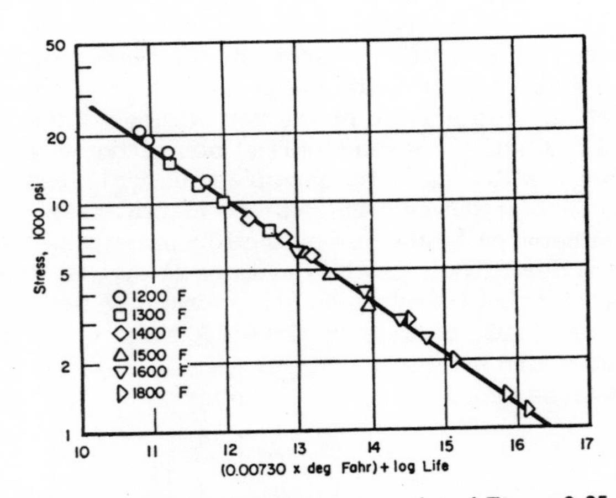

Figure 2-26 – Revised master-rupture plot of Figure 2-25.

isotherms are separated by a constant amount then the partial derivative in equation (2-58) is a constant independent of stress and temperature. It was observed by Clauss that for many high temperature steels the separation between two isotherms which differ by 100°F represents a difference in rupture times corresponding to one log cycle. In this instance, the partial derivative in equation (2-58) will be:

$$\left(\frac{\partial \log t_R}{\partial T}\right)_\sigma = \frac{\Delta \log t_R}{\Delta T} = \frac{\log 10}{-100} = -0.010 \qquad (2\text{-}59)$$

and as a first approximation the general correlating parameter for these materials will be:

$$\log t_R + 0.01T = \text{constant at constant stress} \qquad (2\text{-}60)$$

Now writing the Larson-Miller parameter as:

$$20 \times {}^\circ R + \log t_R \times {}^\circ R \qquad (2\text{-}61)$$

it will be noted that since $\log t_R$ is much smaller than 20, it is possible, without much change in the value of the parameter, to use an average value, $^\circ R_{avg}$, for the absolute temperature with the $\log t_R$ term and make the temperature correction in the first term only; then:

$${}^\circ R\,(20 + \log t_R) \cong 20 \times {}^\circ R + \log t_R \times {}^\circ R_{avg} \qquad (2\text{-}62)$$

Further, if it is considered that the range of the temperature of interest is between 1200° and 1800°F, a value of 2000 can be used for $^\circ R_{Avg}$. It follows therefore that:

$${}^\circ R\,(20 + \log t_R) \cong 20 \times {}^\circ R + 2000 \times \log t_R \qquad (2\text{-}63)$$

Approximate values of the Larson-Miller parameter calculated using the right-hand side of this equation are only 1 or 2 percent different from the true values.

Rearrangement of equation (2-63) yields:

$$\cong 20\,({}^\circ F + 460) + 2000 \log t_R$$

$$\cong 20 \times {}^\circ F + 9200 + 2000 \log t_R$$

$$\cong 2000\,(\log t_R + 0.01 \times {}^\circ F) + 9200 \qquad (2\text{-}64)$$

Since the coefficients 2000 and 9200 are constants and can be neglected in writing the parameter, it follows that in place of the Larson-Miller parameter it is possible to use the quantity ($\log t_R + 0.01T$) where T is in °F. This algebraic manipulation by Clauss has shown that the Larson-Miller parameter yields the parameter shown in equation (2-60).

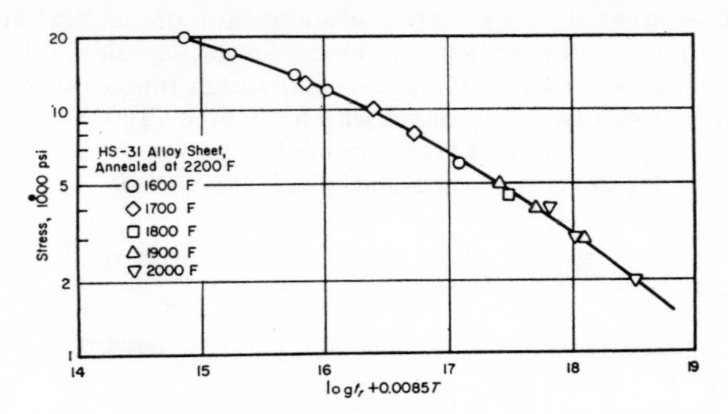

Figure 2-27 – Master-rupture plot for HS-31 alloy[20].

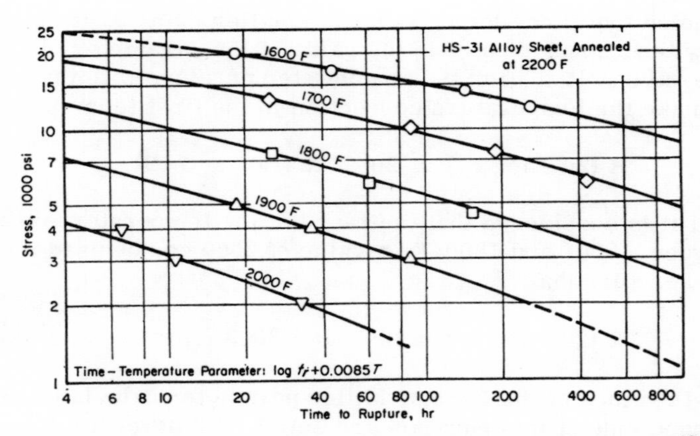

Figure 2-28 – Stress-rupture plot for HS-31 alloy based on Figure 2-27[20].

This parameter has been employed using the data of Figure 2-22 to yield the results shown in Figure 2-25. It will be noted that no better correlation is obtained than when the Larson-Miller parameter was employed. However, this is at least partially due to the incorrect value for $(\partial \log t_R/\partial t)_\sigma$ which was employed. Differentiation of equation (2-55) reveals that this value should be -0.0073 instead of the -0.01 value employed above. It can be noted that this value of -0.0073 can also be obtained by scaling off the horizontal distance between isotherms in Figure 2-22.

Now the correlating parameter for the data shown in Figure 2-22 should be:

$$\log t_R + 0.0073\ T \text{ at constant stress} \qquad (2\text{-}65)$$

and from equation (2-55) this parameter should be linear in log stress. Such a relation is shown in Figure 2-26. Also, a much better correlation is noted than that observed in Figures 2-24 and 2-25.

Class II Behavior

Stress-rupture isotherms which are curved but parallel formed the second type of behavior considered by Clauss. In this case, the stress-rupture results can be expressed as:

$$\log t_R = a\,(\sigma)\,\log \sigma + b\,(T) \qquad (2\text{-}66)$$

where a (σ) is a function of stress and b (T) a function of temperature. If the isotherms are equispaced for equal temperature increments, then the partial derivative in equation (2-58) is a constant independent of stress and temperature. This value can be determined either mathematically as in equation (2-55) or by scaling off the horizontal distance between isotherms on the stress-rupture plot. Such an analysis of the HS-31 alloy data yielded the results shown in Figure 2-27. A slight curvature results because of the curvature of the stress-rupture isotherms. However, a good correlation is observed. Reconstructed isotherms based on the Figure 2-27 correlation are presented in Figure 2-28 to reveal excellent agreement with the experimental data.

Another example[20] of Class II behavior is shown in the master-rupture plot of the A-286 data presented in Figure 2-29. Also, the reconstructed isotherms are presented in Figure 2-30 to indicate the good agreement with the experimental data.

Class III Behavior

This particular type of behavior was described by Clauss as being characterized by isotherms which are linear and have slopes which are less steep (i.e., smaller negative values) as the temperature decreases (see Figure 2-31 for Timken 25-20 stainless steel data). In terms of equation (2-53) the following relation applies:

$$\log t_R = a(T)\,\log \sigma + b(T) \qquad (2\text{-}67)$$

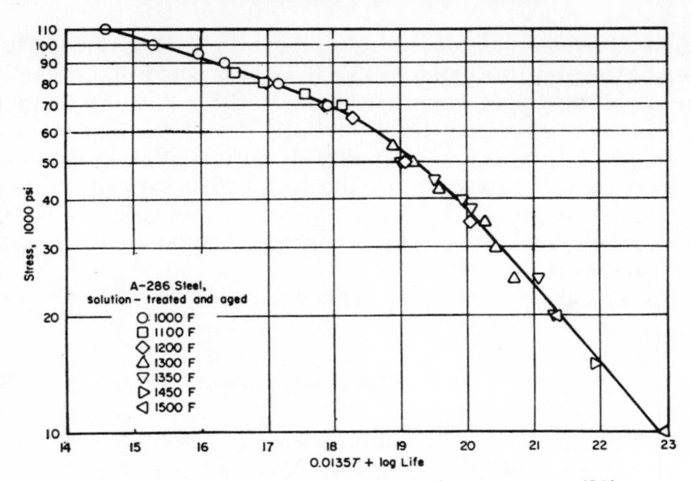

Figure 2-29 – Master-rupture plot of A-286 data[20].

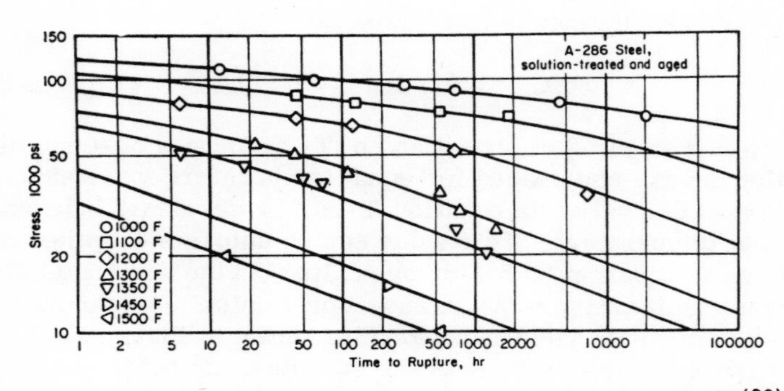

Figure 2-30 – Stress-rupture plot of A-286 data based on Figure 2-29[20].

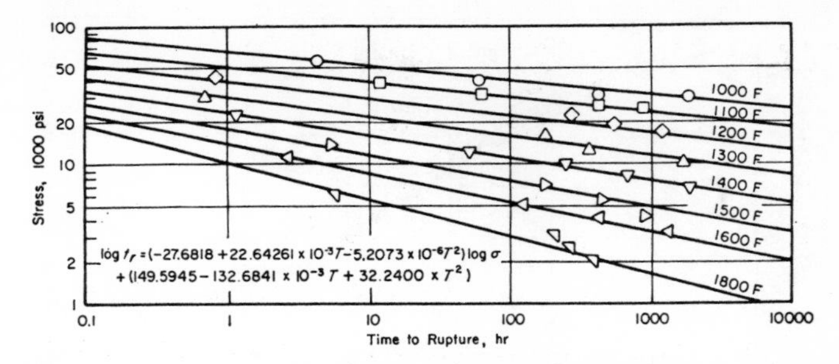

Figure 2-31 – Stress-rupture plot[20] for Timken 25-20 stainless steel data.

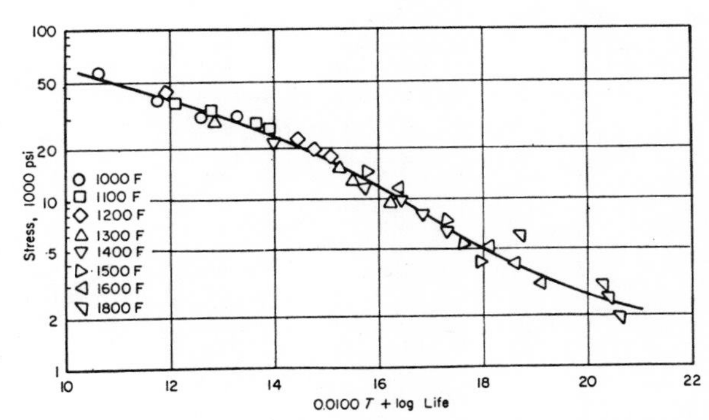

Figure 2-32 – Master-rupture plot of data presented in Figure 2-31.[20]

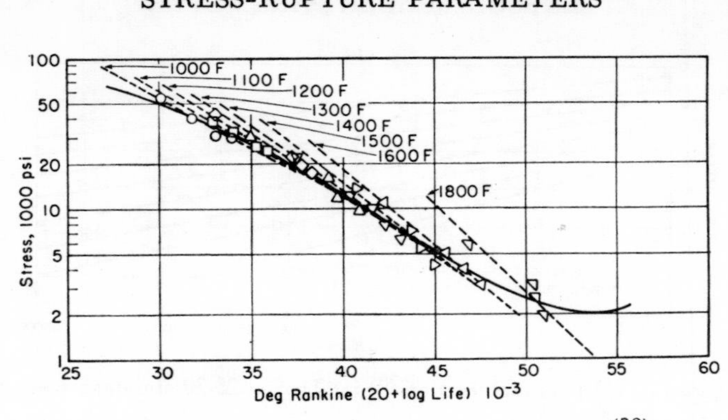

Figure 2-33 – Larson-Miller plot of Figure 2-31 data.[20]

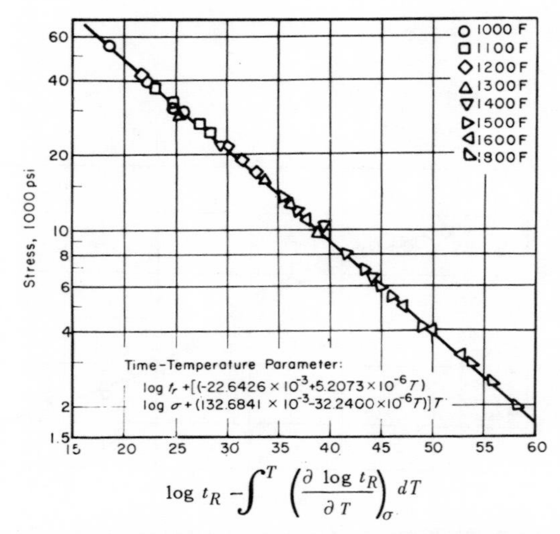

$$\log t_R - \int^{T} \left(\frac{\partial \log t_R}{\partial T}\right)_{\sigma} dT$$

Figure 2-34 – Master-rupture plot for Timken 25-20 stainless steel data using special correlation parameter.[20]

where both a(T) and b(T) represent functions of temperature. A statistical evaluation of all the data was found to yield:

$$\log t_R = -(27.6818 - 22.6426 \times 10^{-3}\ T + 5.207 \times 10^{-6} T^2) \log \sigma$$

$$+ (149.594 - 132.684 \times 10^{-3}\ T + 32.23997 \times 10^{-6}\ T^2) \quad (2\text{-}68)$$

which obviously involves six constants. A reconstruction of the isotherms based on this equation is shown in Figure 2-31. Equation (2-64) was employed in an analysis of these data with the results shown in Figure 2-32. Obviously, the correlation is far from acceptable. A Larson-Miller analysis of these same data led to an equally poor correlation as shown in Figure 2-33. As in Figure 2-23, the data points at each temperature describe individual lines and it is impossible to position a single line or curve to represent all the data. It was concluded[20] that since the correlation in Figure 2-32 is better than that shown in Figure 2-33 the use of the Larson-Miller parameter is not justified in this case.

If equation (2-68) is employed in conjunction with equation (2-58) the correlation parameter for the Timken 25-20 data can be shown to be:

$$\log t_R + [(-22.6426 \times 10^{-3} + 5.207 \times 10^{-6}\ T) \log \sigma$$

$$+ (132.684 \times 10^{-3} - 32.24 \times 10^{-6}\ T)]\ T \quad (2\text{-}69)$$

where T is in °F. An analysis of the data for Timken 25-20 is shown in Figure 2-34 to reveal a very excellent correlation. Of course, the correlating parameter is quite complex and hence some disadvantage must be assigned to this approach. Also, some disadvantage involves the occurrence of a stress term in both the ordinate and abscissa. In other words, if the 100-hour rupture stress were to be calculated at a given temperature, a trial and error procedure would be involved using the correlation plot of Figure 2-34.

Although the Larson-Miller correlation of Figure 2-33 is very poor, this need not lead to the general conclusion that Class III behavior cannot be represented by the Larson-Miller approach. For example, Conway [21] has shown that excellent correlation is obtained with the Larson-Miller parameter when applied to a series of isotherms which are linear but which have different slopes. To obtain this excellent correlation, the slopes must be related in a certain fashion [see equation (2-43)].

Class IV Behavior

This type of behavior stems from a series of curved isotherms which are non-parallel. Clauss cited the data for S-590 as being typical of this behavior. Also, an equation similar to (2-68) was derived and a correlation parameter similar to that shown in Figure 2-34 was

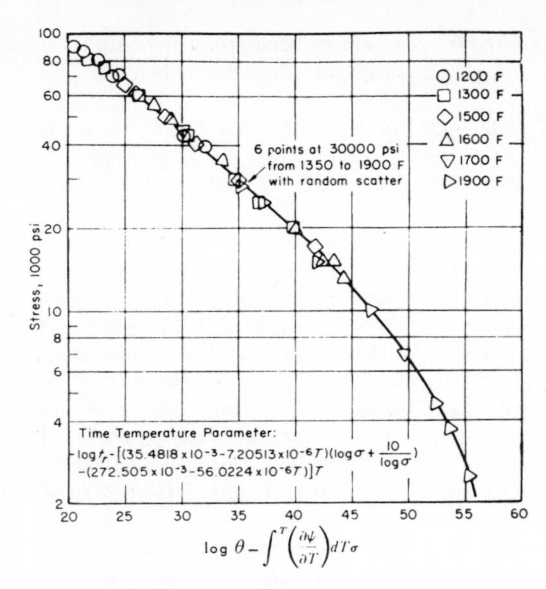

Figure 2-35 – Master-rupture plot for S-590 alloy using special correlating parameter(20).

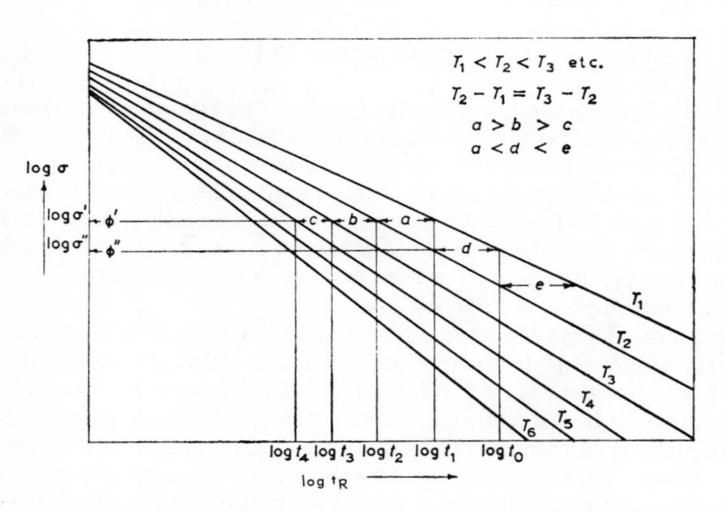

Figure 2-36 – Arrangement of log stress-log time curves(30) based on the Larson-Miller parameter; temperature intervals are equal.

indicated. These results are shown in Figure 2-35 and, as in Figure 2-34, the correlating parameter is quite complex.

THE LARKE AND INGLIS[30] EVALUATION

In this very interesting analysis the type of stress-rupture behavior which is amenable to correlation in terms of the Larson-Miller parameter was identified. It was shown that for the Larson-Miller approach to be applicable the stress-rupture isotherms can be linear or curved but they must be non-parallel. Furthermore, the spacing between any two isotherms must be related to the ratio formed by the absolute temperatures of the isotherms.

Writing the Larson-Miller parameter as:

$$T\ (C + \log t_R) = \phi \tag{2-70}$$

Larke and Inglis[30] employed a simple rearrangement to obtain:

$$\log t_R = \frac{\phi}{T} - C \tag{2-71}$$

where, as usual, C is the Larson-Miller constant, T is in degrees absolute and ϕ is constant at a given stress. It was then stipulated in the Larke-Inglis analysis that isotherms corresponding to equal temperature intervals would be considered; thus:

$$(T_2 - T_1) = (T_3 - T_2) = (T_4 - T_3) \text{ etc.} \tag{2-72}$$

Reference to equation (2-70) and Figure 2-36* reveals that at a stress level of say $\log \sigma'$ a fixed value of ϕ' will be defined. This value can be calculated from equation (2-70) for any stress level once a time-temperature combination is known and once C has been determined. Each stress level then will have a unique value of ϕ. Obviously, if it were necessary it would be possible to replace the log σ scale in Figure 2-36 with a corresponding scale of ϕ values. This procedure, however, is not usually considered necessary. But, it is important to note that no general relation between ϕ and σ has been identified and hence, values of ϕ cannot usually be calculated from stress values. Instead, time-temperature data along with C values must be employed. Based on these observations, Larke and Inglis noted that if two materials were tested at the same temperature, T, and fracture was obtained in the same time, t_R, then if the value of C was the same for both materials, equation (2-70) would give the same value for ϕ even though in general the stress to cause fracture would be different for the two materials. In other words, the functional relationship between ϕ and σ is not the same for all materials. As a matter of fact, it might even

*While linear isotherms are employed the reasonings and conclusions apply just as well to non-linear cases.

be said that no two materials have exactly the same relationship between these two quantities.

Applying equation (2-71) to three temperatures at σ' it follows that:

$$\log t_{R_1} = \frac{\phi'}{T_1} - C \tag{2-73}$$

$$\log t_{R_2} = \frac{\phi'}{T_2} \quad C \tag{2-74}$$

$$\log t_{R_3} = \frac{\phi'}{T_3} - C \tag{2-75}$$

from which:

$$\log t_{R_1} - \log t_{R_2} = \phi' \frac{T_2 - T_1}{T_1 T_2} = a \tag{2-76}$$

and

$$\log t_{R_2} - \log t_{R_3} = \phi' \frac{T_3 - T_2}{T_2 T_3} = b \tag{2-77}$$

when a and b have the significance shown in Figure 2-36. In view of equation (2-72) it can be seen that:

$$a = \frac{T_3}{T_1} b \tag{2-78}$$

and since

$$T_3 > T_1 \tag{2-79}$$

then

$$a > b \tag{2-80}$$

By the same procedure Larke and Inglis employed T_2, T_3 and T_4 at σ' to show that:

$$b = \frac{T_4}{T_2} c \tag{2-81}$$

and

$$b > c \tag{2-82}$$

Hence for equal temperature intervals the Larson-Miller parameter approach requires that:

$$a > b > c \text{ etc.} \tag{2-83}$$

Now at σ'' where $\sigma' > \sigma''$ and selecting a time t_{R_0} at temperature T_1 it is easily shown that:

$$\log t_{R_0} = \frac{\phi''}{T_1} - C \tag{2-84}$$

Also, for t_{R_1} and T_2 at σ'' :

$$\log t_{R_1} = \frac{\phi''}{T_2} - C \tag{2-85}$$

Combining gives:

$$\log t_{R_0} - \log t_{R_1} = \phi'' \frac{T_2 - T_1}{T_2 T_1} = d \tag{2-86}$$

Incorporating equation (2-76) it follows that:

$$a = \frac{\phi'}{\phi''} d \tag{2-87}$$

from which equations (2-73) and (2-85) lead to:

$$a = \frac{T_1}{T_2} d \tag{2-88}$$

and since

$$T_2 > T_1 \tag{2-89}$$

$$a < d \tag{2-90}$$

Similarly, it can be shown that:

$$d = \frac{T_1}{T_2} e \tag{2-91}$$

and

$$d < e \tag{2-92}$$

and

$$a < d < e \tag{2-93}$$

Equations (2-80) and (2-82) reveal that based on the Larson-Miller approach, a comparison at a specified stress level leads to the conclusion that the logarithmic time intervals between $\log \sigma$ versus $\log t_R$ curves corresponding to equally spaced temperatures will decrease with increasing temperatures (see the intervals a, b, and c in Figure 2-36). This relation is true independent of the material. Also noteworthy is the fact that for three equally spaced temperatures the ratio a/b will be the same for all materials and will be given as the ratio of the highest to the lowest of the three temperatures. A similar statement can be made for b/c. Hence it follows that the Larson-Miller concept is only applicable to isotherms which diverge as time increases.

Another interesting observation of the Larke-Inglis analysis involves equation (2-76) which can be rewritten as:

$$a = (C + \log t_{R_2}) \frac{T_2 - T_1}{T_1} = \log t_{R_1} - \log t_{R_2} \tag{2-94}$$

and as:

$$\log t_{R_1} = (C + \log t_{R_2}) \frac{(T_2 - T_1)}{(T_1)} + \log t_{R_2} \tag{2-95}$$

It follows directly, therefore, that for a given set of temperatures T_1

TABLE 2-9

A SUMMARY OF RESULTS OBTAINED IN THE MURRY[31] ANALYSIS EMPLOYING THE LARSON-MILLER APPROACH

Steel	σ_0, kgf/mm²	$f(\sigma_0)$	C	Standard deviation	Linear correlation coefficient
'A37'	8	19 693·00	21·853 12	0·0554	> 0·99
	11	18 229·12	21·175 04	0·0197	> 0·99
	13	19 164·02	23·017 92	0·0714	> 0·99
	15	20 834·99	25·937 42	0·0311	> 0·99
	17	21 001·62	26·926 76	0·0766	> 0·99
	20	23 099·02	30·952 63	0·0559	> 0·99
'2·25% Cr–1% Mo'	5	29 535·93	28·575 66	0·0838	> 0·99
	10	19 498·38	19·982 60	0·0264	> 0·99
	15	18 825·27	20·442 60	0·0193	> 0·99
	20	20 536·75	23·567 59	0·0432	> 0·99
'17–22 A'S	7	20 117·70	19·297 85	0·0633	> 0·99
	14	22 217·64	22·561 27	0·0745	> 0·99
	28	23 173·93	24·811 78	0·1144	> 0·99
	56	25 097·66	29·431 84	0·2552	0·97
'18% Cr–12% Ni–Ti'	6	16 305·53	13·345 58	0·0443	> 0·99
	12	17 799·85	15·958 62	0·0365	> 0·99
	20	16 790·45	15·952 56	0·1267	> 0·99
	35	20 484·17	22·275 84	0·0504	> 0·99

and T_2 the value of C determines the extent of the separation of the two isotherms. A large value of C will naturally lead to greater spacings of adjacent isotherms.

If the ratio a/d given by equation (2-88) is not constant over the entire stress range then it can be deduced from equation (2-87) that C cannot be constant but will vary with stress. Hence if this behavior (i.e., variable a/d ratio) is noted an application of the Larson-Miller approach would lead to erroneous results.

THE MURRY[31] EVALUATION

Applying a statistical approach to the analysis of rupture data for several steels, Murry[31] evaluated the linear relationship given by equation (2-13) in the form:

$$\log t_R = \frac{f(\sigma_0)}{T} - C \tag{2-96}$$

While the data at each stress level for a given material were found to be quite adequately described by a straight line of this form, it was concluded that C was not really constant but rather varied with the initial stress σ_0. A summary of a portion of these results is presented in Table 2-9 where the correlation coefficient, being so close to unity, argues well for the linearity between $\log t_R$ and $(1/T)$. Also noted is the variation of C with the initial stress. These data are presented graphically in Figure 2-37. Of course, since C varies with stress the assumption made by Larson and Miller that all constant stress lines converge to the same point at $(1/T) = 0$ is questioned. As a matter of fact the general form suggested by this behavior is:

$$\log t_R = \frac{F_1(\sigma_0)}{T} - F_2(\sigma_0) \tag{2-97}$$

where the intercept $F_2(\sigma_0)$ is shown as a function of stress.

Considering the Larson-Miller parameter:

$$f(\sigma_0) = T(\log t_R + C) \tag{2-98}$$

and assuming that C is constant a combination of equations (2-97) and (2-98) yields:

$$f(\sigma_0) = F_1(\sigma_0) + T\left[C - F_2(\sigma_0)\right] \tag{2-99}$$

Obviously, the parameter, $f(\sigma_0)$, is not independent of temperature and can be seen to vary more with temperature the greater the difference between the values adopted for C and $F_2(\sigma_0)$. In equation (2-99), the value of T is the test temperature or the average temperature of the tests from which $f(\sigma_0)$ is calculated for a given initial stress. Representing this average temperature as T_m, equation (2-99) becomes:

$$f(\sigma_0) = F_1(\sigma_0) + T_m\left[C - F_2(\sigma_0)\right] \tag{2-100}$$

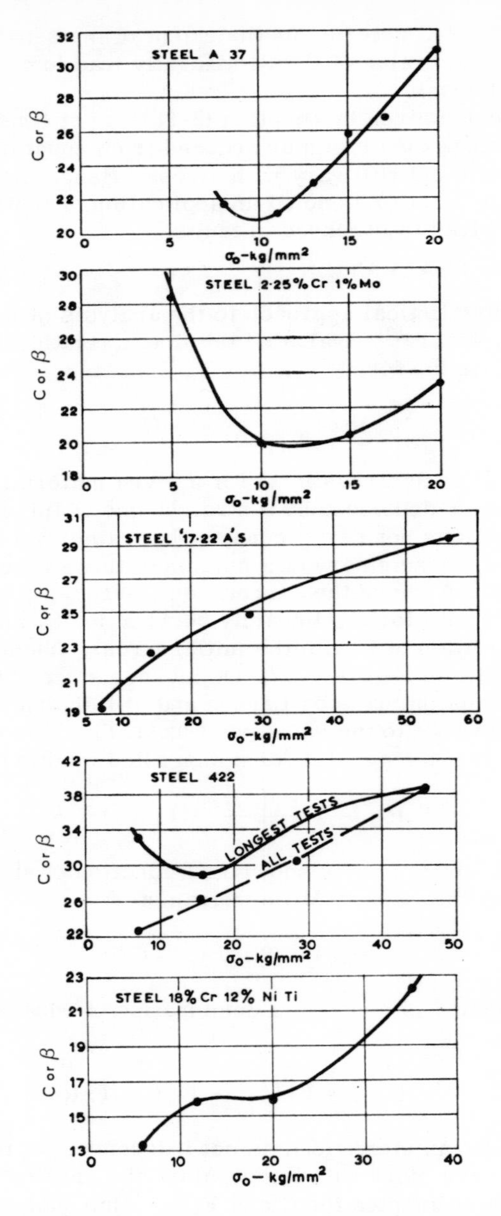

Figure 2-37 – Summary of Larson-Miller C values at various stresses obtained in Murry[31] analysis.

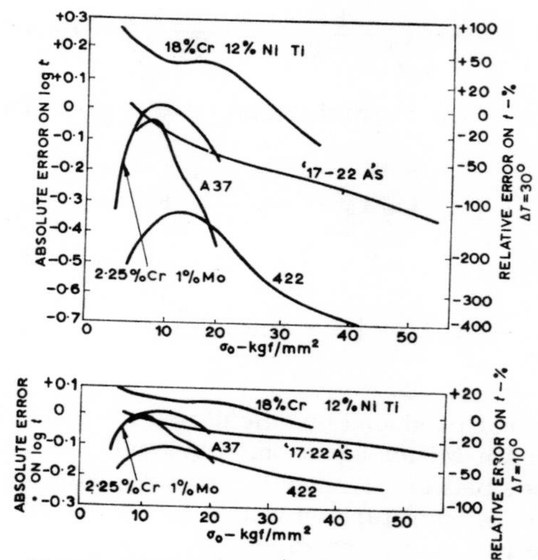

ΔT = difference between average temperature of tests on which the calculation of $f(\sigma_0)$ is based and the temperature of extrapolation.

Figure 2-38 – Errors due to calculating $\log t_R$ by extrapolation using Larson-Miller formula $f(\sigma_0) = T(\log t_R + 20)$(31).

At a given temperature, T_e, a characteristic time can be calculated from equation (2-96) as:

$$\log t_R = \frac{f(\sigma_0)}{T_e} - C \tag{2-101}$$

Substitution of equation (2-100) then leads to:

$$\log t_{R_{L.M.}} = \frac{F_1(\sigma_0)}{T_e} + \frac{T_m}{T_e}[C - F_2(\sigma_0)] - C \tag{2-102}$$

Now the true value of the characteristic time is given by equation (2-97) as:

$$\log t_{R_{true}} = \frac{F_1(\sigma_0)}{T_e} - F_2(\sigma_0) \tag{2-103}$$

Hence the difference:

$$\log t_{R_{L.M.}} - \log t_{R_{true}} = [C - F_2(\sigma_0)]\left(\frac{T_m}{T_e} - 1\right) \equiv \Delta \log t_R \tag{2-104}$$

represents the error produced by calculating the characteristic time by means of the Larson-Miller equation. Obviously, this error increases with the difference between T_m and T_e, that is, with the difference between the average temperature on which $f(\sigma_0)$ is based and the temperature at which the results are extrapolated. Also, $\Delta \log t_R$ is related to the quantity $[C - F_2(\sigma_0)]$ and hence depends on the value chosen for C. In view of the variation shown in Figure 2-37, $\Delta \log t_R$ will also be seen to be a function of σ_0.

Some idea of the error, $\Delta \log t_R$, due to using a constant C value is given in Figure 2-38. This evaluation was based on:

$$C = 20$$

$$T_m = 550\,^\circ C$$

$$T_m - T_e = 30\,^\circ C$$

As noted, the error varies with σ_0 and can be very extensive.

CHAPTER 3

DORN PARAMETER

In a study of the creep behavior of aluminum and various aluminum alloys, Orr, Sherby, and Dorn[32] noted a striking similarity in the strain-time plots for various temperatures at the same stress. It was found possible to correlate their data at a given stress by plotting the creep strain as a function of:

$$\theta = t\, e^{\frac{-\Delta H}{RT}} \tag{3-1}$$

where the quantity θ was referred to as the temperature-compensated time; also t is time, T is the absolute temperature, ΔH is the activation energy for the creep process and R is the gas constant.

A typical strain versus θ plot is presented in Figure 3-1 to reveal that at a given stress this method of plotting causes all the isotherms to be coincident. Hence it was proposed that the strain, ϵ, would be given by:

$$\epsilon = f(\theta, \sigma) \tag{3-2}$$

which describes the instantaneous strain as a function of θ and the stress, σ. It was found that for high temperature creep, the activation energy, ΔH, was constant for a given material independent of temperature, creep stress, creep strain, grain size, sub-structures developed during creep and small alloying additions.

Each point in Figure 3-1 at the highest strain value corresponds to rupture. It is assumed, therefore, that equation (3-2) is valid up to and including the rupture point. This implied to Orr, Sherby, and Dorn that the processes involved in the formation and growth of microcracks that eventually result in rupture are dependent on the processes involved in creep. Assuming that such strain damage depends on the applied stress and the creep strain the strain at rupture following high temperature creep should then depend only on the applied stress. Therefore, from equation (3-2):

$$\epsilon_R = \phi(\sigma) \tag{3-3}$$

or

$$\theta_R = F(\sigma) \tag{3-4}$$

where the subscript refers to rupture and of course:

$$\theta_R = t_R\, e^{\frac{-\Delta H_R}{RT}} \tag{3-5}$$

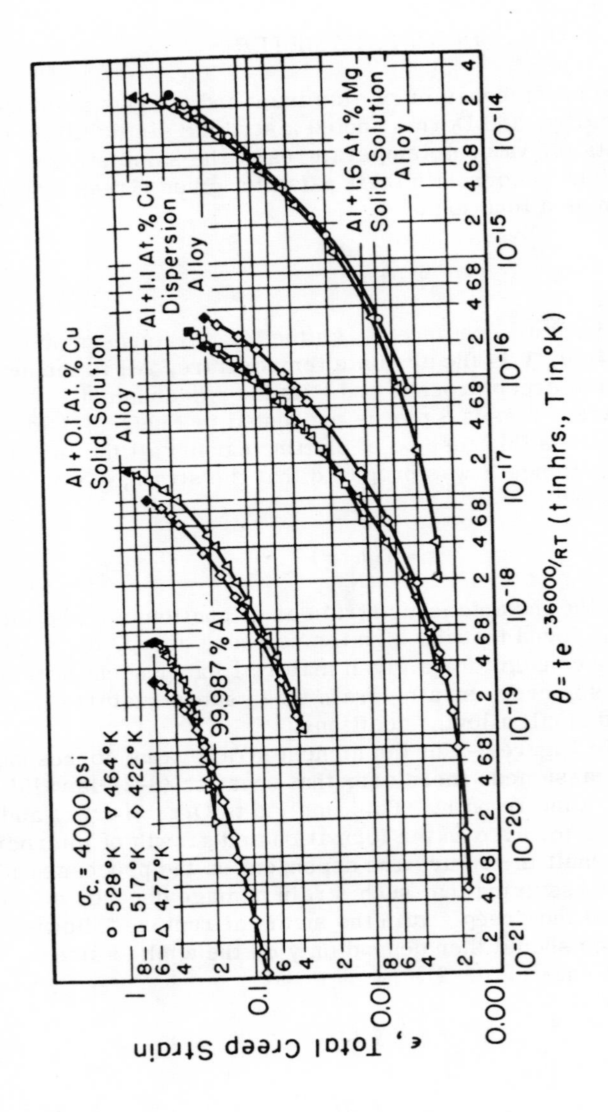

Figure 3-1 — Correlation(32) of creep strain-time data for aluminum and dilute aluminum alloys by means of the relation $\epsilon = f(\theta)$ for a stress of 4,000 psi.

Writing equation (3-5) at a given stress for two rupture points it follows that:

$$t_{R1}\, e^{\frac{-\Delta H_R}{RT_1}} = t_{R2}\, e^{\frac{-\Delta H_R}{RT_2}} \qquad (3\text{-}6)$$

since θ_R is constant at constant stress. Rearrangement allows the activation energy for rupture, ΔH_R, to be calculated as:

$$\Delta H_R = \frac{R \ln \frac{t_{R1}}{t_{R2}}}{\frac{1}{T_1} - \frac{1}{T_2}} \qquad (3\text{-}7)$$

Once ΔH_R is known the value of θ_R given by equation (3-5) can be calculated. This quantity introduced by Orr, Sherby and Dorn[32] has come to be known as the Dorn parameter for use in stress-rupture correlations. According to equation (3-5), this parameter should be a function of stress only and plots of this parameter against stress should yield a single curve or line independent of temperature. Some correlations of this type were provided by Orr, Sherby and Dorn and as shown in Figure 3-2 fairly good results were obtained.

In a more recent paper by Barrett, Ardell and Sherby[58] the use of modulus values in creep correlations was described. Based on the form of the steady state creep equation:

$$\dot{\epsilon}_s = SL^2\, D\left(\frac{\sigma}{E}\right)^n \qquad (3\text{-}8)$$

proposed by Sherby[59], where $\dot{\epsilon}_s$ is the steady state or linear creep rate, L is the grain diameter, D is the self-diffusion coefficient, E is the isotropic polycrystalline unrelaxed elastic modulus and n and S are constants, a more realistic interpretation follows from the use of a modulus correction. These authors have also suggested that this modification should also be reflected in various parametric approaches. For example, the Zener-Hollomon[60] parameter should be:

$$\dot{\epsilon}_s\, e^{\frac{\Delta H}{RT}} = f\left(\frac{\sigma}{E}\right) \qquad (3\text{-}9)$$

and the Dorn parameter:

$$t_R\, e^{\frac{-\Delta H}{RT}} = f\left(\frac{\sigma}{E}\right) \qquad (3\text{-}10)$$

While this modification to include modulus values might well provide more accurate correlations it has not been evaluated too extensively as yet. Of course, one disadvantage is immediately obvious in that the modulus values are implicit functions of the temperature. Hence, a parameter plot of say (σ/E) versus the parameter value would be

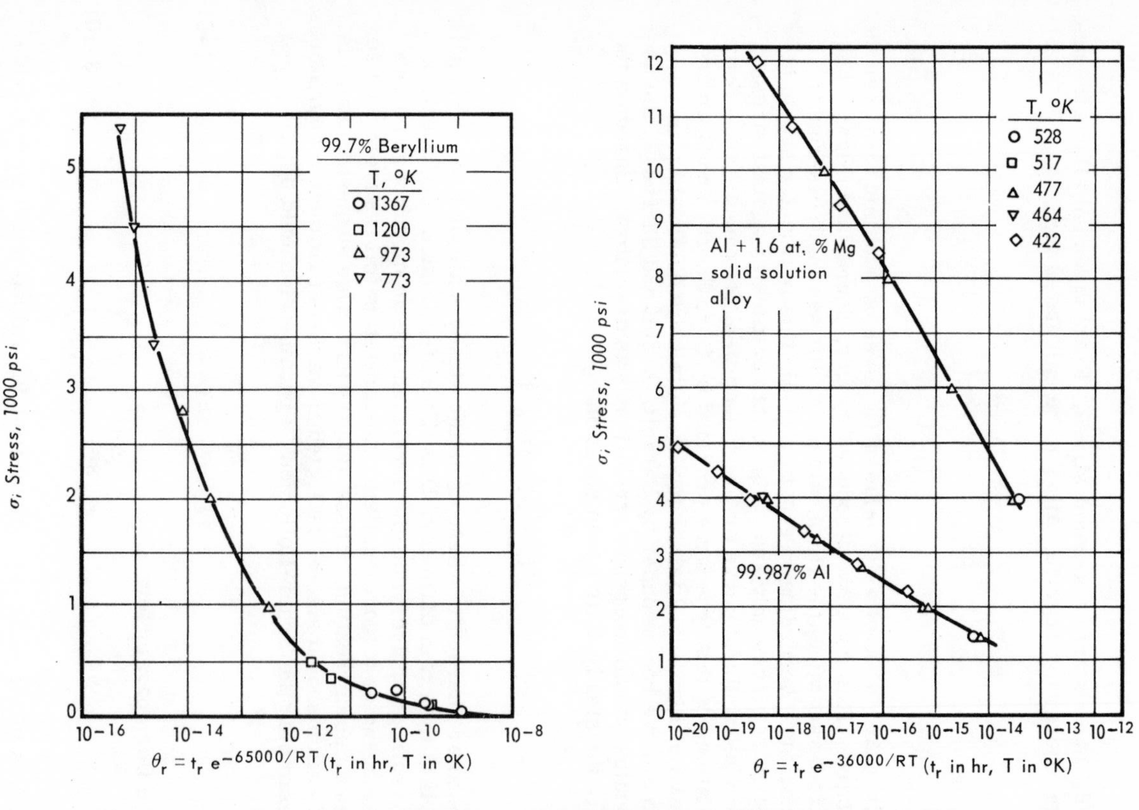

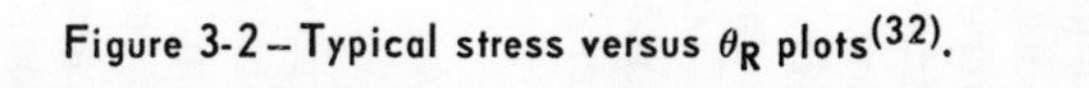
Figure 3-2 – Typical stress versus θ_R plots[32].

slightly inconvenient to employ. Some reference to a T versus E relation would always be required. Additional studies in this area are obviously indicated.

It will be noted that for a given stress equation (3-5) can be written as:

$$\log t_R = \frac{\Delta H_R}{2.3RT} + \log A \qquad (3\text{-}11)$$

where A is a constant. Hence a plot of $\log t_R$ versus $(1/T)$ will yield a linear relationship with a slope equal to $\Delta H_R/2.3R$ and an intercept (at $1/T = 0$) of $\log A$. Data at other stresses will then yield the series of parallel lines shown in Figure 3-3. Each line has the same slope but a different intercept. This observation allows for one other way in which the value of ΔH_R can be calculated; this result should be identical to that obtained through the use of equation (3-7).

It is worth noting that the parallelism given in Figure 3-3 describes a behavior which completely contradicts that observed in the case of the Larson-Miller parameter. It will be remembered that in the Larson-Miller approach a plot of $\log t_R$ versus $(1/T)$ required a series of constant stress lines which were definitely not parallel but rather had a common point of intersection. Obviously, both these characteristics cannot apply to the same material. If a series of parallel iso-stress lines is obtained then the Dorn parameter would be applicable and, of course, vice versa. Any attempt to apply the Larson-Miller concept to a case of parallel constant stress lines would naturally lead to some error.

A discussion similar to that involving Figure 2-6 in Chapter 2 can also be presented for the Dorn parameter plot. Since such a discussion would involve many similar deductions no detailed comments will be presented in this section. It should be obvious, for example, that the relative strengths of materials can be compared on the same Dorn parameter plot if the ΔH values are the same. In this case, the stronger materials will be those closest to the right hand side of the plot. A graphical aid similar to that employed in Figure 2-2 can also be incorporated into the Dorn parameter plot to allow for convenient conversions when ΔH is the same for all materials being compared. When the ΔH values are different for the materials being compared on the same parameter plot then the approach illustrated in Figure 2-8 can be adopted. While this type of graph has not been prepared for inclusion in this section a large version of the nomograph which would be used is presented in Appendix A.

LEAST SQUARES APPROACH TO PARAMETER ANALYSIS

A slight rearrangement of equations (2-15) and (2-16) will allow for a least squares analysis of each iso-stress line in Figure 3-3. However, it is also possible to treat all the data simultaneously to obtain a single value for the activation energy, ΔH_R In this approach[5] equation (3-11) is written in the form:

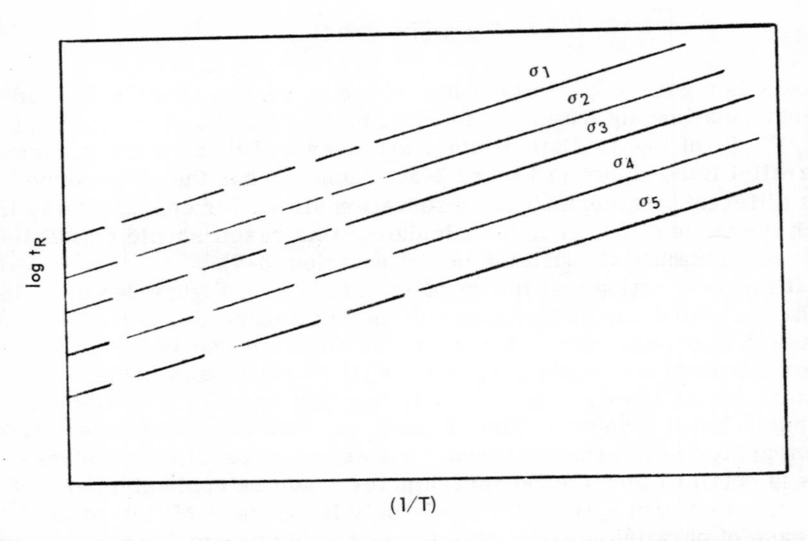

Figure 3-3 – Series of parallel constant stress lines formed by Dorn parameter.

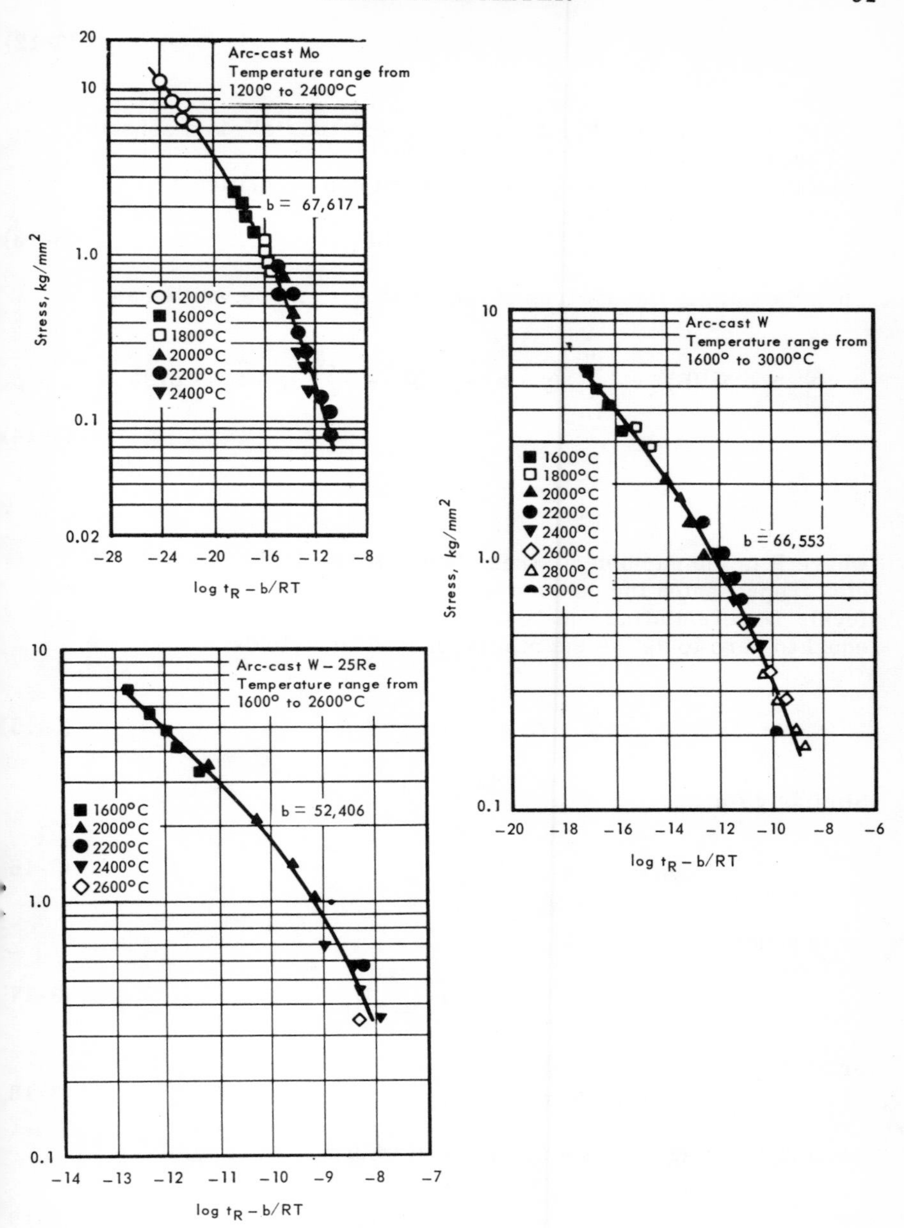

Figure 3-4—Dorn parameter plot for some high temperature refractory metal data[6]

$$y = a + bL \tag{3-12}$$

where:

$$y = \log t_R, \quad L = \frac{1}{T}, \quad b = \frac{\Delta H_R}{2.3R} \text{ and "a" is a constant.}$$

Then the equation for the jth stress level can be written as:

$$y_j = a_j + bL_j \tag{3-13}$$

Then the sum of the squares of the residuals can be written as:

$$S = \Sigma\,(R)^2 = \sum_{i=1}^{N_I} (y - a_I - bL)_I^2 + \sum_{i=1}^{N_{II}} (y - a_{II} - bL)_{II}^2 + \ldots + \sum_{i=1}^{N_P} (y - a_P - bL)_P^2 \tag{3-14}$$

where P is the number of stress levels in the analysis and N_I, N_{II}, etc., represented the number of experimental points at each stress level. Differentiating equation (3-14) with respect to a_I and setting equal to zero to define the minimum condition yields:

$$\sum_{i=1}^{N_I} y_I = N_I\, a_I + b \sum_{i=1}^{N_I} L_I \tag{3-15}$$

Similarly for a_{II}:

$$\sum_{i=1}^{N_{II}} y_{II} = N_{II}\, a_{II} + b \sum_{i=1}^{N_{II}} L_{II} \tag{3-16}$$

or in general:

$$\sum_{i=1}^{N_j} y_j = N_j\, a_j + b_j \sum_{i=1}^{N_j} L_j \tag{3-17}$$

or

$$D_j = N_j\, a_j + b\, A_j \tag{3-18}$$

when equation (2-28) is employed and where:

$$D_j = \sum_{i=1}^{N_j} y_j \tag{3-19}$$

Now differentiating equation (3-14) with respect to b and setting equal to zero yields:

$$\sum_{i=1}^{N_I} (Ly)_I + \sum_{i=1}^{N_{II}} (Ly)_{II} + \ldots + \sum_{i=1}^{N_P} (Ly)_P =$$

$$a_I \sum_{i=1}^{N_I} L_I + a_{II} \sum_{i=1}^{N_{II}} L_{II} + \ldots + a_P \sum_{i=1}^{N_P} L_P + \ldots$$
$$+ b \sum_{i=1}^{N_I} (L)_I^2 + b \sum_{i=1}^{N_{II}} (L)_I^2 + \ldots + b \sum_{i=1}^{N_P} (L)_P^2 \qquad (3\text{-}20)$$

or in general terms:

$$\sum_{j=1}^{P} C_j = \sum_{j=1}^{P} a_j A_j + b \sum_{j=1}^{P} B_j \qquad (3\text{-}21)$$

Now solving equation (3-18) gives:

$$a_j = \frac{D_j - b A_j}{N_j} \qquad (3\text{-}22)$$

which when substituted into equation (3-21) leads to:

$$b = \frac{\sum_{j=1}^{P} C_j - \sum_{j=1}^{P} \frac{A_j D_j}{N_j}}{\sum_{j=1}^{P} B_j - \sum_{j=1}^{P} \frac{A_j^2}{N_j}} \qquad (3\text{-}23)$$

In this approach, b leads to the Dorn constant and is obtained by first evaluating various summation terms and then using these terms in equation (3-23) to yield the desired solution. An illustration of this solution procedure is presented in Table 3-1 for the case where 6, 7 and 8 experimental points are available at stress levels I, II and III, respectively. All summation terms for use in equation (3-23) are thus easily evaluated.

Once the value of b (actually $\Delta H_R/2.3R$) has been obtained, the master-rupture plot can be constructed by plotting this parameter value as a function of log stress. As in the case of the Larson-Miller parameter a single line or curve is found to represent the stress-rupture behavior over a wide range of temperatures, stresses and rupture times.

When experimental data are available in the form of stress-rupture isotherms the preceding analysis can still be performed but as in the Larson-Miller analysis the data must first be converted to constant stress groupings. As before, this slight inconvenience can be avoided in the Manson and Mendelson analysis for handling the stress-rupture data given for several isotherms. As with the Larson-Miller parameter the Dorn parameter (or really the form given in

Table 3-1. Evaluation of Summation Terms for Use in Equation (3-23)

	$y = \log t_R$	$L = (\frac{1}{T})$	$L^2 = (\frac{1}{T})^2$	$y\,L = \frac{\log t_R}{T}$	
= 6	- - - - - -	- - - - - -	- - - - - -	- - - - - -	$\frac{A_I D_I}{N_I}$ and $\frac{A_I^2}{N_I}$
	$\Sigma = D_I$	$\Sigma = A_I$	$\Sigma = B_I$	$\Sigma = C_I$	
I I = 7	- - - - - - -	- - - - - - -	- - - - - - -	- - - - - - -	$\frac{A_{II} D_{II}}{N_{II}}$ and $\frac{A_{II}^2}{N_{II}}$
	$\Sigma = D_{II}$	$\Sigma = A_{II}$	$\Sigma = B_{II}$	$\Sigma = C_{II}$	
I II = 8	- - - - - - - -	- - - - - - - -	- - - - - - - -	- - - - - - - -	$\frac{A_{III} D_{III}}{N_{III}}$ and $\frac{A_{III}^2}{N_{III}}$
	$\Sigma = D_{III}$	$\Sigma = A_{III}$	$\Sigma = B_{III}$	$\Sigma = C_{III}$	
			$\sum_{j=1}^{P} B_j$	$\sum_{j=1}^{P} C_j$	$\sum_{j=1}^{P} \frac{A_j D_j}{N_j}$ and $\sum_{j=1}^{P} \frac{A_j^2}{N_j}$

equation (3-11)) is assumed to be expressed as some polynomial equation in log stress of the form:

$$y - \frac{b}{T} = a_0 + a_1 x + a_2 x^2 + \ldots + a_m x^m \qquad (3\text{-}24)$$

where $y = \log t_R$, $x = \log\sigma$, $b = (\Delta H_R/2.3R)$, a_0, a_1, etc, are constants and m is the degree of the polynomial. Using $L = 1/T$, equation (3-24) becomes:

$$y = bL + a_0 + a_1 x + a_2 x^2 + \ldots a_m x^m \qquad (3\text{-}25)$$

Then the sum of the squares of the residuals will be:

$$S = \Sigma (R)^2 = \sum_{i=1}^{N} (y - bL - a_0 - a_1 x - a_2 x^2 - \ldots - a_m x^m)^2 \qquad (3\text{-}26)$$

Differentiating with respect to b, a_0, a_1, etc., to a_m and setting equal to zero leads to:

$$\sum_{i=1}^{N} yL = b\sum_{i=1}^{N} L^2 + a_0 \sum_{i=1}^{N} L + a_1 \sum_{i=1}^{N} Lx + a_2 \sum_{i=1}^{N} Lx^2 + \ldots + a_m \sum_{i=1}^{N} Lx^m \qquad (3\text{-}27)$$

$$\sum_{i=1}^{N} y = b\sum_{i=1}^{N} L + Na_0 + a_1 \sum_{i=1}^{N} x + a_2 \sum_{i=1}^{N} x^2 + \ldots + a_m \sum_{i=1}^{N} x^m \qquad (3\text{-}28)$$

$$\sum_{i=1}^{N} yx = b\sum_{i=1}^{N} Lx + a_0 \sum_{i=1}^{N} x + a_1 \sum_{i=1}^{N} x^2 + a_2 \sum_{i=1}^{N} x^3 + \ldots + a_m \sum_{i=1}^{N} x^{m+1} \qquad (3\text{-}29)$$

$$\vdots$$

$$\sum_{i=1}^{N} yx^m = b\sum_{i=1}^{N} Lx^m + a_0 \sum_{i=1}^{N} x^m + a_1 \sum_{i=1}^{N} x^{m+1} + a_2 \sum_{i=1}^{N} x^{m+2} + \ldots + a_m \sum_{i=1}^{N} x^{2m} \qquad (3\text{-}30)$$

As can be noted the number of equations involved is equal to the degree of the polynomial plus two. Simultaneous solution leads to the value of b to enable Dorn parameter values to be calculated; values of a_0, a_1, etc., then enable the master-rupture curve to be positioned.

Applying the above approach to the analysis of high temperature rupture data[6] yielded the results shown in Figure 3-4. These plots were used to construct the stress-rupture isotherms as shown in Figure 3-5. A good agreement with the experimental points is noted although it should be observed that the correlation is not as good as that obtained using the Larson-Miller approach.

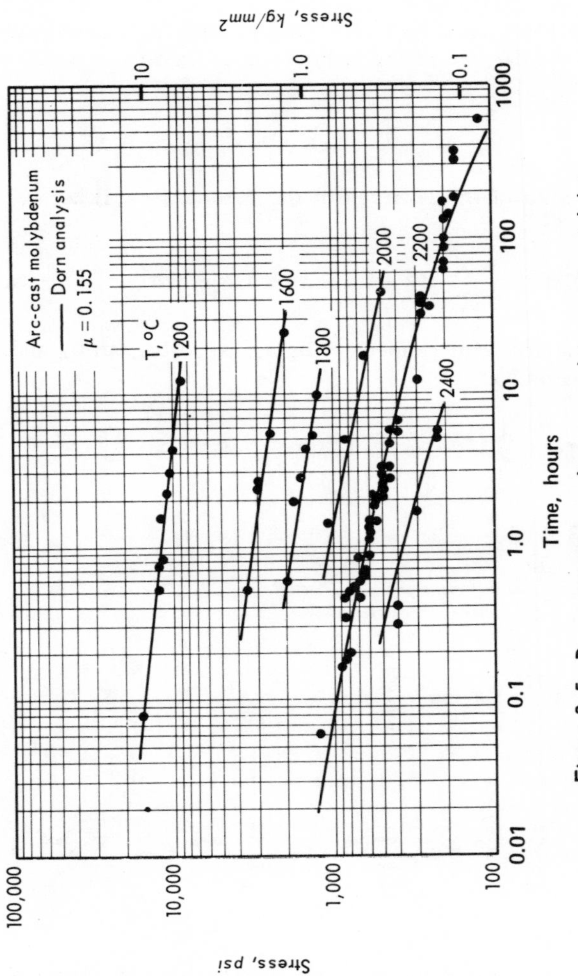

Figure 3-5 — Dorn parameter results compared to experimental data.

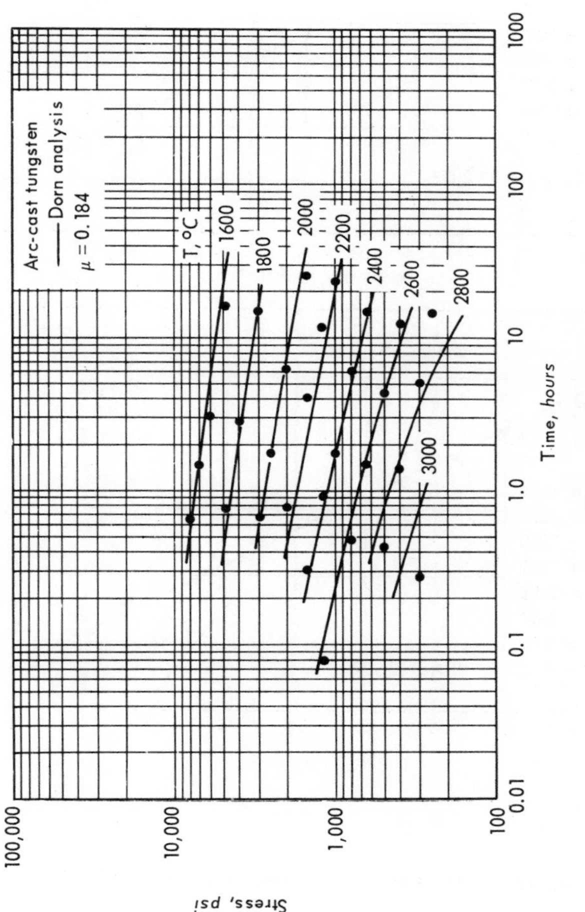

Figure 3-5 (continued)

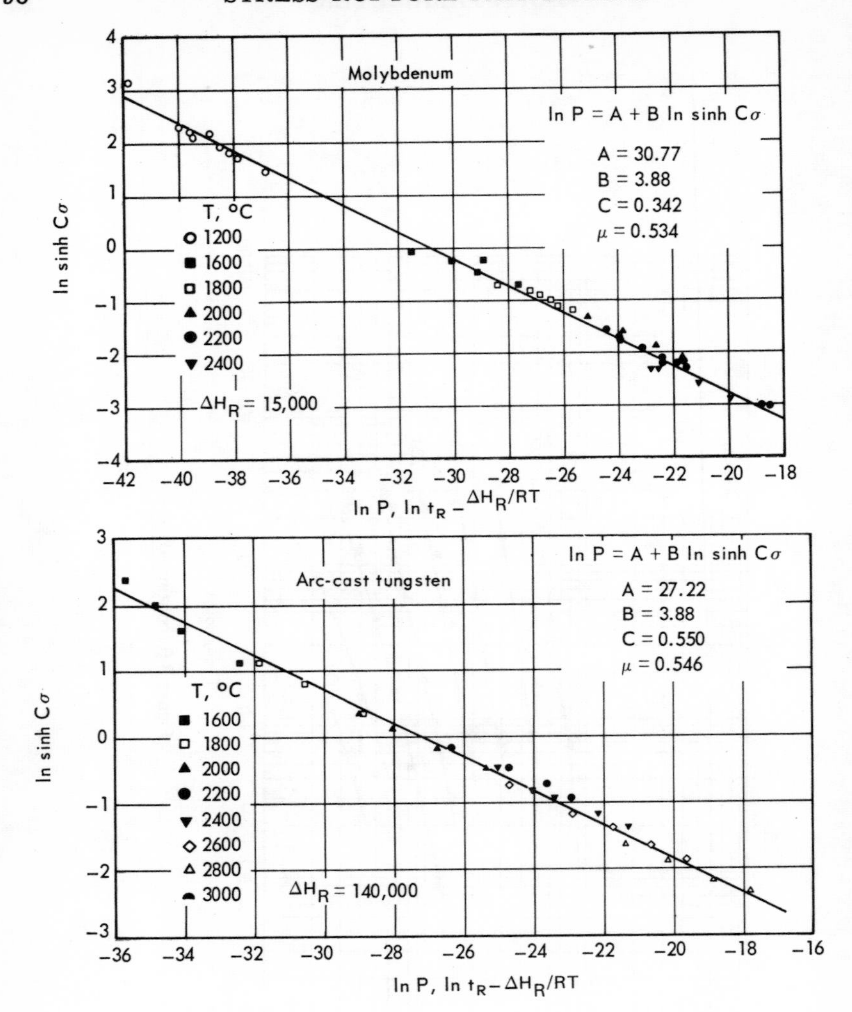

Figure 3-6 – Dorn parameter expressed as hyperbolic sine function of stress.

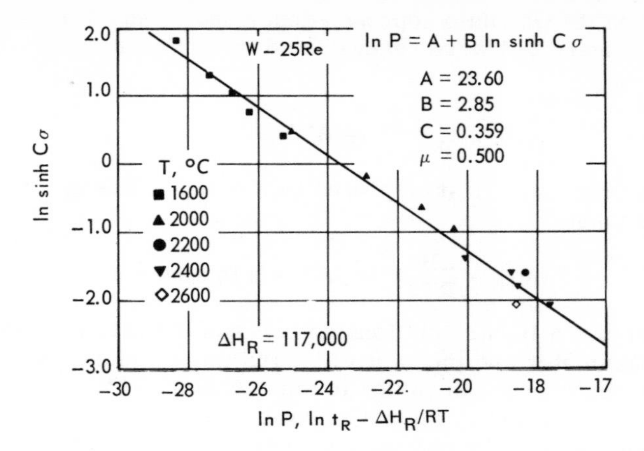

Figure 3-6 (continued)

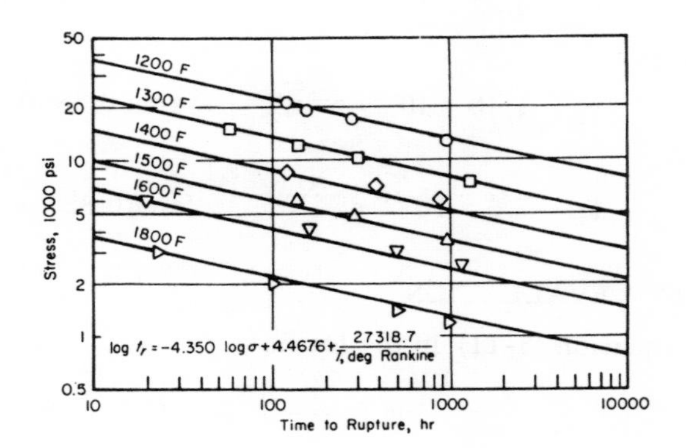

Figure 3-7 – Data for Timken 35-15 steel compared to results from equation (3-37)[20].

Based on the Garofalo approach described by equation (1-13) the data of Figure 3-4 were re-evaluated in terms of:

$$t_R e^{\frac{-\Delta H_R}{RT}} = A''' (\sinh a\,\sigma)^{-n} \tag{3-31}$$

following a procedure first employed by Smith.[54] Taking natural logarithms yields:

$$\ln t_R - \frac{\Delta H_R}{RT} = \ln A''' - n \ln \sinh a\,\sigma \tag{3-32}$$

which describes a linear relationship between the natural logarithm of the Dorn parameter and the natural logarithm of sinh a σ (a non-linear regression analysis led to values for the constant "a"). Results of this analysis are presented in Figure 3-6 where excellent linearity is noted. This behavior allows the following expressions to be proposed (for t_R in hours and σ in kg/mm^2):

For Mo

$$t_R = 4.27 \times 10^{-14}\, e^{\frac{-115{,}000}{RT}} (\sinh 0.342\,\sigma)^{-3.88} \tag{3-33}$$

For W

$$t_R = 1.48 \times 10^{-12}\, e^{\frac{-140{,}000}{RT}} (\sinh 0.55\,\sigma)^{-3.88} \tag{3-34}$$

For W-25Re

$$t_R = 5.5 \times 10^{-11}\, e^{\frac{-117{,}000}{RT}} (\sinh 0.359\,\sigma)^{-2.85} \tag{3-35}$$

THE CLAUSS[20] EVALUATION

Writing equation (3-11) in the form:

$$\log t_R - \frac{\Delta H_R}{2.3RT} = f(\sigma) \tag{3-36}$$

Clauss observed that for the data for Timken 35-15 steel shown in Figure 2-22, log t_R was linear in log σ. Hence equation (3-36) become

$$\log t_R - \frac{\Delta H_R}{2.3RT} = A \log \sigma + B \tag{3-37}$$

or

$$\log t_R = A \log \sigma + B + \frac{\Delta H_R}{2.3RT} \tag{3-38}$$

This equation differs from equation (2-55) only in the temperature term. In equation (3-38) the (1/T) term is employed whereas a term linear in T was used in equation (2-55). An analysis of these data defined the temperature function in equation (2-54) as follows:

$$b(T) = B + \frac{\Delta H_R}{2.3RT} = 4.4676 + \frac{27318.7}{T} \tag{3-39}$$

where T is in °R.

Substituting equation (3-39) and using the coefficient on stress from equation (2-55) yields:

$$\log t_R = -4.35 \log \sigma + 4.4676 + \frac{27318.7}{T} \qquad (3\text{-}40)$$

as the general equation for Timken 35-15 steel. A plot of these data with the isotherms calculated using equation (3-40) is shown in Figure 3-7. Excellent agreement with the experimental points is indicated.

Rearrangement of equation (3-40) at constant stress leads to:

$$\log t_R - \frac{27318.7}{T} = \text{constant} \qquad (3\text{-}41)$$

which, of course, is the Dorn Parameter in logarithmic form. A plot based on this approach is shown in Figure 3-8 and, as noted, an excellent correlation is indicated.

THE LARKE AND INGLIS[30] EVALUATION

Writing the Dorn parameter in logarithmic form:

$$\log t_R = \log \phi + \frac{B}{T} \qquad (3\text{-}42)$$

Larke and Inglis employed Figure 3-9 in an analysis similar to that performed in conjunction with Figure 2-36. For example, at the stress level σ', equation (3-42), for isotherms representing equal temperature increments, yields:

$$\log t_{R_1} = \log \phi' + \frac{B}{T_1} \qquad (3\text{-}43)$$

$$\log t_{R_2} = \log \phi' + \frac{B}{T_2} \qquad (3\text{-}44)$$

and

$$\log t_{R_3} = \log \phi' + \frac{B}{T_3} \qquad (3\text{-}45)$$

from which:

$$\log t_{R_1} - \log t_{R_2} = B\left(\frac{T_2 - T_1}{T_1 T_2}\right) = a \qquad (3\text{-}46)$$

and

$$\log t_{R_2} - \log t_{R_3} = B\left(\frac{T_3 - T_2}{T_3 T_2}\right) = b \qquad (3\text{-}47)$$

Since it has been stipulated that:

$$T_2 - T_1 = T_3 - T_2 \qquad (3\text{-}48)$$

then, from equations (3-46) and (3-47):

$$a = \frac{T_3}{T_1}\, b \qquad (3\text{-}49)$$

and since $T_3 > T_1$ it follows that:

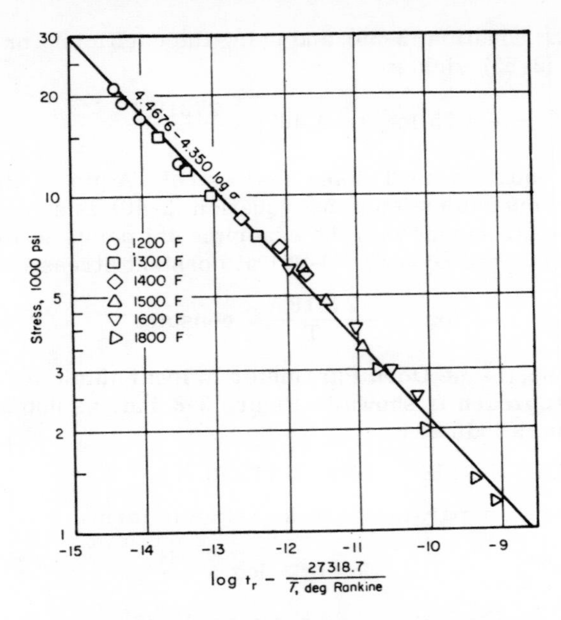

Figure 3-8 – Dorn parameter plot for Timken 35-15 steel[20].

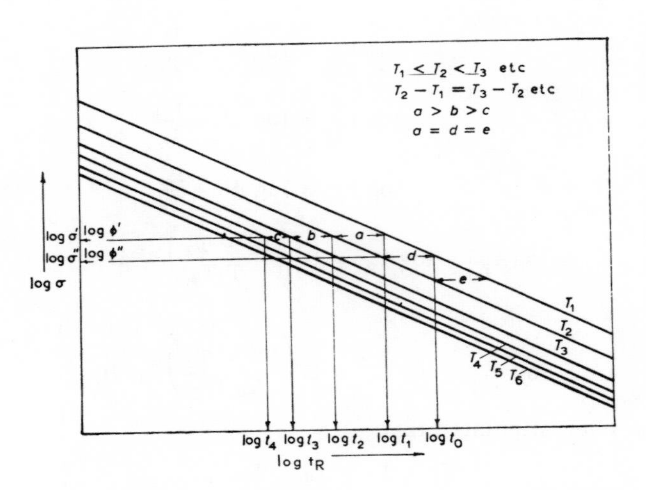

Figure 3-9 – Isotherms spaced at equal temperature intervals for use in evaluation of Dorn parameter [30].

$$a > b \tag{3-50}$$

A similar procedure reveals that

$$b > c \tag{3-51}$$

hence,

$$a > b > c \tag{3-52}$$

At a lower stress σ'' and at a temperature equal to T_1 it is possible to write:

$$\log t_{R_0} = \log \phi'' + \frac{B}{T_1} \tag{3-53}$$

Similarly for t_{R_1} and T_2 at σ'':

$$\log t_{R_1} = \log \sigma'' + \frac{B}{T_2} \tag{3-54}$$

Subtracting:

$$\log t_{R_0} - \log t_{R_1} = B \frac{T_2 - T_1}{T_2 T_1} = d \tag{3-55}$$

Comparing this with equation (3-46) it follows that:

$$a = d \tag{3-56}$$

It is easily shown further that:

$$a = d = e \tag{3-57}$$

Equation (3-52) will be recalled as describing the same relationship as that written for the Larson-Miller parameter in Chapter 2. However, it is important to note that the characteristic defined in equation (3-57) is completely different from that applying to the Larson-Miller parameter. For the Dorn parameter then, any material tested at two temperatures will exhibit log time intervals a, d, e, between adjacent $\log \sigma/\log t_R$ curves or lines (see footnote on page 77 of Chapter 2) which are equal independent of the stress level employed. In the analysis of both the Dorn and Larson-Miller parameters, it was found that for equi-spaced temperatures, and independent of the material, the ratios a/b, b/c, etc. are dependent on temperature only. Specifically:

$$\frac{a}{b} = \frac{T_3}{T_1} \tag{3-58}$$

and

$$\frac{b}{c} = \frac{T_4}{T_2} \quad \text{etc.} \tag{3-59}$$

As concluding remarks, Larke and Inglis pointed out that for the same two temperatures the same value for "a" is not to be expected

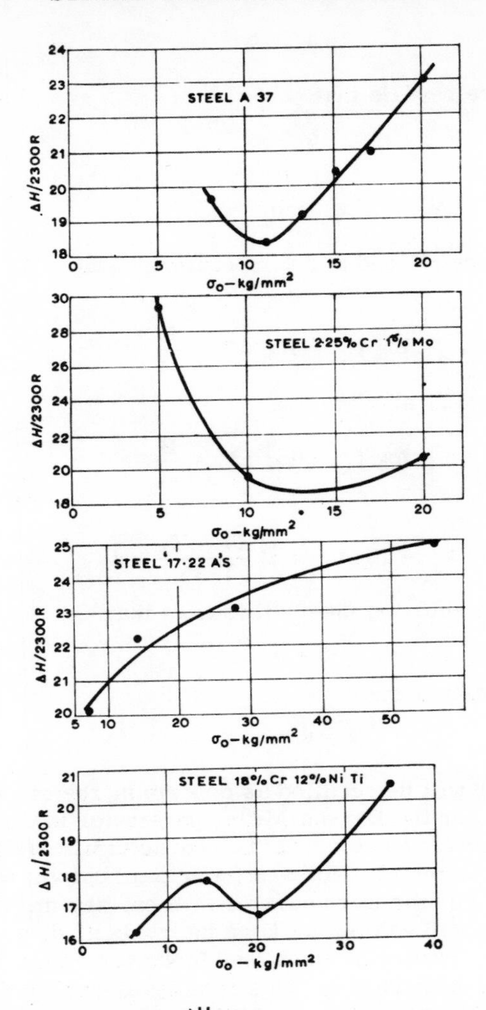

Figure 3-10 – Variation of $\frac{\Delta H}{2.3R}$ values in Dorn parameter based on Murry analysis[31].

for different materials. Furthermore, it was pointed out that the value of B in equation (3-42) is another material characteristic. Finally, if the conditions defined by equation (3-57) are not in evidence for a given set of data then it is to be expected that large errors will occur if the Dorn analysis is applied.

THE MURRY[31] EVALUATION

Writing the Dorn parameter in logarithmic form as:

$$\log t_R = \frac{\alpha}{T} - \beta \tag{3-60}$$

Murry emphasized the similarity of this expression and equation (2-96). In other words, both the Larson-Miller and Dorn parameters describe a linear relationship between $\log t_R$ and $(1/T)$. Analyzing the same data as employed in Table 2-9 of Chapter 2 it must follow that the constants α and β in equation (3-60) would be identical to those presented for $f(\sigma_0)$ and C of equation (2-96). A listing of the α and β values resulting from a least squares analysis of this equation would obviously lead to the same results presented in Table 2-9. It need only be mentioned that α, which of course is equal to $(\Delta H/2.3R)$, replaces $f(\sigma_0)$ and β replaces C. With this simple exchange the data in Table 2-9 represent the results of the analysis based on equation (3-60).

Based on the results of the least squares analysis of equation (3-60) Murry noted that the assumption of Orr, Sherby and Dorn[32] that $(\Delta H/2.3R)$, or α in equation (3-60), was a constant independent of stress, did not seem to apply. Variation of this quantity with stress can be noted in Table 2-9 in the $f(\sigma_0)$ column. This variation is presented graphically in Figure 3-10 for the same four steels listed in Table 2-9. These results lead to the conclusion that while the constant stress lines on a plot of $\log t_R$ versus $1/T$, are linear they are not parallel. Hence the general equation for this behavior is:

$$\log t_R = \frac{F_1(\sigma_0)}{T} - F_2(\sigma_0) \tag{3-61}$$

to suggest that both α and β from equation (3-60) are functions of the initial stress.

If, as in the Dorn parameter approach, it is assumed that $F_1(\sigma_0)$ is a constant independent of stress then it follows that:

$$f(\sigma_0) = \frac{\Delta H}{2.3RT} - \log t_R \tag{3-62}$$

Combining equation (3-61) with (3-62) leads to:

$$f(\sigma_0) = \frac{1}{T}\left[\frac{\Delta H}{2.3R} - F_1(\sigma_0)\right] + F_2(\sigma_0) \tag{3-63}$$

which reveals that $f(\sigma_0)$ is not independent of temperature but rather varies with it in a way which is directly proportional to the difference between the value adopted for $\Delta H/2.3R$ and $F_1(\sigma_0)$.

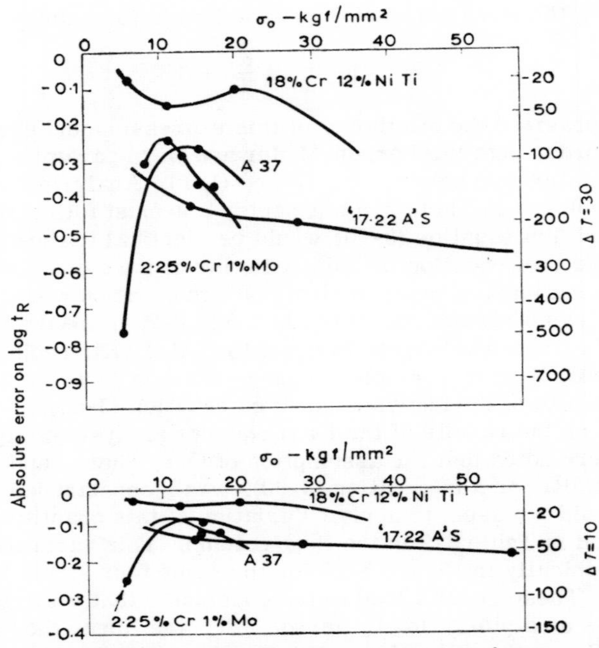

ΔT = difference between the average temperature of tests from which $F(\sigma_0)$ is calculated and the temperature of extrapolation.

$\Delta H = 60$ kcal/mol for α structures

$\Delta H = 67$ kcal/mol for γ structures

Fig. 3-11 – Errors [31] due to the determination of log t_R by extrapolation with the Dorn parameter;

$$f(\sigma_0) = \frac{\Delta H}{2.3RT} - \log t_R$$

In equation (3-63) the value of T corresponds to the temperature of the test or the average temperature of the tests from which $f(\sigma_0)$ is calculated for the particular initial stress. Expressing this temperature as T_m then:

$$f(\sigma_0) = \frac{1}{T_m}\left[\frac{\Delta H}{2.3R} - F_1(\sigma_0)\right] + F_2(\sigma_0) \qquad (3\text{-}64)$$

A characteristic time is then determined at a given temperature, T_e, by application of equation (3-62). Thus:

$$\log t_{R_{Dorn}} = \frac{\Delta H}{2.3RT_e} - f(\sigma_0) \qquad (3\text{-}65)$$

and substitution of equation (3-64) yields:

$$\log t_{R_{Dorn}} = \frac{\Delta H}{2.3RT_e} - \frac{1}{T_m}\left[\frac{\Delta H}{2.3R} - F_1(\sigma_0)\right] - F_2(\sigma_0) \qquad (3\text{-}66)$$

Now the true value for the characteristic time is given by equation (3-61) as:

$$\log t_{R_{true}} = \frac{F_1(\sigma_0)}{T_e} - F_2(\sigma_0) \qquad (3\text{-}67)$$

and the difference:

$$\log t_{R_{Dorn}} - \log t_{R_{true}} = \left[\frac{\Delta H}{2.3R} - F_1(\sigma_0)\right]\left(\frac{1}{T_e} - \frac{1}{T_m}\right) = \Delta \log t_R \qquad (3\text{-}68)$$

represents the error in the calculation of characteristic time using the Dorn parameter. Murry noted that this error increases with the difference between T_m and T_e, that is, between the average temperature of the tests from which $f(\sigma_0)$ is calculated and the temperature at which the results are extrapolated. Furthermore, $\Delta \log t_R$ is proportional to:

$$\frac{\Delta H}{2.3R} - F_1(\sigma_0) \qquad (3\text{-}69)$$

and this depends on the value of ΔH. However, since $F_1(\sigma_0) = \alpha$ then $\Delta \log t_R$ also varies with σ_0. From the shape of the plots in Figure 3-10 the variations of $\Delta \log t_R$ with σ_0 will be quite unpredictable.

Some indication of the error involved in the use of the Dorn parameter is presented in Figure 3-11 where the variation of $\Delta \log t_R$ with σ_0 is plotted. This analysis was based on:

ΔH = 60 kcal/mole for α-structure steels
ΔH = 67 kcal/mole for γ-structure steels
$T_m = 550°C = 823°K$
$T = T_m - T_e = 10°$ or $30°$

Extrapolation using the Dorn approach is seen to lead to substantial errors in certain situations.

CHAPTER 4

MANSON-HAFERD PARAMETER

Another very common parametric approach to the correlation of stress-rupture data involves the Manson-Haferd[36] parameter. In a very detailed study of the Larson-Miller parameter, Manson and Haferd, while noting the simplicity of the Larson-Miller approach, also noted that in certain applications the effectiveness of the approach left a lot to be desired. In some cases, for example, where extrapolations are made into the range of long rupture times and only short-term rupture data are available, the errors involved can be as high as one order of magnitude. Attempts to explain such discrepancies revealed certain inconsistencies in the basic Larson-Miller approach. For example, in analyzing some data for 18-8 stainless steel it was noted that while a plot of $T(20 + \log t_R)$ versus log stress seemed to describe a single curve, the deviations were too systematic to be attributed to experimental scatter. Although all the data points appeared to fall close to a mean curve, it was clear that data for different temperatures described individual and different smooth curves considerably removed from the mean curve. Such a situation for 18-8 stainless steel is shown in Figure 4-1. Also shown in Figure 4-1 is the different master-rupture curve which is obtained when only rupture data in the range below 100 hours are analyzed. Obviously serious error can be introduced if such a rupture curve is employed in extrapolations to yield rupture information in the range of several thousand hours. An illustration of this situation was presented by Manson and Haferd and is shown in Figure 4-2. As can be seen, the curves in Figure 4-2, based on the curve in Figure 4-1 corresponding to rupture times less than 100 hours, are not in good agreement with the actual experimental data points. This is particularly true in the range of large rupture times and obviously serious extrapolation errors can result. At 1200°F, for example, the measured rupture life at a stress close to 1500 psi is 1000 hours compared to a predicted value (based on data for rupture times less than 100 hours) of 8000 hours.

While investigating the possible source of the extrapolation errors obtained in certain cases when the Larson-Miller parameter was employed, Manson and Haferd found reason to question the assumption of the linearity of the $\log t_R$ versus $(1/T)$ plots. Such linearity, it will be recalled, is the entire basis for the Larson-Miller parameter. When plots of $\log t_R$ versus $(1/T)$ were prepared for a number of materials, definite deviations from linearity were noted as shown schematically in Figure 4-3. Noting that the non-linear trends were too general and

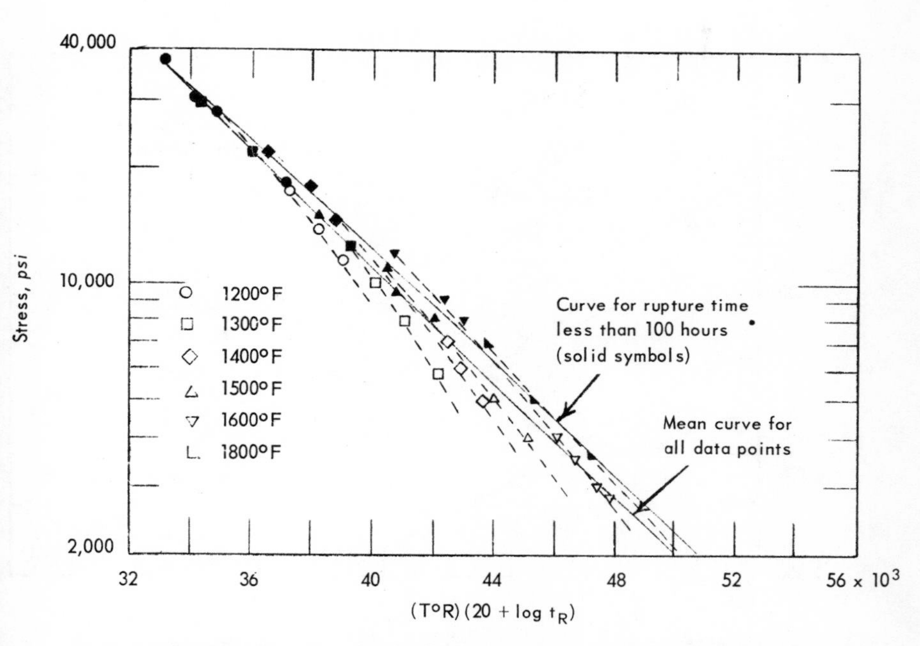

Figure 4-1 – Master-rupture plot for 18-8 stainless steel based on Larson-Miller parameter.

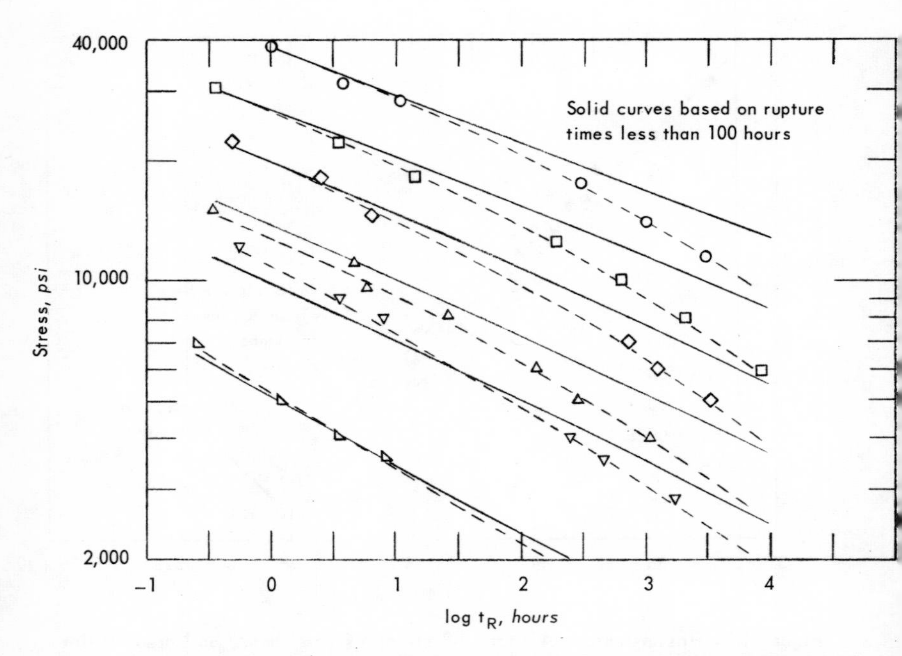

Figure 4-2 – Stress-rupture plots for 18-8 stainless steel based on Figure 4-1.

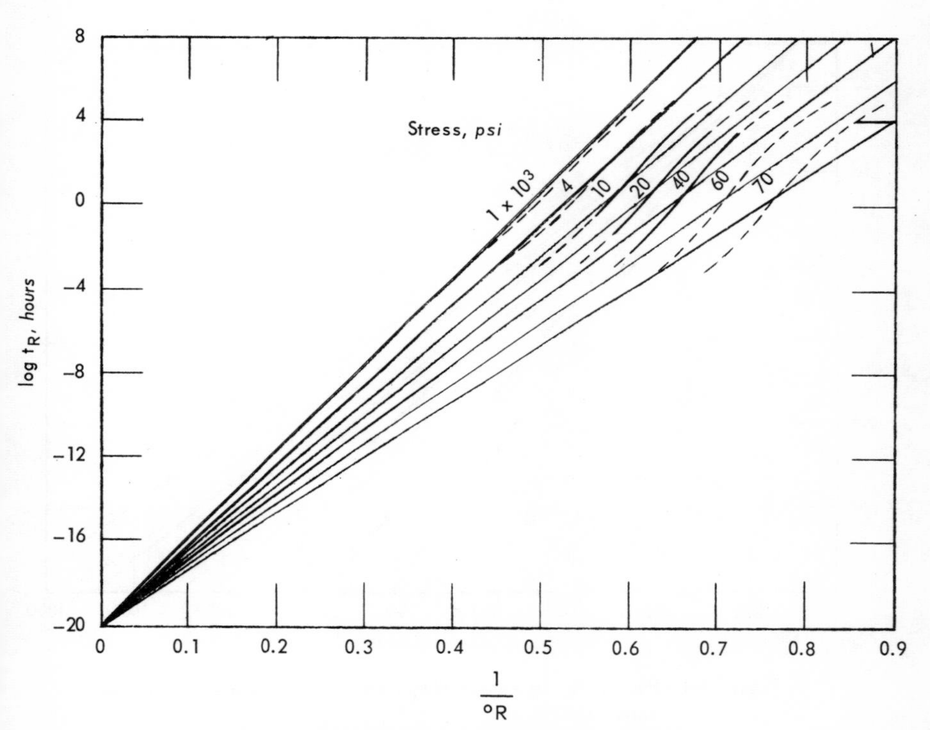

Figure 4-3 – Schematic log t_R versus (1/T) plot.

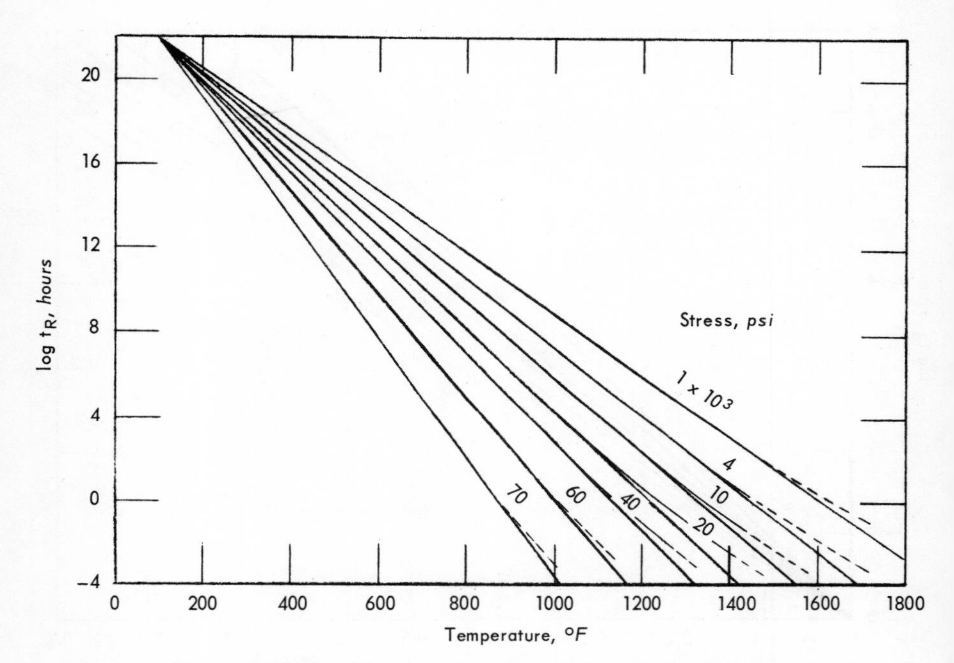

Figure 4-4 – Plot of log t_R versus temperature to define Manson-Haferd parameter.

systematic to be attributable to data scatter or to the method of cross-plotting used in preparing this plot, it was concluded that no such linearity exists. In this figure lines converging to C = 20 have been drawn to emphasize the deviations from linearity noted in the region of the experimental data. Curvature is seen to occur at both the very short and the very long rupture times and hence, when intermediate data are used to extrapolate to long rupture times, the errors noted above are understandable.

During the course of the analysis of the Larson-Miller parameter, Manson and Haferd noted that for rupture times greater than 10 hours good linearity was obtained in a plot of log t_R versus temperature at constant stress. A plot of this type is shown in Figure 4-4 for the same data used in Figure 4-3. At the very short rupture times considerable curvature is noted in the constant stress lines whereas in the practical rupture time range between 10 and 10,000 hours, a close approach to linearity is observed. Furthermore, these constant stress lines exhibit a common convergence point. Therefore, over the time range in which these constant stress lines are linear, a new stress-rupture parameter was proposed of the form:

$$\frac{T - T_a}{\log t_R - \log t_a} = \phi \tag{4-1}$$

where ϕ is the reciprocal of the slope of a given constant stress line and defines the Manson-Haferd parameter; T_a and log t_a are material constants which describe the common point of convergence as shown in Figure 4-4. Once the constants T_a and log t_a are identified, a master-rupture plot of the Manson-Haferd parameter versus log stress can be prepared as was the case in the treatment of the stress-rupture parameters discussed previously. Since the Manson-Haferd parameter is based on the linear relationship between log t_R and temperature, it is often referred to as the linear time-temperature parameter.

Some similarity between the Manson-Haferd and Larson-Miller parameters will be noted. Both define a series of linear and non-parallel constant stress lines. Both also require a common point of intersection for the constant stress lines. However, whereas the Larson-Miller approach requires a common point of intersection at $(1/T) = 0$, the Manson-Haferd approach allows this intersection to occur at abscissa values corresponding to finite temperatures.

A brief study of equation (4-1) will reveal that the calculation of the constants T_a and log t_a is not exactly straightforward. More than two rupture-time-temperature combinations are necessary. If two pairs of t_R-T values are known at a given stress, σ_I, then a rearrangement of equation (4-1) yields

$$T_1 = \phi_I (\log t_{R1} - \log t_a) + T_a \tag{4-2}$$

and

$$T_2 = \phi_I (\log t_{R2} - \log t_a) + T_a \tag{4-3}$$

Since T_a and $\log t_a$ are constants, and for the given stress value the same value of ϕ applies, subtraction gives:

$$\phi_I = \frac{T_1 - T_2}{\log t_{R1} - \log t_{R2}} \tag{4-4}$$

A similar calculation using two other pairs of t_R-T values at another stress σ_{II} yields:

$$\phi_{II} = \frac{T_3 - T_4}{\log t_{R3} - \log t_{R4}} \tag{4-5}$$

With ϕ_I and ϕ_{II} now known, simultaneous solution of:

$$T_1 = \phi_I \left(\log t_{R1} - \log t_a\right) + T_a \tag{4-6}$$

and

$$T_3 = \phi_{II} \left(\log t_{R3} - \log t_a\right) + T_a \tag{4-7}$$

yields

$$\log t_a = \frac{T_1 - T_3 - \phi_I \log t_{R1} + \phi_{II} \log t_{R3}}{\phi_{II} - \phi_I} \tag{4-8}$$

With $\log t_a$ known, the value of T_a can be obtained from either equation (4-6) or (4-7). Hence, if values of the Manson-Haferd constants are to be calculated, it is necessary to have at least two t_R-T combinations at each of two different stresses. It must be pointed out, however, that such a calculation, based on only four data points, might not lead to the most representative values for T_a and $\log t_a$. A calculation of these constants which employs the entire set of data simultaneously will be described below.

A discussion of the Manson-Haferd plot in terms of the considerations involving Figure 2-6 of Chapter 2 would lead to similar deductions. Because of the use of two constants in the Manson-Haferd approach, some slight additional complications are, of course, introduced. But, nevertheless, it can be seen that if materials have the same T_a and $\log t_a$ values, the relative strengths can be compared directly in a Manson-Haferd plot. As in the case of the other two parameters already discussed, the stronger materials occupy positions to the right of the weaker materials. It may also be noted that the graphical aid illustrated in Figure 2-7 can be incorporated into the type of plot presented in Figure 4-7, as long as all the materials being compared have the same T_a and $\log t_a$ values. For the case of materials with different T_a and $\log t_a$ values, the approach illustrated in Figure 2-8 could be employed. A large version of the nomograph which would be applicable in such a plot is presented in Appendix A.

A simplified procedure, based on isostatic testing, was described by Manson, Succop and Brown[52] for use in establishing the master curve for the Manson-Haferd parameter (this approach was acknowledged as being applicable also to the Larson-Miller and Dorn parameters). In selecting the two stresses to be employed, it was recommended that these be chosen far enough apart to allow fairly large differences to be obtained in the slopes of the lines in the log t_R versus T plot. It was suggested that the tensile strength data be used as a guide in the selection of stresses (see Figure 4-5). For the lowest stress value a point is selected in the high temperature region. In Figure 4-5, this is shown to be 10,000 psi at about 1450°F for the "17-22-A"S data.

In selecting the higher stress, attention is given to the range in which rupture life is not too sensitive to temperature change so that excessive data scattering will be avoided. For this reason, the region of very high stress should not be considered. Referring to Figure 4-5 attention should be directed to the temperature range in which the strength decreases rapidly, i.e., 800° to 1300°F for this material. A stress of 80,000 psi (1150°F) was chosen in this example.

Isostatic testing at the two chosen stresses is then initiated, but at temperatures some 50°F below the tensile temperature. Failure in these tests should occur in perhaps 1 hour. Another point on the isostatic is then measured by again reducing the test temperature by another 50°F. With these data available, a line joining the two points on a log t_R versus T plot is then drawn to yield an approximate slope. This line is used to select the next test temperature in this constant-stress testing, and the next point is used to make any necessary adjustments in the line defined by the previous points. Continuing this procedure, the isostatics shown in Figure 4-6 were established.

It was stated that some curvature in the constant stress lines of Figure 4-6 might be observed for short-term data. If this is the case, the testing must continue into the longer rupture life region until sufficient data are obtained to clearly establish a linear portion. Also, it was recommended that testing continue until the rupture life obtained is within two log cycles of the longest rupture life desired in any intended extrapolation of the data (100-hour data needed for 10,000-hour predictions). It was not considered possible to recommend any specific number of tests which should be employed in the determination of Figure 4-6. In this study, four points (solid circles) were considered sufficient in view of the uniform behavior observed.

A least squares fit (see Chapter 10 for this procedure) of the straight constant stress lines in Figure 4-6 was employed to accurately determine the point of intersection of the two isostatics. In this way the T_a and log t_a values given in Figure 4-6 were established.

As a final step in establishing the master-rupture curve, the parameter values (4 values at each stress) are calculated for the data points obtained. This is done using the T_a and log t_a values given in Figure 4-6 and yields the results presented in Figure 4-7. A straight line is then drawn between the two clusters of points to yield an "idealized" master-rupture curve. Following this, some additional tests (open circles in Figure 4-6) are made at stress levels between the values shown in Figure 4-6. These data serve to define the master-rupture curve very accurately. In this additional testing, the rupture

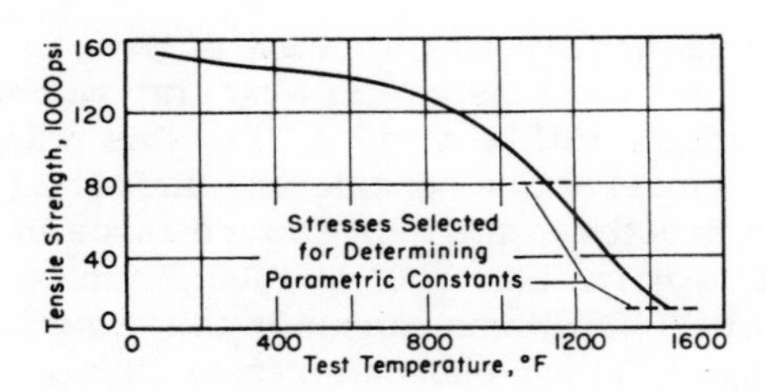

Figure 4-5 – Tensile strength data for "17-22-A"S(52).

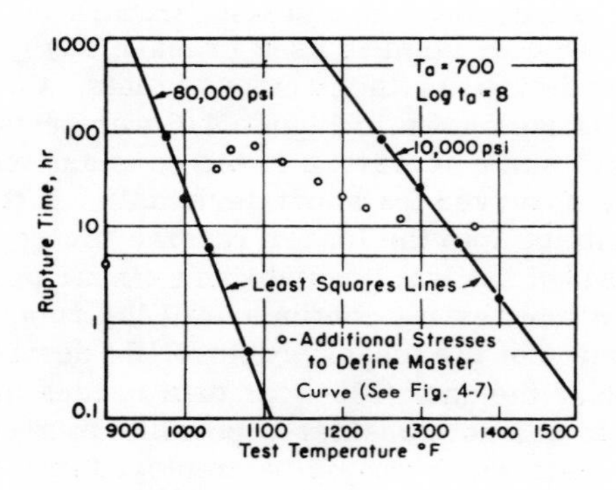

Figure 4-6 – Constant stress data for "17-22-A"S(52).

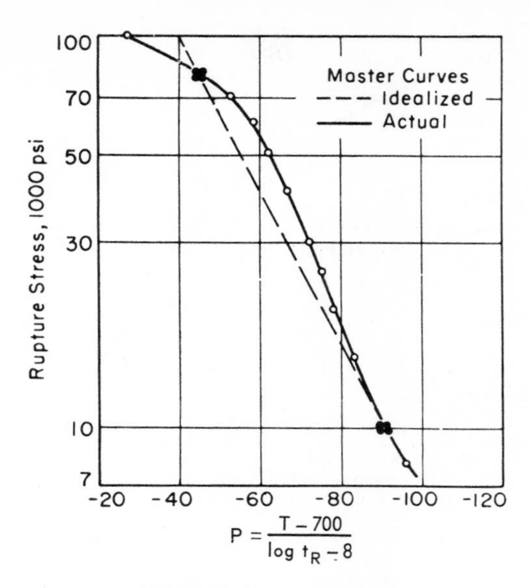

Figure 4-7 – Manson-Haferd master-rupture plot for "17-22-A"S(52).

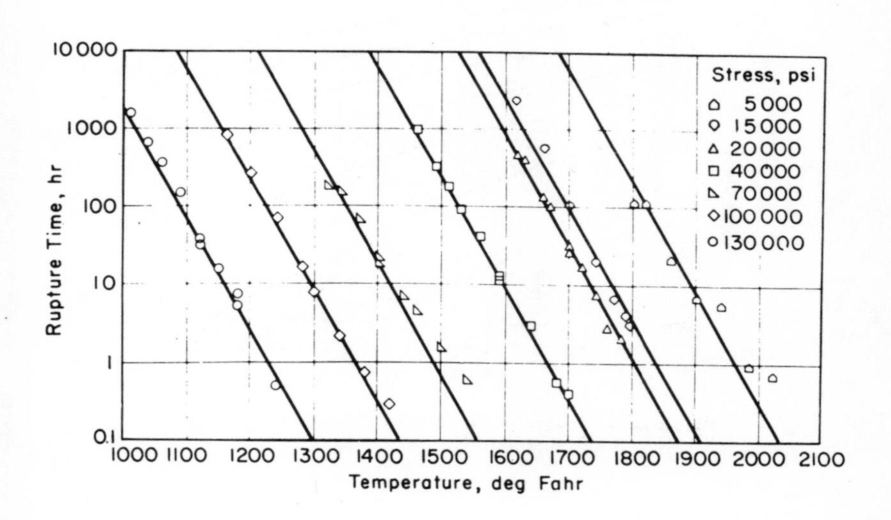

Figure 4-8 – Rupture time versus temperature for Inconel 700(46).

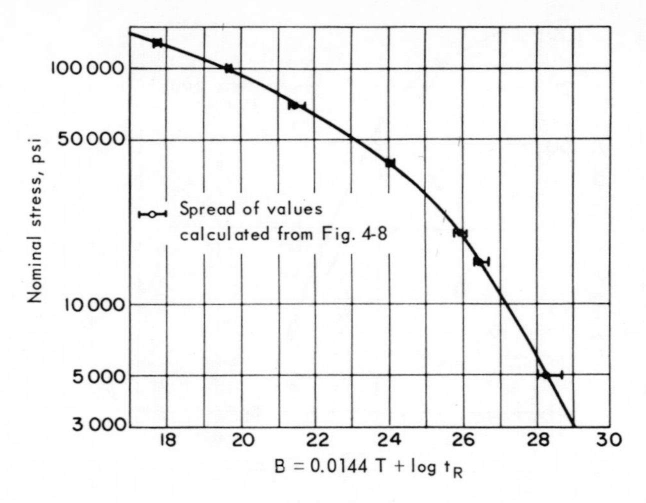

Figure 4-9 – Manson-Haferd master-rupture plot for Inconel 700[46].

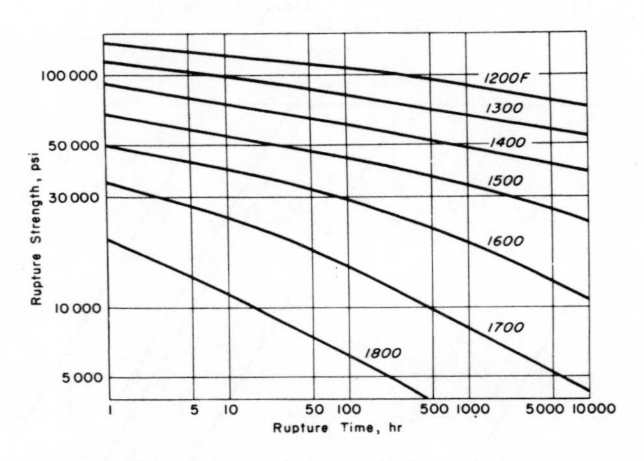

Figure 4-10 – Isotherms for Inconel 700 constructed using Figure 4-9[46].

times should be equal to the longest tests in the isostatic tests. However, it was felt that in the interest of reducing the test time the objectives could be realized by employing conditions which lead to shorter term tests. As a suggestion, the idealized master-rupture curve (line in Figure 4-7) is employed to calculate test temperature at various stresses which will yield rupture times equal to the geometric mean of the highest and lowest rupture times observed in the linear range of the isostatic data (lowest time restricted to a value greater than 1.0 hour). In the supplementary tests shown as open circles in Figure 4-6, a rupture time of 10 hours was selected, but as shown, the actual data obtained were in the 10- to 70-hour range. These additional data points are shown in Figure 4-7 to define the actual master-rupture curve. Two additional tests at stresses outside the 10,000 to 80,000 psi range are also shown in Figure 4-7.

With Figure 4-7 established, the stress-rupture isotherms can be established for the "17-22-A"S material. Extrapolation of the master-rupture curve is not recommended, although the isotherms can be extended to any desired rupture time within the experimental stress range. In the experience of Manson, Succop and Brown extrapolation beyond two log cycles of rupture time is not recommended. Additional studies dealing with this parameter will be necessary before the validity of such extrapolations can be evaluated.

In a study of the Inconel 700 rupture data, Manson and Succop[46] noted that a certain temperature change caused about the same percent change in rupture time over a fairly wide stress range. As a result, a plot of log t_R versus T yielded constant stress lines which were nearly parallel. Hence for the Manson-Haferd analysis the convergence point would be far removed from the range of data resulting in extremely large values for log t_a and extremely low values for T_a. In cases of this type it is possible to consider the log t_R versus T plot at constant stress to consist of a series of parallel lines as shown in Figure 4-8. Mathematically at a given stress:

$$\log t_R = AT + B \qquad (4\text{-}9)$$

where A = -0.0144 in Figure 4-8. Then:

$$B = 0.0144T + \log t_R \qquad (4\text{-}10)$$

to define the stress-rupture parameter, B, (particular attention should be given to the close similarity between these forms and that proposed by Clauss in equation (2-60) in Chapter 2) for use in this case. A plot of this parameter as a function of stress is shown in Figure 4-9 to define a smooth curve. Constructing the isotherms from this parameter plot leads to the results shown in Figure 4-10. Extrapolation of the linear isotherms in Figure 4-8 led to the prediction of 10,000-hour results for this material.

Only one constant is needed in using the parameter, B, just

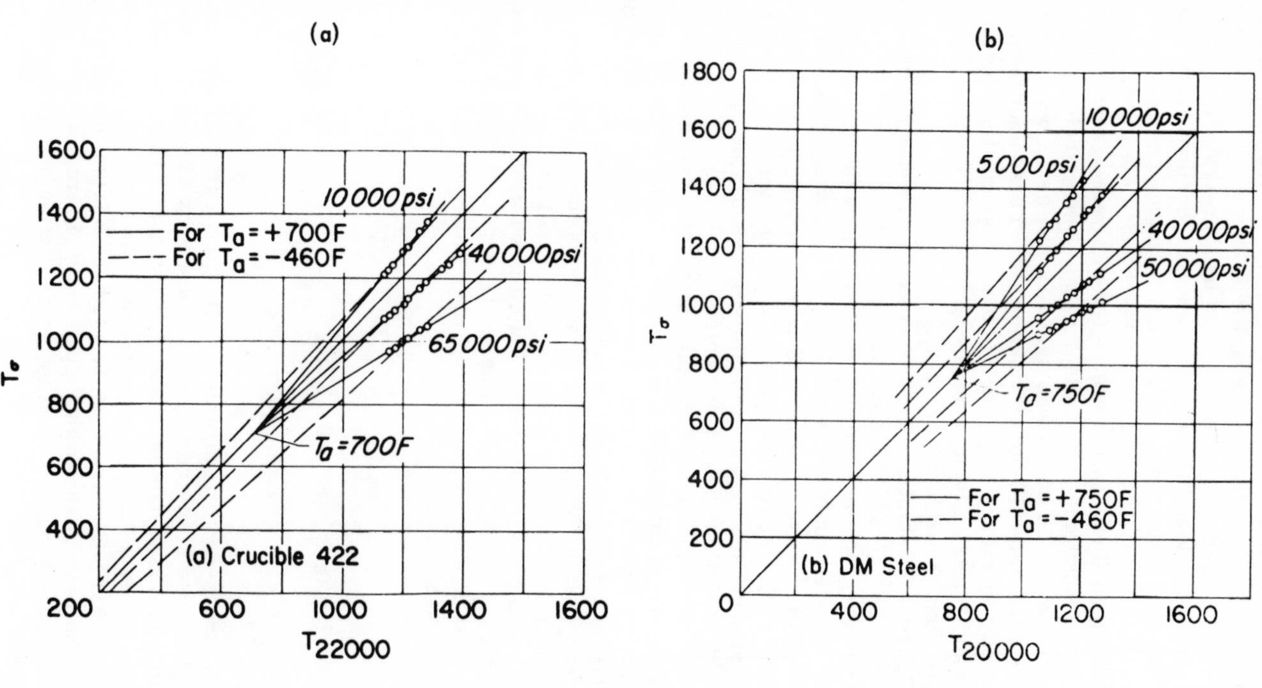

Figure 4-11 – Corresponding-temperature plot(50).

described. As was shown, this value can be obtained from the slope of the lines given in Figure 4-8. A least squares approach to the analysis of this parameter will be described below.

Noting that some definite curvature appears in the log t_R versus T plots at constant stress for certain materials (see data for Crucible 422 steel, for example, in Figure 9-32), Manson and Brown[50] described a general approach to the correlation of stress-rupture data in order to accommodate this behavior. When linear isostatics are obtained, then this approach leads to the Manson-Haferd parameter. A correlation between time, temperature and stress was assumed in the form:

$$F(t_R) \cdot G(T) = P(\sigma) \tag{4-11}$$

where F, G and P represent functions to be determined. Comparing this with the Larson-Miller parameter it was noted that $G(T) = T + 460$, $F(t_R) = C + \log t_R$ and $P(\sigma)$ is represented by the master-rupture curve. Similar comparisons can be made for the Dorn and Manson-Haferd parameters.

Quoting directly from Manson and Brown, "For the purpose of generalizing the results, it is convenient to introduce the concept of a corresponding-temperature plot. This plot was first used to ascertain the possibility of correlating stress-rupture data on the basis of the Larson and Miller parameter, $(T + 460)\ (C + \log t_R)$, where C is a constant other than 20. Let it be assumed, for example, that a suitable value of C can be found for perfect correlation of the data for Crucible 422 steel. Then the equation of the 22,000 psi constant stress line would be:

$$(T_{22,000} + 460)\ (C + \log t_{22,000}) = P_{22,000} \tag{4-12}$$

and that for the 10,000 psi line would be:

$$(T_{10,000} + 460)\ (C + \log t_{10,000}) = P_{10,000} \tag{4-13}$$

Now select identical values of rupture time on each of the two curves and divide equation (4-12) by (4-13). Since C is the same in each equation and since log t_R is the same by selection, the term $(C + \log t_R)$ cancels upon dividing and the relation obtained becomes:

$$\frac{T_{20,000} + 460}{T_{10,000} + 460} = \frac{P_{22,000}}{P_{10,000}} = \text{constant} \ldots \tag{4-14}$$

Thus a plot of $T_{22,000}$ against $T_{10,000}$ at arbitrarily selected identical values of rupture time should, by equation (4-14), yield a straight line intersecting the 45-degree line at the point $T_{22,000} = T_{10,000} = -460$. Similarly using the 22,000 psi data as the base curve, plotting corresponding temperatures for identical rupture times for each of the other stress

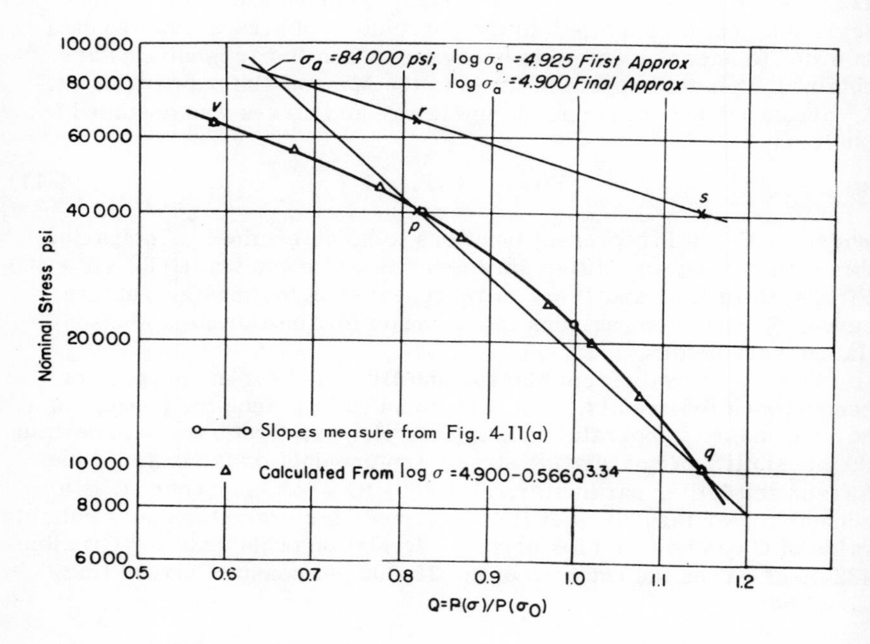

Figure 4-12 – Relation between Q and nominal stress[50].

curves in Figure 9-32 against the temperature on the 22,000 psi curve should yield a series of straight lines all converging to the point -460°F on the 45-degree line. The corresponding-temperature plot for Crucible 422 steel is shown in Figure 4-11a. It is seen that the lines are quite straight, but their apparent point of convergence on the 45-degree line is at 700° rather than at -460°F. The compromise that must be made if the temperature term in the parameter is to be taken as (T + 460) is shown by the dotted lines which converge to the point -460 on the 45-degree line. Thus, on the basis of the corresponding-temperature plot, it can be concluded that although a better value of C than 20 might be found for correlation purposes, some error must in any case be accepted because of the use of absolute temperature as the multiplier for the $(C + \log t_R)$ term.

"Figure 4-11b shows the corresponding-temperature plot for DM steel on which more data were obtained than on Crucible 422 steel, and for which the point of convergence is more distinctly defined as a value in the vicinity of 750°F rather than -460°F. The corresponding-temperature plot thus serves the purpose of assisting in the identification of suitable forms for the temperature characteristic G(T).

"Consider two constant stress curves σ_1 and σ_0. Then by equation (4-11), the equations of these curves are:

$$F(t_{R1}) \cdot G(T_1) = P(\sigma_1) \tag{4-15}$$

$$F(t_{R0}) \cdot G(T_0) = P(\sigma_0) \tag{4-16}$$

Using the concept of the corresponding-temperature plot, select identical rupture time values on each of the two curves and plot the corresponding temperatures T_1 against T_0. The equation of the relation between T_1 and T_0 is obtained by dividing equations (4-15) and (4-16), thereby cancelling the time function which is identical for all selected values:

$$\frac{G(T_1)}{G(T_0)} = \frac{P(\sigma_1)}{P(\sigma_0)} = Q_1, \text{ a constant} \tag{4-17}$$

When such plots are made using the various stress curves in combinations, the corresponding temperatures lie on very nearly straight lines which converge to a point T_a on the 45-degree line. This representation should obviously yield the same value for T_a as obtained using the linear time-temperature parameter provided the constant nominal stress curves are linear and converge to the point T_a, $\log t_a$. However, the property of linearity and convergence of the corresponding temperature plots was found to be characteristic for Crucible 422 where curvature exists in the constant stress curves.

"It can be seen either by inspection or by setting up a suitable differential equation, expressing the fact that equation (4-17) must define a straight-line relation between T_1 and T_0 which is satisfied at a common point on the 45-degree line for all assigned constant values of Q, that a general form for the function G is found to be $(T - T_a)^z$. For this form, equation (4-17) becomes:

$$\left(\frac{T_1 - T_a}{T_0 - T_a}\right)^z = \text{constant} \tag{4-18}$$

which establishes the necessary linear convergent relation when the zth root is taken of both sides of the equation. At this point of the analysis, z is completely arbitrary, since substitution for G in equation (4-11) can be followed by taking zth roots of both sides of this equation without destroying the generality of F and P which have not as yet been established. The simplest temperature characteristics result when z is taken as unity. Hence, without destroying the generality of the analysis:

$$G(T) = T - T_a \tag{4-19}$$

where T_a is the apparent point of convergence on the 45-degree lines of the corresponding-temperature plots. In some cases, particularly if there is scatter in the basic data, the convergence of corresponding-temperature plots to a point T_a may not be as distinct as in the case of Figure 4-11. However, the arbitrary selection of an approximate point that best satisfies the linearity and convergence property is usually found to give good results if consistency is maintained in the subsequent analysis. The value of T_a is not critical, and good correlation can be obtained for a fairly wide range of selected values for a given material.

"A point of practical significance in the construction of the corresponding-temperature plot is the proper selection of the constant nominal stress curve used as a base. It will be recognized that an experimental scatter in the base curve will be reflected in each of the corresponding-temperature lines. Since it may in certain cases be difficult to ascertain which one of the constant stress curves is not the most suitable as a base, it would be desirable to establish a reference curve on the basis of all the available data. This can be done as follows. The numerical average of the temperatures on each of the available constant stress curves is found for an arbitrary time level. The temperature so obtained can be shown to correspond to that on some constant nominal stress curve. This curve may then be defined as completely as desired by selecting another arbitrary time level, again averaging the temperatures. The average curve so obtained should then be the most suitable base for fairing the data.

"It should also be pointed out that although from the standpoint of correlation of stress-rupture data the selection of G(T) as $(T - T_a)$ is adequate, there may be other forms of G(T) which characterize linearity and convergence of corresponding-temperature plots as an approximate property. Such forms would not be derivable from the differential equation which expresses this as an exact property. For example, the form

$$G(T) = \frac{1}{T + 460} - \frac{1}{T_a + 460},$$

which might be obtained from the rate process equation if plots of t_R versus $[1/(T + 460)]$ were linear but converged to a point at absolute temperature $T_a + 460$, would show some tendency to produce approximately linear and convergent corresponding-temperature plots in a limited temperature range. This function is usually inferior for representing the experimental data; however, it is conceivable that there may be forms of functions derivable from physical theory and consistent with the observed properties of corresponding-temperature plots. If the correlation method is to provide insight into the fundamental mechanism of the stress-rupture process, the temperature characteristic may have to be re-examined.

"The corresponding-temperature plot also provides considerable information about the stress characteristic. Substituting equation (4-19) into equation (4-17) gives:

$$\frac{T_1 - T_a}{T_0 - T_a} = \frac{P(\sigma_1)}{P(\sigma_0)} = Q_1 \ldots \qquad (4\text{-}20)$$

Since

$$\frac{T_1 - T_a}{T_0 - T_a}$$

is the slope of line associated with T_1 on the corresponding-temperature plot, the value of Q_1 may be determined. Similarly, the values of

$$Q_2 = \left(\frac{P(\sigma_2)}{P(\sigma_0)}\right), \quad Q_3 = \left(\frac{P(\sigma_3)}{P(\sigma_0)}\right), \text{ etc.}$$

for each of the experimentally available constant stress curves can be determined. The Q function can thus be plotted against stress. Figure 4-12 shows the values for Crucible 422 steel based on the corresponding-temperature plot of Figure 4-11 in which the 22,000-psi constant nominal stress curve was used as the baseline.

"Once G(T) and Q have been determined as described above, the time characteristic can be obtained from equation (4-11). Because experience has indicated that

$$\frac{T - T_a}{\log t_R - \log t_a}$$

is suitable in most cases for correlation and since G(T) has already been determined as $T - T_a$, it will be convenient to solve equation (4-11) for $[1/F(t_R)]$ rather than $F(t_R)$. Thus,

$$\frac{1}{F(t_R)} = \frac{G(T)}{P(\sigma)} = \frac{T - T_a}{P(\sigma)} = \frac{1}{P(\sigma_0)} \cdot \frac{T - T_a}{\frac{P(\sigma)}{P(\sigma_0)}} = \frac{1}{P(\sigma_0)} \cdot \frac{T - T_a}{Q} \ldots \qquad (4\text{-}21)$$

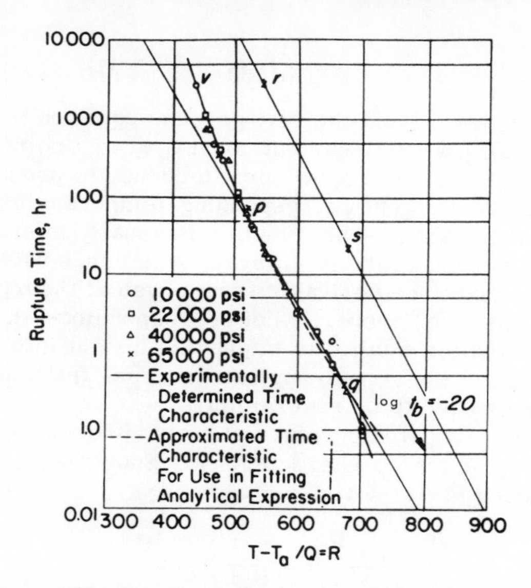

Figure 4-13 – Experimentally determined time characteristic for Crucible 422[50].

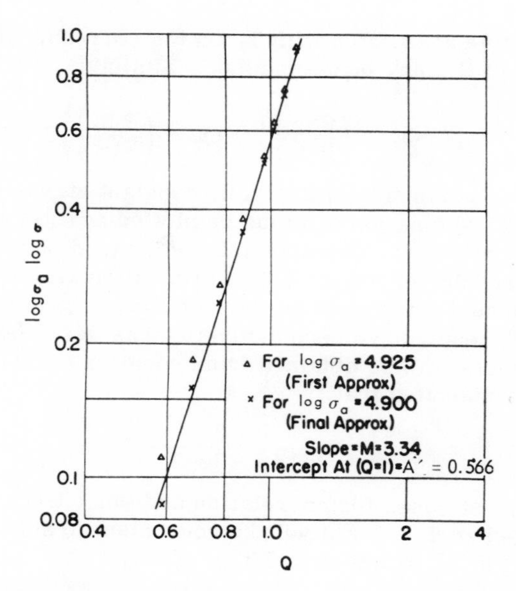

Figure 4-14 – Method for determining M and A′ for Crucible 422[50].

Hence a plot of t_R versus $(T - T_a)/Q$ should yield a single curve for all the data and this will define $F(t_R)$.

"For Crucible 422 a plot of the time characteristic is shown in Figure 4-13 where $\log t_R$ has been plotted versus $(T - T_a)/Q$ using the values of Q plotted in Figure 4-12. It is evident that the data correlate very well. The change in curvature in the time range below one hour is not well established by the few available data points. The curve has, however, arbitrarily been drawn to pass through as many of the data points as possible, necessitating the introduction of a change of curvature. It is evident that the time characteristic obtained in this manner, can be made to conform as closely as possible to the original data points, and does not necessitate that the characteristic have any pre-established shape, such as straight lines in cases where the linear parameter is valid and hyperbolas where the $(T + 460)(C + \log t_R)$ parameter is valid.

"The individual, constant nominal stress curves can be reconstructed from the time characteristic in Figure 4-13 and the Q value for each stress level as shown in Figure 4-12. The short-dashed curves in Figure 9-32 were constructed in this manner for each of the experimentally investigated stress levels for Crucible 422. It will be seen that the curves so obtained agree very well with the data over the entire experimental range.

"Since the time characteristic can be extended up to the longest rupture time experimentally available, regardless of the particular stress level at which the data point was obtained, the curve essentially serves the purpose of permitting extrapolation for those stress levels where only lower rupture times are experimentally available. In addition, a certain amount of extrapolation of the time characteristic curve should be possible, thereby extending the experimental time range with a degree of confidence. Thus, in Figure 4-13, in the absence of more suitable methods of extrapolation, the last portion of the time characteristic could probably be extended linearly up to about 10, 000 hours. The results would, of course, be slightly different from those obtained on the basis of the linear time-temperature parameter when only the 30- to 300-hour data are used for the determination of T_a and $\log t_a$. The latter case corresponds to the linear extension of the tangent to the time characteristic curve in the 30- to 300-hour range.

"When the individual constant nominal stress curves are linear, the time characteristic will also be linear, intersecting the vertical axes at a time corresponding to $\log t_a$.

"It has been shown in Figures 4-12 and 4-13 that the characteristics of stress and time can be defined graphically. It is possible to fit an analytical expression to each of the curves and by combining these with the temperature function already determined, to write an explicit analytical expression in terms of time, temperature, and stress.

"If Crucible 422 is taken as an example, the stress function in Figure 4-12 can be taken analogous to the temperature characteristic:

$$Q = A(\log \sigma_a - \log \sigma)^m \ldots \qquad (4\text{-}22)$$

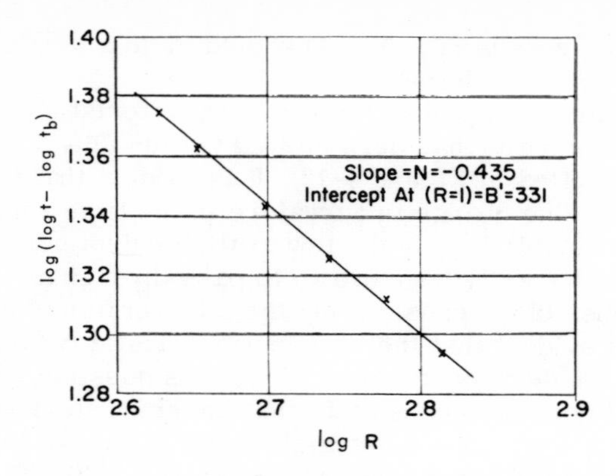

Figure 4-15 – Method for determining N and B′ for Crucible 422(50).

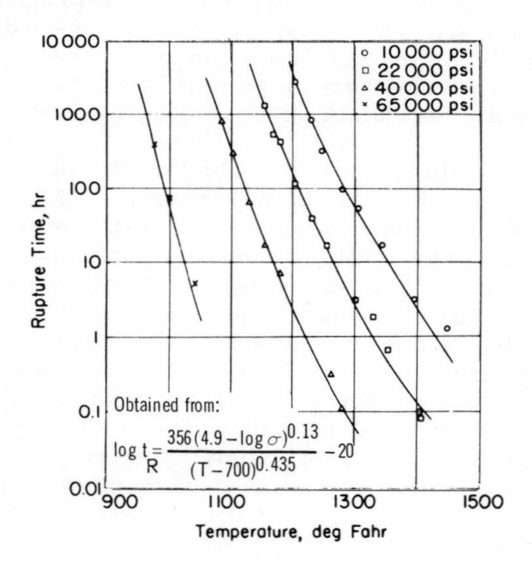

Figure 4-16 – Comparison between experimental and calculated data for Crucible 422(50).

or

$$\log \sigma = \log \sigma_a - A' Q^M \ldots \quad (4\text{-}23)$$

The curve in Figure 4-12 may be fitted to this equation by a method outlined by Running.[64] The point p is selected on the curve with an abscissa value equal to the mean proportional between the abscissa values of the end points v and q. The point r is selected to have the same abscissa as p and the same ordinate as v, while the point s is selected to have the same abscissa as q and the same ordinate as p. The intersection of the lines drawn through r and s, p and q gives a value for the first approximation to σ_a, in this case equal to 84,000 psi. Since equation (4-23) can be rewritten in the following form:

$$\log (\log \sigma_a - \log \sigma) = (\log A' + M \log Q) \quad (4\text{-}24)$$

a plot of $\log (\log \sigma_a - \log \sigma)$ versus $\log Q$ should be linear with a slope equal to M and an intercept at $\log Q = 1$ of $\log A'$. The linearity of this plot is a test for the suitability of the selected value of σ_a by the method outlined above. Such a plot is shown in Figure 4-14. The results for $\sigma_a = 84,000$ ($\log \sigma_a = 4.925$) exhibit some deviation from linearity. The arbitrary selection of $\log \sigma_a = 4.900$ improved the linearity and this value was, therefore, chosen. The values of M and A' are shown in Figure 4-14, and these values can now be substituted in equation (4-23) to yield the following expression:

$$\log \sigma = 4.900 - 0.566\, Q^{3.34} \quad (4\text{-}25)$$

or

$$Q = 1.186\, (4.900 - \log \sigma)^{0.3} \quad (4\text{-}26)$$

The results calculated from the expression agree well with the curve as shown in Figure 4-12.

"For the time characteristic represented in Figure 4-13, the form by analogy with the temperature and stress characteristic and for consistency with the linear parameter may be taken as:

$$R = B(\log t_R - \log t_b)^a \quad (4\text{-}27)$$

or

$$\log t_R = \log t_b + B' R^N \quad (4\text{-}28)$$

The expression in equation (4-28) will not fit the curve drawn through the experimental points in Figure 4-13 because of the previously discussed slight change in curvature at times around 1 hour. To provide a smooth curve for the purpose of fitting, the dotted line has been taken to represent all the data. This curve may now be fitted by the same procedure as outlined for the stress characteristic. The value of $\log t_b = -20$ is large and not too critical. The values of B' and N were determined from the plot in Figure 4-15. The equation so obtained for the time equation becomes:

$$\log t_R = 331R^{-0.435} - 20 \tag{4-29}$$

or

$$R = \frac{T - T_a}{Q} = \frac{6.20 \cdot 10^5}{(20 + \log t_R)^{2.30}} \tag{4-30}$$

By combining equation (4-26) with (4-30) the following explicit expression is obtained in terms of time, temperature, and stress:

$$(T - 700)\ (20 + \log t_R)^{2.30}$$

$$= 7.4 \cdot 10^5\,(4.900 - \log \sigma)^{0.30} \tag{4-31}$$

or

$$\log t_R = 356\ \frac{(4.900 - \log \sigma)^{0.130}}{(T - 700)^{0.435}} - 20 \tag{4-32}$$

Using this expression, the constant nominal stress curves at each of the four experimentally investigated stress levels were calculated and are shown in Figure 4-16. It is evident that these curves represent the data very well and, therefore, demonstrate the suitability of the form of equation (4-31).

"Single equations relating stress, temperature, and time to rupture have also been obtained for the other four materials investigated (see Figure 4-17). In these cases, where the linear parameter:

$$\frac{T - T_a}{\log t_R - \log t_a}$$

was suitable for characterizing the data in the entire experimental range, it was necessary merely to fit an equation of the (4-22) form to the master curve, where Q in this case is replaced by the linear parameter. No difficulty was encountered in this process except for DM steel in which the master curve showed a reversal of curvature at stresses below 10,000 psi (similar to the reversals in the master curves shown by Manson and Haferd,[36] especially for Inconel X). For DM, therefore, the curve was fitted only for stresses above 10,000 psi, and it was expected that poor agreement between the formula and the experimental data would occur at 5000 psi. The equations deduced for each of the four materials are as follows:

16-25-6M: $\dfrac{T - 750}{\log t_R - 9} = -111.3(5.060 - \log \sigma)^{-0.650}$

"17-22 A"S: $\dfrac{T - 600}{\log t_R - 9.5} = -81.8(5.131 - \log \sigma)^{-0.341}$ (4-33)

16-13-3: $\dfrac{T - 100}{\log t_R - 15} = -106.8(5.114 - \log \sigma)^{-0.427}$

$$\text{DM:}\quad \frac{T - 750}{\log t_R - 8} = -77.25(4.786 - \log \sigma)^{-0.398} \qquad (4\text{-}33)$$

Figure 4-17 (a to d) shows the comparison between the experimental data and the computed results based on equation (4-33). In general, the agreement is seen to be very good except for the 5000 psi curve for DM steel, the reason for which was previously described. Thus, it can be seen that over a fairly wide range of time, temperature, and stress, the variables can be related by an explicit expression in the form:

$$(T - T_a)\ (\log t_R - \log t_a)^{\alpha} = A(\log \sigma_a - \log \sigma)^{\beta} \qquad (4\text{-}33A)$$

where in most cases $\alpha = -1$. It will be observed that equation (4-33A) is very similar to the linear parameter, but in this case an explicit functional relationship in terms of stress is provided. Instead of referring to a master-rupture plot, the temperature-time relations are seen to be obtained analytically."

A fairly general form of the Manson-Haferd parameter was introduced recently[56] in the form:

$$P(\sigma) = \frac{\dfrac{\log t_R}{\sigma^Q} - \log t_a}{(T - T_a)^R} \qquad (4\text{-}34)$$

where Q, R, T_a and $\log t_a$ are constants. In this form it was noted that when $Q = 0$ and $R = 1$, the standard form of the Manson-Haferd parameter is obtained; when $Q = 0$, $R = -1$, $T_a = -460°F$ and $\log t_a = -20$, the Larson-Miller parameter is obtained; if $Q = 1$ and $R = 1$, the Murry[31] parameter is obtained; and finally when $Q = 0$, the Manson-Brown form of the linear parameter is obtained.

While equation (4-34) does not readily reduce to the Dorn or the Manson-Succop modification, it can provide a close approximation of these parameters. For example, if $Q = 0$ and $R = 1$ and both T_a and $\log t_a$ are very large numbers, then the Manson-Succop behavior is fairly accurately described; when R is about -0.2 and Q is close to 0.1, then the Dorn parameter is found to be closely approximated.

Typical $\log t_R$ versus T plots resulting from equation (4-34) are presented in Figure 4-18. Various Q and R combinations reveal the different types of behavior which can be expected. Each curve represents a constant stress condition; those lines which are labeled with the same letter have the same coordinates at 10 hours and 10,000 hours in order to represent approximately the same data in this time range. Manson also pointed out that by suitable selection of Q and R values the constant stress curves can take on positive or negative curvatures and a large variety of characteristics can be obtained relating the spacing of these constant stress curves. Hence equation (4-34) can describe a wide range of material behavior.

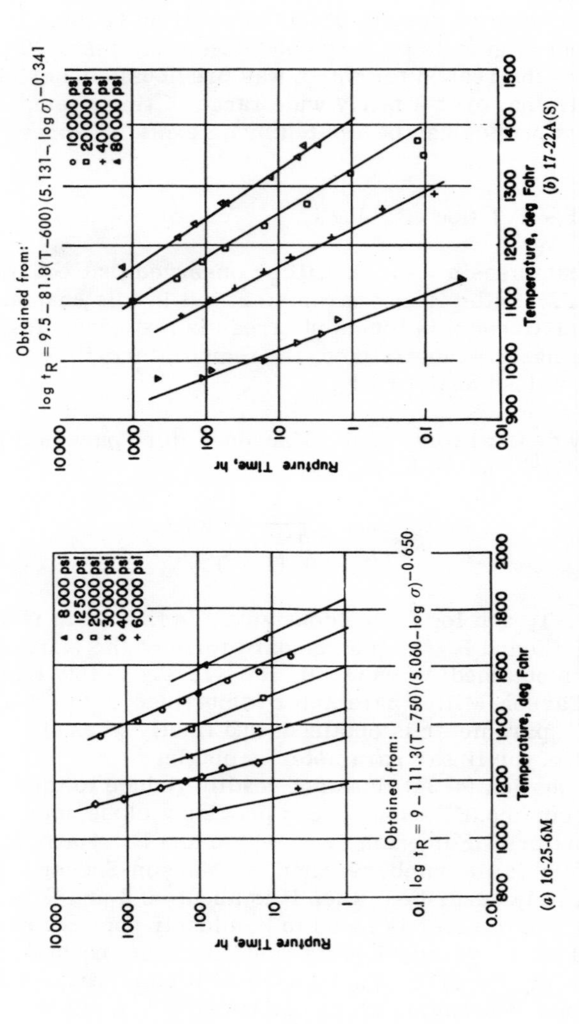

Figure 4-17 — Comparison between experimental and calculated data for various steels(50).

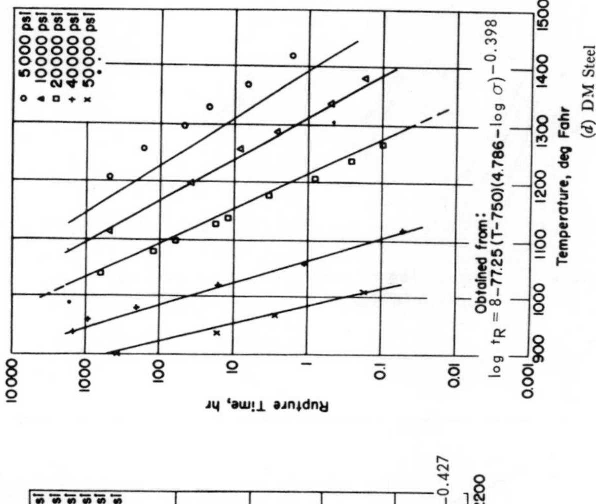

(*d*) DM Steel

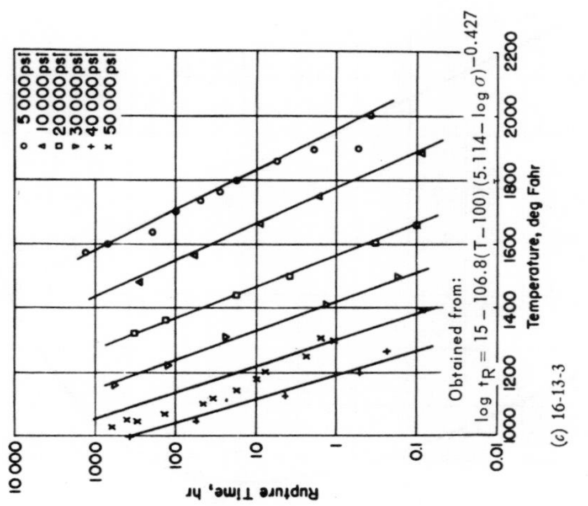

(*c*) 16-13-3

Figure 4-17 (continued)

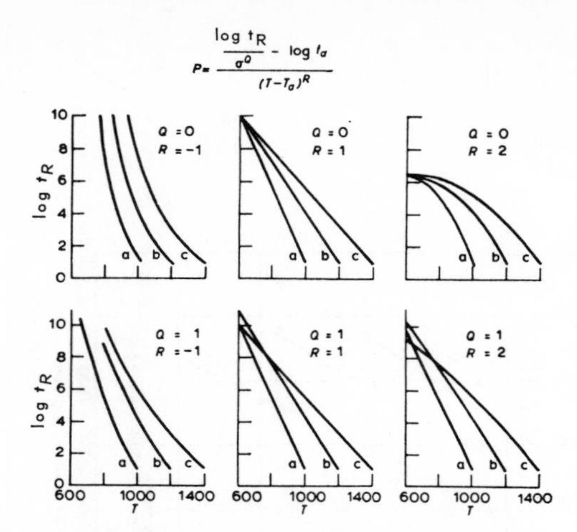

Figure 4-18 – Various log t_R versus T plots based on equation (4-34).

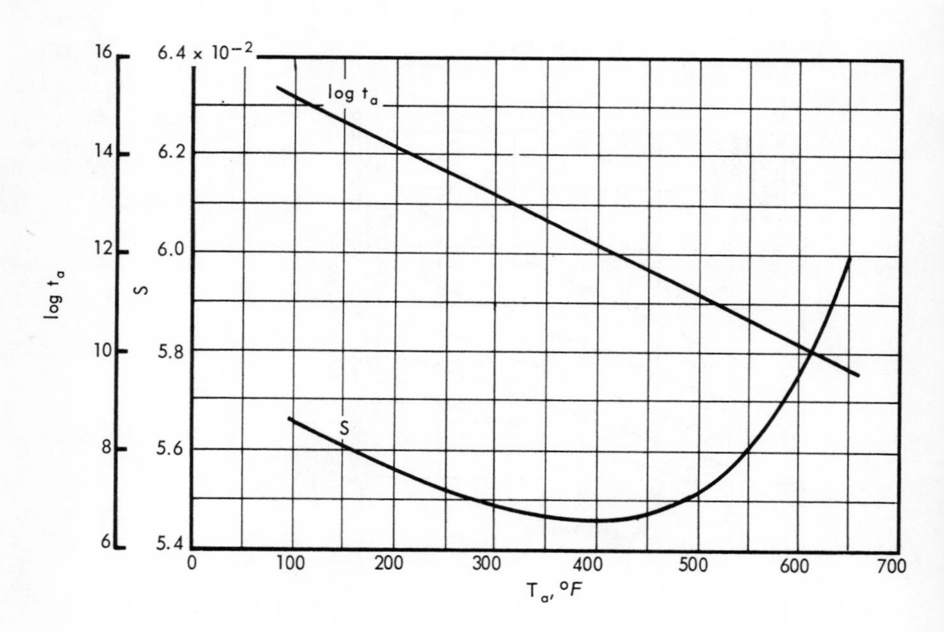

Figure 4-19 – Manson-Haferd[5] analysis of Nimonic 80A data to yield T_a and log t_a values.

It was noted by Manson that none of the well-known parameters yields constant stress lines which are concave downward. However, when $R > 1$, this type of behavior will evolve. In connection with the value of Q, it was noted that its use has not as yet been found to improve the data correlation. It is included to allow for more generality as might be required in future applications.

Due to the relative complexity of the parameter defined in equation (4-34), some difficulty can be expected in the identification of the parameter constants. A mathematical approach to this problem will be covered in a later section. In Chapter 9 the use of this parameter in the analysis of rupture data will be discussed.

LEAST SQUARES APPROACH TO PARAMETER ANALYSIS

Constants for use in equation (4-1) may be obtained by means of a least squares approach described by Manson and Mendelson.[5] For any of the constant stress lines in Figure 4-4:

$$y_j = y_a + b_j T - b_j T_a \tag{4-35}$$

where $y_j = \log t_R$ for the jth set of data, $y_a = \log t_a$ and b_j (actually the reciprocal of ϕ) is the slope of the jth constant stress line. It can be noted that equation (4-35) is non-linear in the unknown constants because of the $b_j T_a$ product, and hence, a straightforward least squares approach is not possible. However, equation (4-35) can be written as:

$$y_j = y_a + b_j (T - T_a) \tag{4-36}$$

to yield a form similar to equation (2-20). Then for a selected value of T_a, equations (2-33) and (2-31) will yield the values for y_a and b_j, respectively. Of course, in these evaluations the quantity $(T - T_a)$ replaces L in all summation terms. Now, with both y_a and b_j known, the sum of the squares of the residuals can be calculated using a form similar to equation (2-21). Other values of T_a are then assumed until the minimum sum in equation (2-21) is identified. At this point the correct values for y_a, b_j and T_a are all identified for use in conjunction with equation (4-1) (ϕ is given by the reciprocal b value). Results[5] obtained in this type of calculation are presented in Figure 4-19 for some rupture data for Nimonic 80A. Note that the minimum in the sum, S, of the squares of residuals occurs at a value of $T_a = 400°F$, and that the corresponding value of $\log t_a$ is close to 12.2.

In an alternate procedure Manson and Mendelson described a method of analysis whereby the trial and error solution just described can be eliminated. Initially, the $b_j T_a$ term in equation (4-35) is temporarily grouped with y_a to give:

$$y_j = d_j + b_j T \tag{4-37}$$

where $d_j = y_a - b_j T_a$. This expression is now linear in the unknown constants d_j and b_j and a direct least squares approach can be applied. For the sum of the squares of the residuals:

$$S = \Sigma (R)^2 = \sum_{i=1}^{N_I} (y - d_I - b_I T)_I^2 + \sum_{i=1}^{N_{II}} (y - d_{II} - b_{II} T)_{II}^2 +$$

$$\ldots + \sum_{i=1}^{N_P} (y - d_P - b_P T)_P^2 \tag{4-38}$$

for P stress groups. Now differentiating with respect to d_j and b_j and equating to zero to define the minimum condition yields the two general equations:

$$D_j = N_j d_j + b_j A_j \tag{4-39}$$

and

$$C_j = d_j A_j + b_j B_j \tag{4-40}$$

using the notation of Chapter 2 although now temperatures are used in the summation terms instead of (1/T) values. Solving gives:

$$d_j = \frac{B_j D_j - A_j C_j}{N_j B_j - A_j^2} \tag{4-41}$$

and

$$b_j = \frac{N_j C_j - A_j D_j}{N_j B_j - A_j^2} \tag{4-42}$$

Since all the summation terms in these equations can be easily evaluated, the identification of b_j and d_j follows directly. Then since:

$$d_j = y_a - b_j T_a \tag{4-43}$$

the best values for y_a and T_a can be obtained by considering a new sum of the squares of the residuals defined as:

$$\sum_{j=1}^{P} (d_j - y_a + b_j T_a)^2 \tag{4-44}$$

where the b_j and d_j values are obtained from equations (4-42) and (4-41). Differentiating then with respect to y_a and then T_a and setting equal to zero yields:

$$\sum_{j=1}^{P} d_j = P y_a - T_a \sum_{j=1}^{P} b_j \tag{4-45}$$

and

$$\sum_{j=1}^{P} d_j b_j = y_a \sum_{j=1}^{P} b_j - T_a \sum_{j=1}^{P} (b_j)^2 \quad (4\text{-}46)$$

Solving simultaneously yields:

$$T_a = \frac{\sum_{j=1}^{P} b_j d_j - \sum_{j=1}^{P} d_j \sum_{j=1}^{P} b_j}{\left(\sum_{j=1}^{P} b_j\right)^2 - P \sum_{j=1}^{P} b_j^2} \quad (4\text{-}47)$$

and

$$y_a = \frac{\sum_{j=1}^{P} d_j + T_a \sum_{j=1}^{P} b_j}{P} \quad (4\text{-}48)$$

Hence a direct solution for y_a and T_a is offered.

When only isothermal stress-rupture data are available, conversion to constant stress groupings for use in the above solution is avoided by employing the Manson and Mendelson technique proposed for the isothermal case. As in the analysis of the two other parameters already discussed, a polynomial variation is assumed in the form:

$$\frac{y - y_a}{T - T_a} = a_0 + a_1 x + a_2 x^2 + \ldots + a_m x^m \quad (4\text{-}49)$$

Then:

$$y = y_a + a_0 (T-T_a) + a_1 x(T-T_a) + a_2 x^2 (T-T_a) + \ldots + a_m x^m (T-T_a) \quad (4\text{-}50)$$

It will be noted that equation (4-50) is similar to equation (2-35) with L replaced by $(T-T_a)$ and -C replaced by y_a. Hence equations (2-37), (2-38), (2-39) and (2-40) can be employed to yield the values for y_a, T_a and a_i values. Of course, a trial and error approach is necessary since equation (4-50) is not linear in all the constants. Values of T_a are assumed and then y_a, a_0, a_1, etc., are calculated. Then the sum of the squares of the residuals is evaluated using an equation similar to equation (2-36). Other values of T_a are assumed until the minimum value for the sum of the squares of the residuals is identified. At this point all of the required values for the constants are found for use in equation (4-49).

One of the master-rupture plots calculated in the Manson-Haferd studies of the linear parameter is shown in Figure 4-20. As may be noted, $T_a = 100°F$ and $\log t_a = 15$. All the data points for this material (18-8 stainless steel) describe a fairly smooth curve and the stress-rupture isotherms constructed from this curve are shown in Figure 4-21 to be in excellent agreement with the experimentally measured rupture values. It was also noted by Manson and Haferd that this

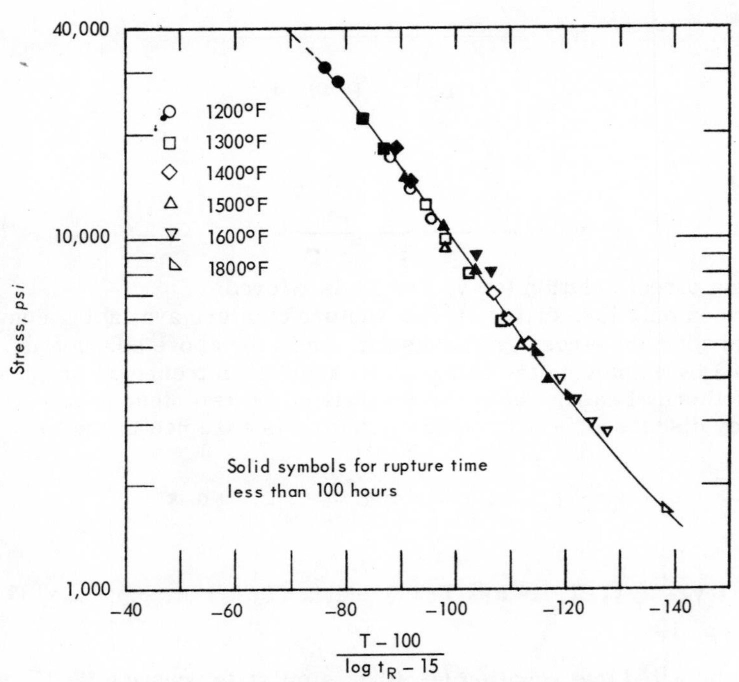

Figure 4-20 – Master-rupture plot for 18-8 stainless steel based on linear parameter(36).

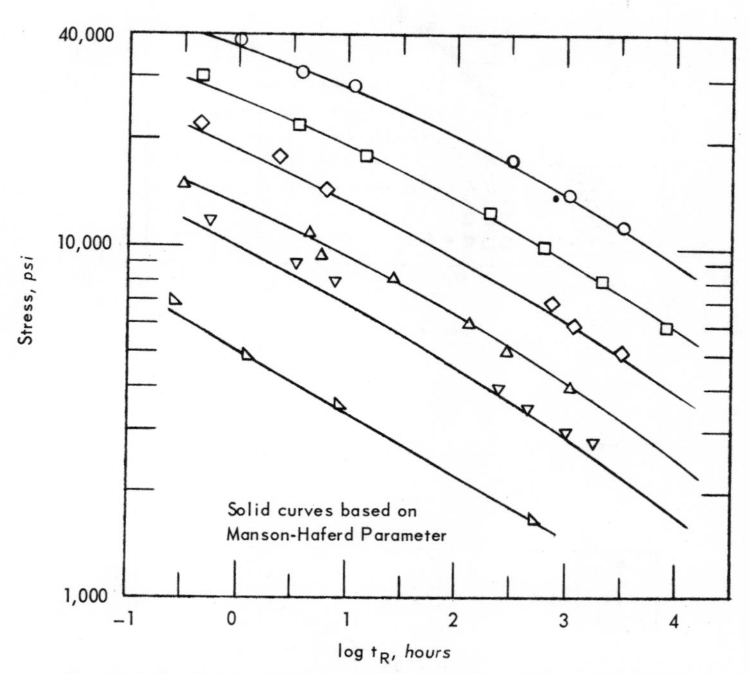

Figure 4-21 – Stress-rupture isotherms constructed from Figure 4-20.

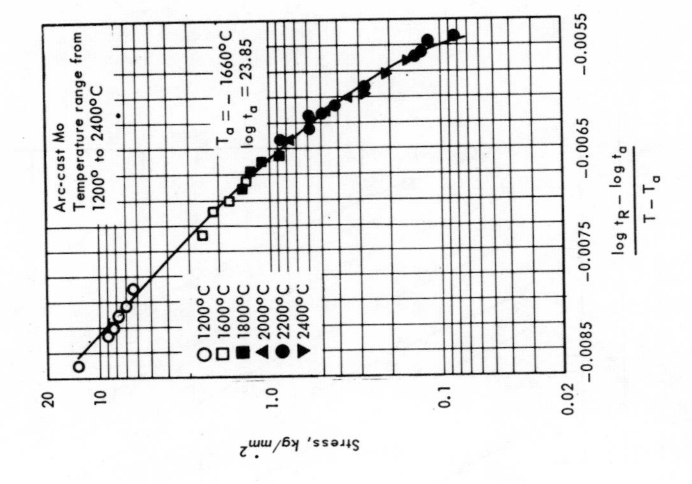

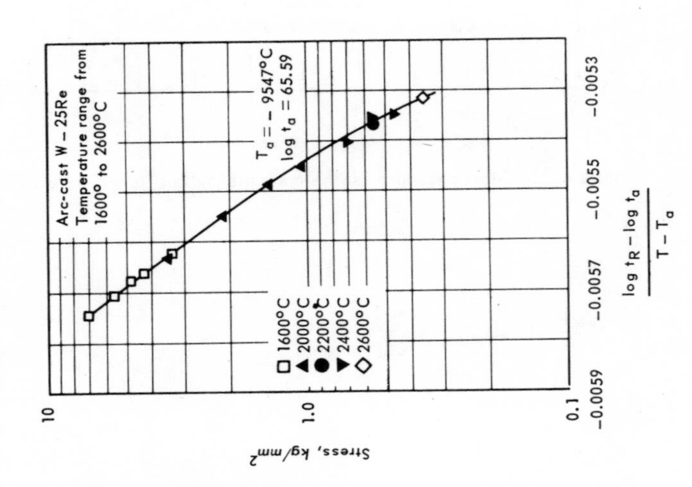

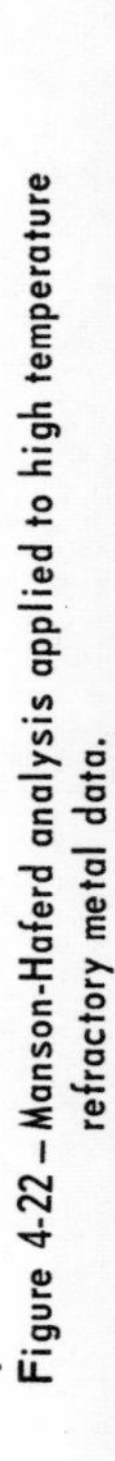
Figure 4-22 – Manson-Haferd analysis applied to high temperature refractory metal data.

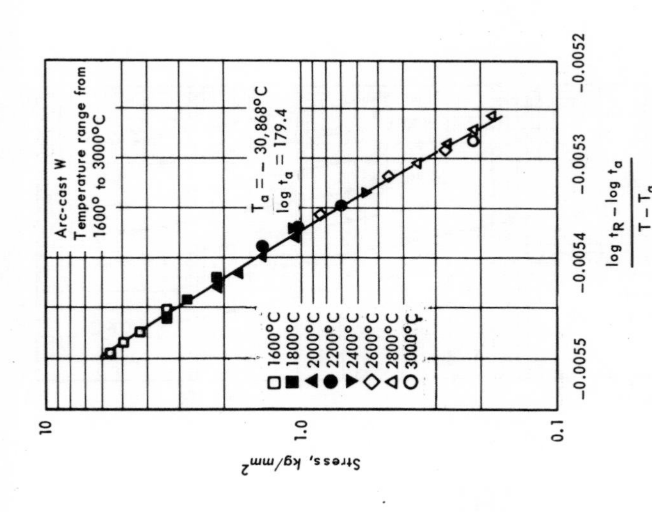

Figure 4-22 (continued)

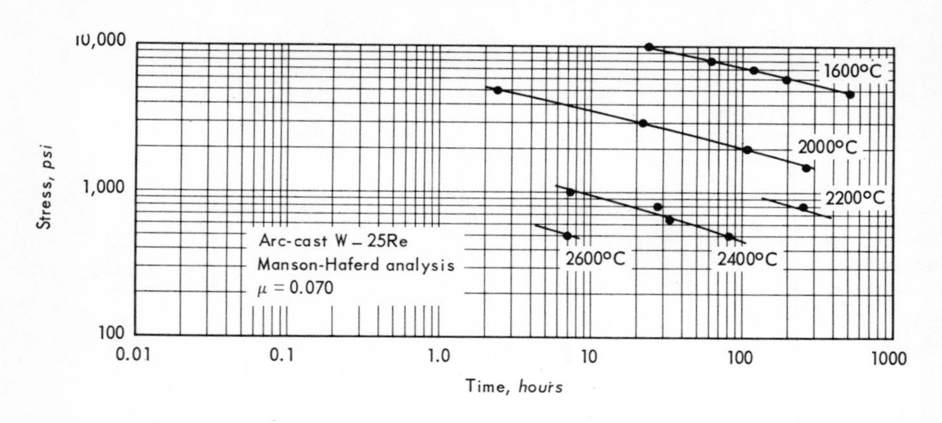

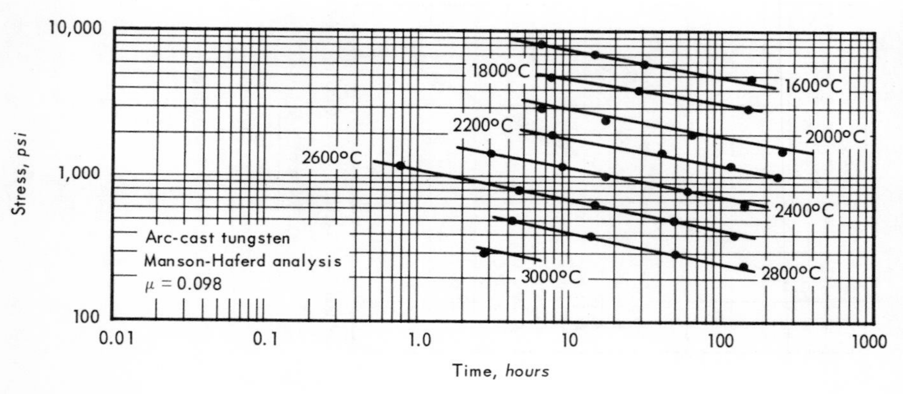

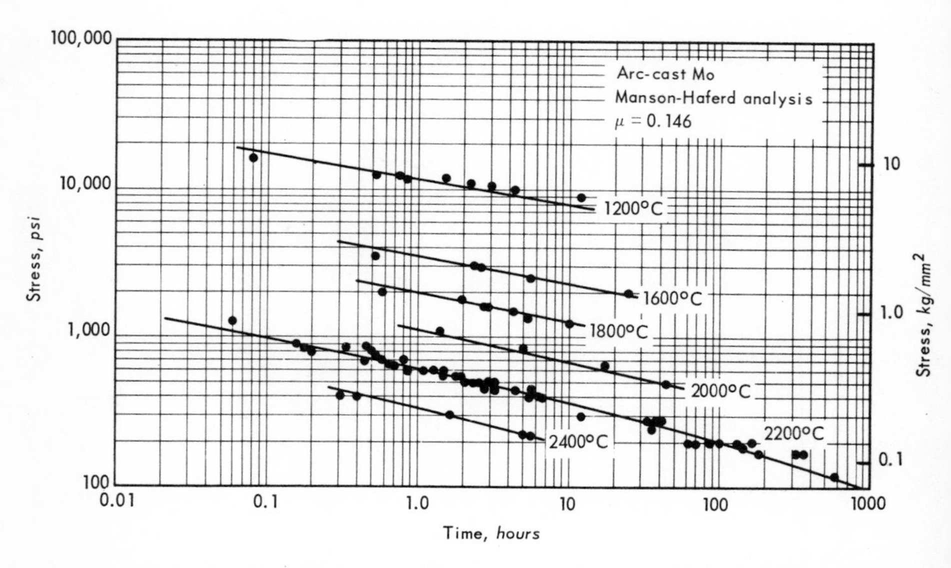

Figure 4-23 – Stress-rupture isotherms constructed from Figure 4-22.

agreement is much better than that obtainable using the Larson-Miller parameter. In this latter case the isotherms constructed from a master-rupture plot do not yield a very good reproduction of the experimental results.

It was also noted by Manson and Haferd (see Figure 4-20) that points corresponding to rupture in less than 100 hours were positioned on the master-rupture plot on the same curve with the points calculated using extrapolated rupture time to 10,000 hours. This is usually not the case in master-rupture plots based on the Larson-Miller parameter as was shown in Figure 4-2.

Employing a given set of stress-rupture data Manson and Mendelson showed that the values for T_a and log t_a calculated using equations (4-47) and (4-48) based on constant stress groupings are identical to those obtained when the polynomial approach based on equation (4-50) is employed. Also an interesting result was obtained when data were analyzed in terms of equation (4-50) using second, third, fourth, and fifth degree polynomials. Values for T_a and log t_a were:

	T_a	$\log t_a$	
m = 2	-400°F	17.3	
m = 3	-200°F	15.3	
m = 4	-200°F	15.3	(4-51)
m = 5	-200°F	15.6	

Hence all polynomial approaches except that of the second degree gave what appear to be identical results. Also noted was the fact that the sum of the squares of the residuals using T_a = -400°F was not much different from that using T_a = -200°F. Therefore, satisfactory results obtain with any of the polynomial forms employed. This observation has prompted the comment that correlations of stress-rupture data in terms of the linear parameter are usually fairly insensitive to the precise values of the T_a and log t_a values. It was offered that this insensitivity is due to the fact that the intersection point of the constant stress lines is usually far removed from the actual data points. Therefore, moving the point of intersection along an average line through all the data would not appreciably change the individual lines. Changes in T_a amounting to several hundred degrees can, therefore, be tolerated without affecting the excellence of the correlation to any great extent.

An evaluation of some high temperature refractory metal data[6] in terms of equation (4-50) has led to the results presented in Figure 4-22. Isotherms constructed from these parametric analyses are presented in Figure 4-23 to indicate excellent agreement with experimental results.

One illustration of the use of the Manson-Haferd approach to the analysis of strain-time data is worth citing (similar approaches can, of course, be made using other parameters). In a study of creep data for the niobium alloy FS-85, Mendelson, Roberts and Manson[57] employed the linear parameter in the analysis of time to various strain

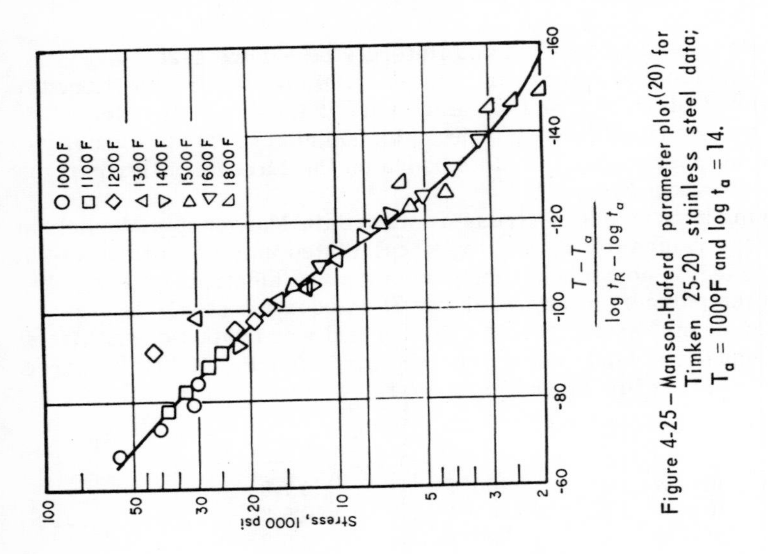

Figure 4-25 — Manson-Haferd parameter plot[20] for Timken 25-20 stainless steel data; $T_a = 100°F$ and $\log t_a = 14$.

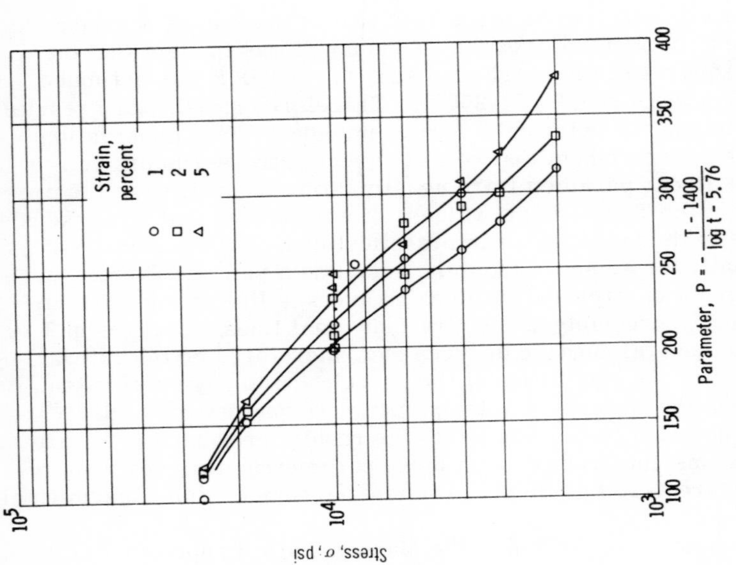

Figure 4-24 — Manson-Haferd master plot for FS-85 data at various strain values[57].

values. These results are shown in Figure 4-24 where the same values of T_a and log t_a are assumed to apply to all strain values.

When the Manson-Succop type of parameter is applicable, a least squares approach similar to that shown in equation (4-50) can be employed. In this instance, though, the parameter is less complicated and the approach more direct. As a matter of fact, no trial and error or iterative solution need be used as the analysis is essentially identical to that for equation (3-24). It will be seen that the only modification necessary is to substitute AT from equation (4-9) for the b/T term in equation (3-24).

Applying an approach similar to that employed in equation (4-50), Mendelson, Roberts and Manson[57] outlined a solution when the parameter given in equation (4-34) is to be used. In this analysis the following quantities were introduced:

$$\tau = \sigma^Q (T - T_a)^R \quad (4\text{-}52)$$

$$y = \log t_R \quad (4\text{-}53)$$

$$x = \log \sigma \quad (4\text{-}54)$$

and

$$y_a = \log t_a \quad (4\text{-}55)$$

Based on equation (4-34) it follows that:

$$y = \sigma^Q y_a + \tau F(x) \quad (4\text{-}56)$$

where F(x) is to be represented in polynomial form as:

$$F(x) = a_0 + a_1 x + b_2 x^2 + \ldots + a_m x^m \quad (4\text{-}57)$$

In this case the sum of the squares of the residuals will be given by:

$$S = \sum_{i=1}^{n} [y_i - \sigma_i^Q y_a - \tau_i F(x_i)]^2 \quad (4\text{-}58)$$

Differentiating this with respect to the constants y_a, a_0, a_1, etc., and setting to zero defines m + 2 equations. However, equation (4-58) is not linear in Q, R or T_a and hence the m + 5 equations needed for a direct solution are not obtainable. Hence a trial and error solution is employed in which values of Q, R and T_a are assumed. Values for the other constants are then calculated and the summation in equation (4-58) evaluated. Those values of Q, R and T_a which minimize this summation are chosen as the correct constants for use in equation (4-56). Some difficulty in this solution was noted by Mendelson, et al.,[57] in dealing with polynomials above the second degree. In these cases the determinants employed to solve the necessary simultaneous equations are close to zero, and number precision is hard to maintain. Even using double-precision arithmetic the results are not too satisfactory. When orthogonal polynomials were employed, however, these difficulties were avoided and a satisfactory solution was obtained. A computer program for use in this type of analysis was described.[57]

THE CLAUSS[20] EVALUATION

In a rather brief discussion of the Manson-Haferd parameter, Clauss considered the reciprocal:

$$\frac{\log t_R - \log t_a}{T - T_a} = \text{constant at constant stress} \qquad (4\text{-}59)$$

and recognized that in this form the parameter,

$$\frac{\Delta \log t_r}{\Delta T},$$

was suggested. In differential form this is

$$\frac{\partial \log t_R}{\partial T}$$

which is a part of the general form of the correlating parameter given by equation (2-58).

Furthermore, the Manson-Haferd analysis of Timken 25-20 stainless steel data was cited in which $\log t_a = 14$ and $T_a = 100°F$. This parameter plot is presented in Figure 4-25 where, except for the short term data for less than 30 hours which were not included in the analysis a good correlation is indicated. It was pointed out by Clauss that the reciprocals of the maximum and minimum parameter values in Figure 4-25 were -0.0167 and -0.0062, respectively. These values are seen to be of the same order of magnitude as the value -0.010 which was pointed out in Chapter 2 to be an approximate value for use with many high temperature steels and alloys. In other words, if the reciprocal of the ratio in equation (4-1) is considered equal to -0.01 then a simple rearrangement yields:

$$\log t_R - \log t_a = -0.01T + 0.01\, T_a \qquad (4\text{-}60)$$

which is very similar to equation (2-65). Despite the apparent differences between the approaches employed by Manson and Haferd and by Larson and Miller, a close similarity seems to exist. It was concluded that while, in general, the Manson-Haferd parameter led to a better correlation than the Larson-Miller parameter some improvement can still be effected. Part of this improvement, it was offered, must come from the realization that plots of $\log t_R$ versus either T or (1/T) do not yield linear constant stress lines. Further, these data do not extrapolate to a common point of intersection.

Deviations from the ideal behavior assumed by Manson and Haferd require that the factor,

$$\left(\frac{\partial \log t_R}{\partial T}\right)_\sigma,$$

in the general correlating parameter given by equation (2-58) be a function of temperature as well as stress and material. When these were taken into account, the excellent correlation for the Timken 25-20 data presented in Figure 2-34 was obtained.

THE LARKE AND INGLIS[30] EVALUATION

In dealing with the Manson-Haferd parameter Larke and Inglis employed the form:

$$\log t_R = \frac{T - T_a}{\phi} + \log t_a \tag{4-61}$$

in which T_a was considered to be less than any value of test temperature, T. Referring to Figure 4-26 where the temperature difference between adjacent isotherms is constant and selecting three temperatures at the same stress, σ', it follows that:

$$\log t_{R_1} = \frac{T_1 - T_a}{\phi'} + \log t_a \tag{4-62}$$

$$\log t_{R_2} = \frac{T_2 - T_a}{\phi'} + \log t_a \tag{4-63}$$

$$\log t_{R_3} = \frac{T_3 - T_a}{\phi'} + \log t_a \tag{4-64}$$

where ϕ' is the parameter value at σ'. Appropriate subtraction yields:

$$\log t_{R_1} - \log t_{R_2} = \frac{T_1 - T_2}{\phi'} = a \tag{4-65}$$

and

$$\log t_{R_2} - \log t_{R_3} = \frac{T_2 - T_3}{\phi'} = b \tag{4-66}$$

Since adjacent isotherms represent equal temperature intervals, it follows from the above that:

$$a = b \tag{4-67}$$

It can be readily shown further that:

$$a = b = c \tag{4-68}$$

which applies independent of the material itself.

Selecting a lower stress σ'' and considering temperatures T_1 and T_2 equation (4-61) yields:

$$\log t_{R_0} = \frac{T_1 - T_a}{\phi''} + \log t_a \tag{4-69}$$

and

$$\log t_{R_1} = \frac{T_2 - T_a}{\phi''} + \log t_a \tag{4-70}$$

Subtraction gives:

$$\log t_{R_0} - \log t_{R_1} = \frac{T_1 - T_2}{\phi''} = d \tag{4-71}$$

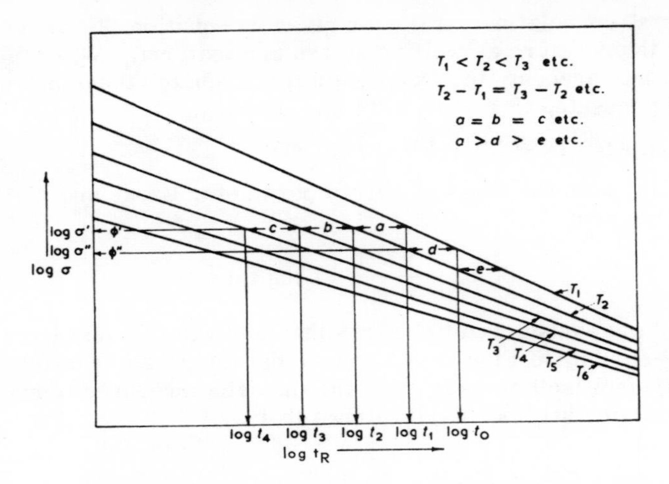

Figure 4-26 – Displacement of log stress-log time curves according to Manson and Haferd; isotherms correspond to equal temperature intervals and T_a is less than lowest test temperature(30).

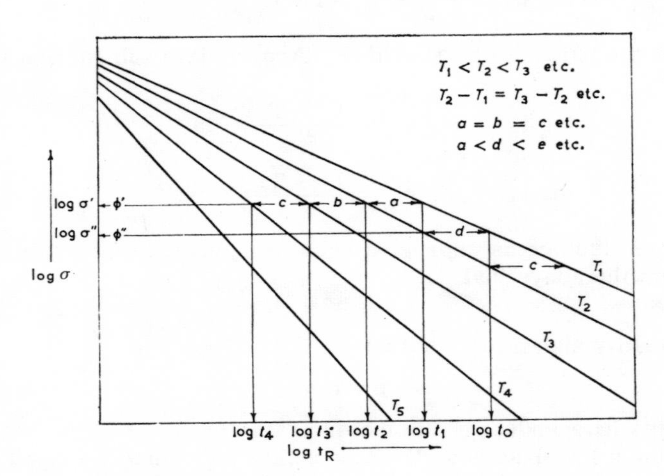

Figure 4-27 – Displacement of log stress-log time curves similar to Figure 4-26 but for T_a greater than any test temperature(30).

Based on equations (4-65) and (4-71) it follows that:

$$\frac{a}{d} = \frac{\phi''}{\phi'} \tag{4-72}$$

which converts to:

$$\frac{a}{d} = \frac{T_2 - T_a}{T_1 - T_a} \tag{4-73}$$

when equations (4-62) and (4-70) are employed. It is easily shown that:

$$a > d \tag{4-74}$$

or in general that:

$$a > d > e \tag{4-75}$$

Equation (4-68) defines a type of behavior completely different from that observed in the discussion of both the Larson-Miller and Dorn parameters. For the Manson-Haferd parameter to be applicable, it is necessary, as defined by equation (4-68), that at any stress level the ratio a/b be equal to unity for equi-spaced temperatures.

When T_a is greater than any test temperature, the schematic representation shown in Figure 4-27 can be employed to confirm that:

$$a = b = c \tag{4-76}$$

a situation identical to the previous case. However, an analysis similar to that employed above will show that:

$$\frac{a}{d} = \frac{T_a - T_2}{T_a - T_1} \tag{4-77}$$

or that

$$a < d < e \tag{4-78}$$

This result is, of course, opposite to that for Figure 4-26.

If Figures 4-26 and 4-27 are consulted, data at various stress levels will yield the type of plots shown in Figure 4-28. Heavy lines have been drawn to represent the data within the experimental range and these lines have been extrapolated to a common point of intersection. In one case this intersection occurs at a temperature below the experimental range of temperatures whereas in the other case the reverse is true. Special caution was recommended when this point of intersection is being located for the graphical approach illustrated in Figure 4-28 can only lead to approximate results. Certainly the least squares approach considered in a previous section should be employed whenever possible.

It was pointed out by Larke and Inglis that in view of equations (4-73) and (4-77) the T_a value is reflected in the a/d ratio and causes appropriate adjustments in this ratio when different materials are

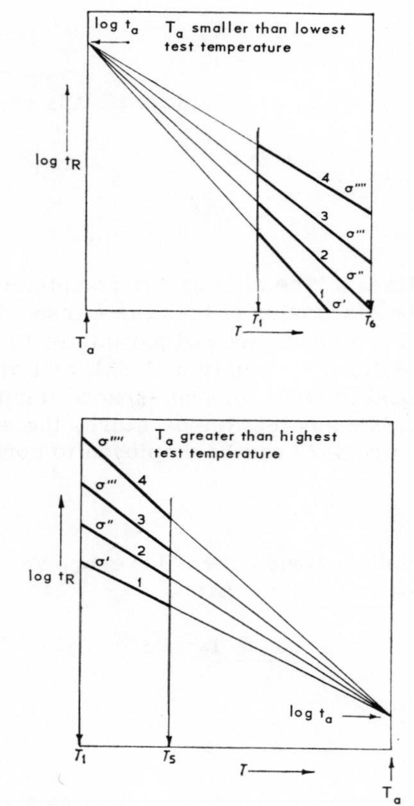

Figure 4-28 – Manson-Haferd plot of log t_R versus T at constant stress[30].

tested at the same two temperatures. Also since $T_2 > T_1$ equation (4-73) can be written as:

$$\frac{a}{d} = 1 + \frac{k}{T_1 - T_a} \text{ for } T_a < T_1 \tag{4-79}$$

and equation (4-77) as:

$$\frac{a}{d} = 1 - \frac{k}{T_a - T_1} \text{ for } T_a > T_1 \tag{4-80}$$

where $k = (T_2 - T_1)$. These expressions make it clear that when T_a is less than the lowest test temperature, or greater than the highest, the magnitude of T_a will decrease when a/d decreases. Furthermore, when large negative values of T_a occur adjacent $\log \sigma / \log t_R$ curves are tending to become parallel, i.e., the ratio a/d is approaching unity. This also happens when large positive values of T_a are encountered. This condition of equal a and d values, it will be seen, is closely approaching the behavior characterized by the Dorn parameter (see equation (3-57) from Chapter 3).

When $\log t_a$ is the same for several different materials, a particular situation develops. Employing equation (4-73) it can be shown that:

$$\frac{a}{d} = \frac{\log t_{R_2} - \log t_a}{\log t_{R_1} - \log t_a} \tag{4-81}$$

and

$$\log t_a = \log t_{R_2} - \frac{a}{(d/a) - 1} \tag{4-82}$$

Referring to Figures 4-26 and 4-27 it will be observed that at the point of intersection of the isotherms it is necessary that $a = 0$; then from equation (4-82) it follows that at this point $\log t_{R_2}$ is equal to $\log t_a$. Now if the data for several materials, all with the same $\log t_a$ value, are presented in the same graph, then the points of intersection will all occur at the same abscissa value. For the same isotherm, say T_2, all the data for materials A, B and C can be made to fall along a common line* (line 1 at T_2 in Figure 4-29). Isotherms corresponding to T_1 will then be as shown in Figure 4-29; intersection with the T_2 isotherm will occur at the same point now since the log scales are adjusted and the $\log t_a$ values are assumed equal. These other isotherms occupy positions dictated by the value of T_a, since, according to equation (4-73), the a/d ratio will be different for each material. Hence the a', a'' and a''' values dictating the displacement $\log t_1 - \log t_2$ between the two isotherms T_1 and T_2 will be different for each material.

*A small change in the length of the log cycle will cause an isotherm, T_2, for material A to be parallel to the same isotherm for material B; a vertical displacement can then bring them into coincidence. In doing this, though, each material will have a different stress scale on the ordinate; also other isotherms such as T_1, T_3, etc., will not be coincident.

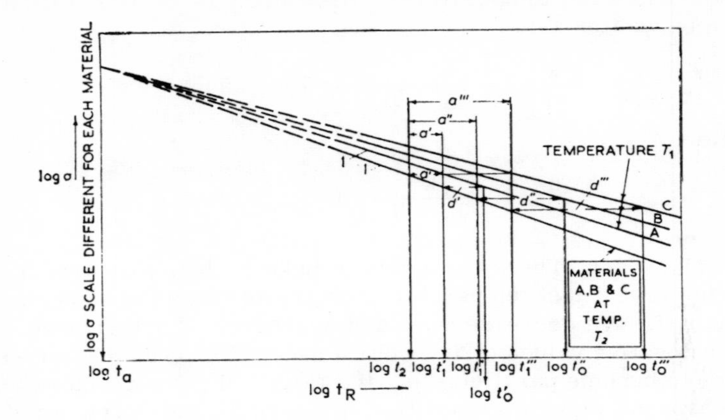

Figure 4-29 – Plot of log σ versus log t_R used in Manson-Haferd analysis involving same log t_a values(30)

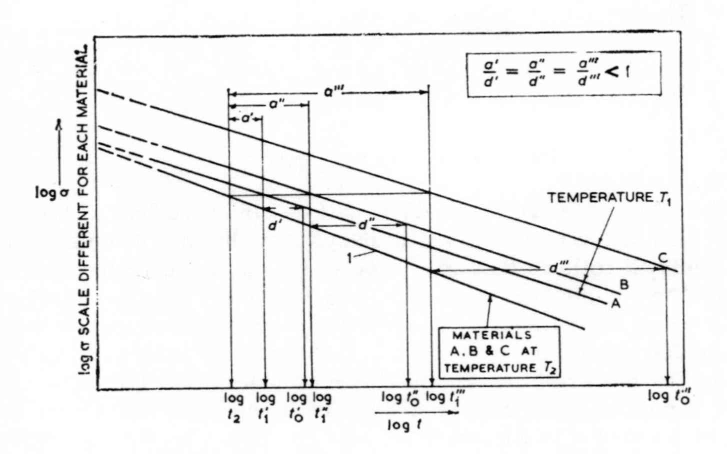

Figure 4-30 – Plot of log σ versus log t_R used in Manson-Haferd analysis involving same T_a values(30)

TABLE 4-1

SUMMARY OF MURRY[31] RESULTS BASED ON MANSON-HAFERD PARAMETER APPLIED TO SEVERAL STEELS

Steel	σ_0, kgf/mm²	a	b	Standard deviation	Linear correlation coefficient
'A37'	8	26·871 12	0·030 11	0·0656	> 0·99
	11	25·325 08	0·029 62	0·0145	> 0·99
	13	28·100 64	0·034 03	0·0725	> 0·99
	15	30·385 21	0·038 02	0·0346	> 0·99
	17	31·121 52	0·040 08	0·1016	> 0·99
	20	36·045 18	0·048 56	0·0532	> 0·99
'2·25% Cr–1% Mo'	5	31·273 64	0·030 30	0·0808	> 0·99
	10	24·269 66	0·025 05	0·0320	> 0·99
	15	24·675 41	0·027 00	0·0426	> 0·99
	20	27·210 07	0·031 37	0·0664	> 0·99
'17–22 A'S	7	22·557 37	0·021 74	0·0688	> 0·99
	14	24·491 93	0·024 82	0·0906	> 0·99
	28	27·255 43	0·029 18	0·1053	> 0·99
	56	31·040 07	0·036 39	0·2722	0·96
'18% Cr–12% Ni–Ti'	6	18·137 84	0·015 19	0·0550	> 0·99
	12	20·713 13	0·018 86	0·0215	> 0·99
	20	25·291 32	0·025 02	0·0790	> 0·99
	35	27·000 00	0·029 57	0·0598	> 0·99

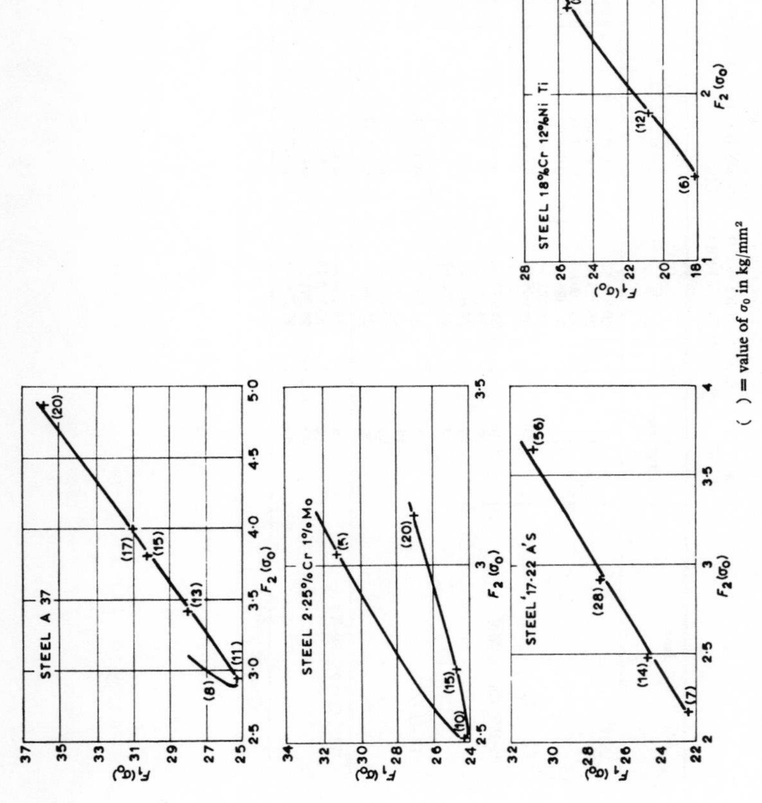

( ) = value of σ_0 in kg/mm²

Figure 4-31 – Plot(31) of F_1 (σ_o) versus F_2 (σ_o) based on Table 4-1 data.

It was pointed out by Larke and Inglis that this concept of varying a/d values is not inherent in the Larson-Miller concept. Instead the Larson-Miller approach requires that a/d be the same for all materials. Hence the Manson-Haferd approach affords this flexibility and from this point of view allows for more extensive application. Another point was made in terms of the converging-diverging possibilities associated with the Manson-Haferd approach as shown in Figures 4-26 and 4-27. Only the divergent behavior can be described by the Larson-Miller parameter. A restriction of the Manson-Haferd was

Although Manson and Haferd did not contend that a/d should be the same for all materials, it was admitted that certain similar materials might exhibit this type of behavior. Constant a/d values, of course, require equal values for T_a. In Figure 4-30 data for materials A, B and C are plotted to show coincidence for the T_2 isotherm. Since the T_2, T_1 isotherms for all the materials will have the same a/d ratio, these T_1 isotherms can be positioned accordingly. Such a construction, and this is easily shown, will result in the T_1 isotherms being parallel. When T_a is the same and a/d is less than unity, the magnitude of $\log t_a$ decreases when the log time interval "a" increases. However, when convergence is observed and a/d is greater than unity, the magnitude of $\log t_a$ increases when the log time interval increases.

THE MURRY[31] EVALUATION

Considering the Manson-Haferd parameter in the form:

$$\log t_R = a - bT \text{ at constant stress} \tag{4-83}$$

where:

$$a = \log t_a - \frac{T_a}{\phi} \tag{4-84}$$

and

$$b = 1/\phi \tag{4-85}$$

Murry applied a least squares approach to the calculation of the constants "a" and "b." Results of this analysis are presented in Table 4-1 where the correlation coefficient is strongly indicative that a linear relation exists. In other words, equation (4-83) seems to be substantiated. Since both a and b in Table 4-1 appear to be dependent on stress, equation (4-83) is written as:

$$\log t_R = F_1(\sigma_0) - F_2(\sigma_0)\, T \tag{4-86}$$

Murry observed that since the Manson-Haferd approach assumes a common point of intersection for all constant stress lines at $T = T_a$ and $\log t_R = \log t_a$ then the following relationship must apply:

$$F_1(\sigma_0) = \log t_a + T_a\, F_2(\sigma_0) \tag{4-87}$$

Applying the data from Table 4-1, the plots in Figure 4-31 were prepared from which the validity of equation (4-87) was not substantiated. In other words, while the linearity described by the Manson-Haferd parameter in equation (4-83) seems confirmed, the existence of a common point of intersection for the constant stress lines could not be substantiated. Over certain ranges of σ_0 the linearity in Figure 4-31 is consistent with equation (4-87) and in these ranges the Manson-Haferd approach would be applicable.

CHAPTER 5

GRAHAM-WALLES PARAMETER

Two scientists, A. Graham and K. F. A. Walles, in Great Britain have contributed extensively(67,68,69) to the literature dealing with stress-rupture and creep parameters and the extrapolation of data. From this work has evolved the Graham-Walles parameter in the form:

$$\theta = t(T' - T)^{-A} = \text{constant} \tag{5-1}$$

where θ is the Graham-Walles time-temperature parameter, t is time, T is temperature and T' and A are constants. These authors have applied this approach in the analysis of well over 100 sets of data and claim notable effectiveness. However, the fact remains that this approach has not been widely adopted as yet since the general impression seems to be that it is slightly too complicated to apply and use.

Actually the Graham-Walles parameter has its origin in strain-time analyses in which a quantitative relationship between stress, strain, time and temperature during creep was being sought. It was acknowledged, of course, that other studies of this same subject have been made and reported; but as far as the extrapolation of data was concerned, Graham and Walles felt that these approaches were not detailed enough to accommodate the complexities of the creep process. For example, it was noted by these authors that as far as extrapolation of data is concerned the existing methods either:

a) extrapolate an assumed law relating time to stress at constant temperature; this approach corresponds to the direct extrapolation of graphs of log stress versus log time (or stress versus log time); or
b) extrapolate an assumed law relating time and temperature at constant stress; examples of this are found in the Larson-Miller, Dorn and Manson-Haferd analyses.

In connection with the latter methods it was felt that these viewed the laws governing the creep process as being so simple that a change in stress in (a) or a change in temperature in (b) affected the creep rate of each deformation process taking place in the material by exactly the same amount. A more involved approach was considered necessary if all the intricacies of the creep process were to be accurately described. With this in mind the Graham-Walles concept was introduced.

In the Graham-Walles method for creep analysis the following relation is assumed to apply:

$$\epsilon = at^{1/3} + bt + ct^3 \qquad (5\text{-}2)$$

where ϵ is the creep strain after subtraction of the elastic strain that occurs during loading, t is time measured from the instant of loading when the creep strain may be regarded as zero and a, b and c are constants at a particular temperature and stress. In this equation the exponents 1/3, 1 and 3 will be recognized as corresponding to the transient (first stage), steady state (second stage) and accelerating (third stage) stages of the creep process. Studies of many sets of creep data were cited as having confirmed the general applicability of this expression.

Reference to the Nutting[70] equation in the form:

$$\epsilon = C\,\sigma^{\beta}\,t^{k} \qquad (5\text{-}3)$$

where σ is the stress, t is the time and C, β and k are constants led to the modification of equation (5-2) to yield the general form:

$$\epsilon = C_1\,\sigma^{\beta_1}\,t^{k_1} + C_2\,\sigma^{\beta_2}\,t^{k_2} + C_3\,\sigma^{\beta_3}\,t^{k_3} + \ldots \qquad (5\text{-}4)$$

In this expression each term accounts for a different portion of the creep process and k has values of 1/3, 1 or 3 consistent with equation (5-2). Actually, more than one term with the same k exponent can be involved in which case equation (5-4) would become:

$$\epsilon = C_1\,\sigma^{\beta_1}\,t^{k_1} + C_2\,\sigma^{\beta_2}\,t^{k_2} + (C_3\,\sigma^{\beta_3} + C_4\,\sigma^{\beta_4})\,t^{k_3} \qquad (5\text{-}5)$$

for the case of a two-term coefficient on the time term involving the k_3 exponent. Then temperature was introduced, not as T but rather as $(T - T')^{\alpha}$, based on the effect which exposure at previous temperatures had on the behavior at T. Combining the time term with this temperature term led to:

$$t^{k}\,(T - T')^{\alpha} \qquad (5\text{-}6)$$

or

$$[t(T - T')^{-A}]^{k} = \theta \qquad (5\text{-}7)$$

where $\alpha = -kA$; in this way a "time-modified temperature" was introduced representing the Graham-Walles parameter. Since T' can be either greater or less than T, some consideration of sign must be made. When $T' > T$

$$\theta = t(T' - T)^{-A} \qquad (5\text{-}8)$$

and when $T' < T$

$$\theta = t(T - T')^{+A} \qquad (5\text{-}9)$$

Considering for the moment the time to a given strain or rupture times, both these expressions will be seen to be consistent with observed behavior. As the temperature, T, is increased at a constant stress then, at constant θ, the time is decreased.

Introducing the θ concept into equation (5-4) it follows that:

$$\epsilon = C_1 \sigma^{\beta_1} \theta_1^{k_1} + C_2 \sigma^{\beta_2} \theta_2^{k_2} + C_3 \sigma^{B_3} \theta_3^{k_3} + \ldots \qquad (5\text{-}10)$$

Total strain is thus described by a summation of terms each of which describes a portion of the creep process in terms of the stress and the Graham-Walles parameter applicable to that creep mechanism. Based on the materials analyzed to date, Graham and Walles observed no definite indication that A and T' varied from term to term. Hence:

$$\epsilon = C_1 \sigma^{\beta_1} \theta^{k_1} + C_2 \sigma^{\beta_2} \theta^{k_2} + C_3 \sigma^{\beta_3} \theta^{k_3} + \ldots \qquad (5\text{-}11)$$

As a matter of fact, the value of A = 20 has been found to afford acceptable representations and is recommended for general usage (the agreement of this value with the value of 20 commonly accepted as the Larson-Miller constant is considered fortuitous).

For a situation such as given by equation (5-11) the identification of all the unknown constants poses no easy problem. If written in the form of equation (5-5) it will be clear that attention must be given to the identification of C_1, C_2, C_3, C_4, β_1, β_2, β_3, β_4, T' and A (k_1, k_2 and k_3 are taken as 1/3, 1 and 3, respectively) if this is not accepted as equal to 20. Hence nine or perhaps ten constants require identification if a proper Graham-Walles analysis is to be made of a given set of creep data. Such an analysis is best performed graphically according to Graham-Walles and should proceed as follows:

(1) an experimental creep curve of the form shown in Figure 5-1 is broken down into the three components given in equation (5-2); this is done by employing a set of master curves[71] and noting that for each of the three stages of creep a log strain versus log time plot yields a linear relation; the slopes are, of course, 1/3, 1 and 3 as indicated in equation (5-2); the results of a typical analysis in which the creep curve is resolved into three component parts are shown as the dashed lines in Figure 5-1; intercept measurements from the log-log plots yield values for the coefficients on the time terms in equation (5-11); for example, the intercept of the line representing the first stage data would be equal to:

$$C_1 \sigma^{\beta_1} (T' - T)^{-k_1 A}; \qquad (5\text{-}12)$$

repeating the above analysis procedures at other temperatures and stresses allows the effects of these variables on the coefficients to be determined; only after T' is determined (see below) can the exact value of C_1, etc., be identified.

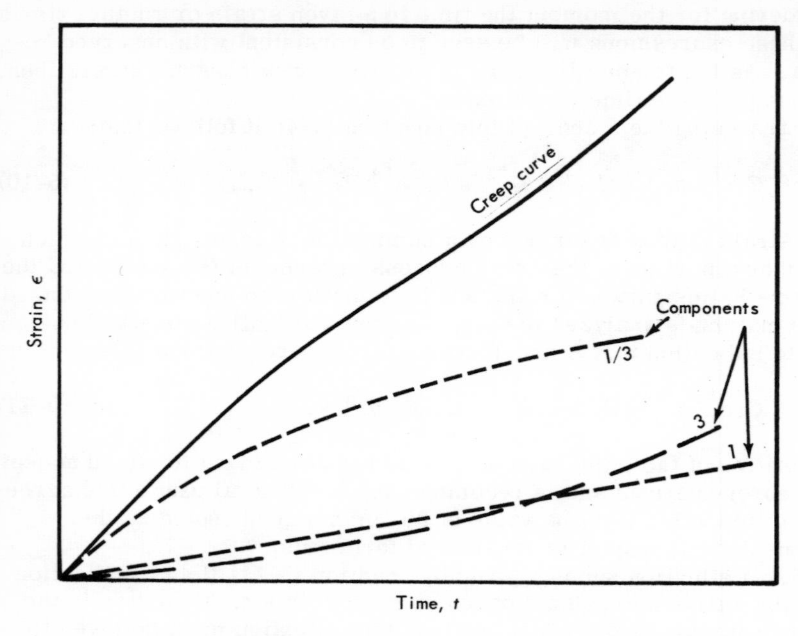

Figure 5-1 – Resolution of creep curve into component parts.

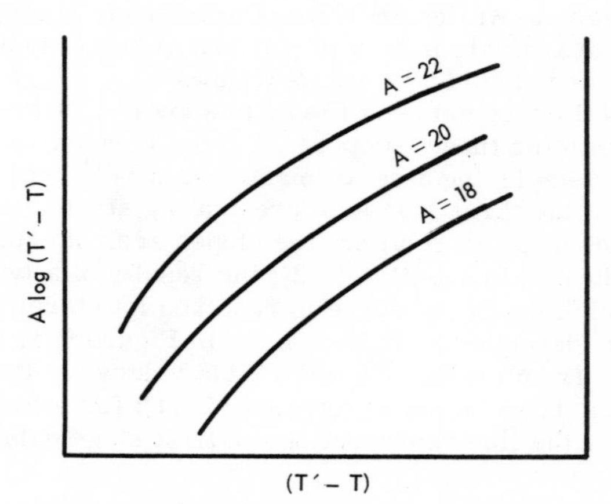

Figure 5-2 – Plot of A log (T′ – T) versus (T′ – T)

(2) employing the dashed curves shown in Figure 5-1, time values corresponding to a certain strain level, say 10^{-3}, are obtained; then for each exponent, 1/3, 1 and 3, plots are made of log σ versus log time for the 1/3 and 1 regions; these will be linear at a given temperature in accordance with equation (5-10) and slope values identify k/β values; since k values are known the β values follow directly for each stage of creep; for the tertiary stage, if the two-term coefficient in equation (5-5) were applicable, the log σ versus long time plot would not be linear but instead would be concave downward; for this curve though the extremities approach a linear form which might allow the constants in the two terms (i.e., C_3 and C_4) to be evaluated; in the above the introduction of temperature results in a series of parallel lines for the 1/3 and 1 data and a series of parallel two-segment lines for the t^3 data.

(3) in (2) above the amount of displacement between adjacent isotherms enables the constants in the time-temperature function, θ, to be determined; in any one group, say the $t^{1/3}$ group for illustration purposes, the times to a given strain at the same stress for temperatures T_1 and T_2 can be used in equation (5-8) to yield:

$$t_1(T' - T_1)^{-A} = t_2(T' - T_2)^{-A} \qquad (5\text{-}13)$$

and when logarithms are employed:

$$\log t_1 - \log t_2 = A[\log(T' - T_1) - \log(T' - T_2)] \qquad (5\text{-}14)$$

It will be noted that the left- hand side is equal to the displacement of the isotherms on a log σ versus log t plot of the $t^{1/3}$ data. A solution for the right-hand side of equation (5-14) requires a set of master curves prepared especially for this purpose. In this preparation values for $(T' - T)$ are assumed and values of A log $(T' - T)$ are calculated for various A values as shown in Figure 5-2. The curve in this set which gives the correct relation between Δ log t and any two temperatures T_1 and T_2 enables the A value to be determined. In identifying the proper curve the Δ log t value is obtained from the experimental data corresponding to the temperatures T_1 and T_2 at a given stress (and, of course, for the same strain value); and when two points on any curve in Figure 5-2 are found such that the ordinate values differ by this Δ log t value and the abscissa values are separated by $(T_1 - T_2)$, then the desired curve is located. This then identifies the value of A to be used (this will be close to 20 as already stated). As yet no indication of the T' value has been obtained. However, if now, the data for the A curve just identified are used properly the T' value can be obtained. First of all a given temperature interval is selected, say equal to 50°C, and the ordinates on the proper A curve in Figure 5-2 are located at $(T' - T)$ values of 450 and 400. In accordance with equation (5-14), subtraction of these ordinate values yields a value for Δ log t. This value

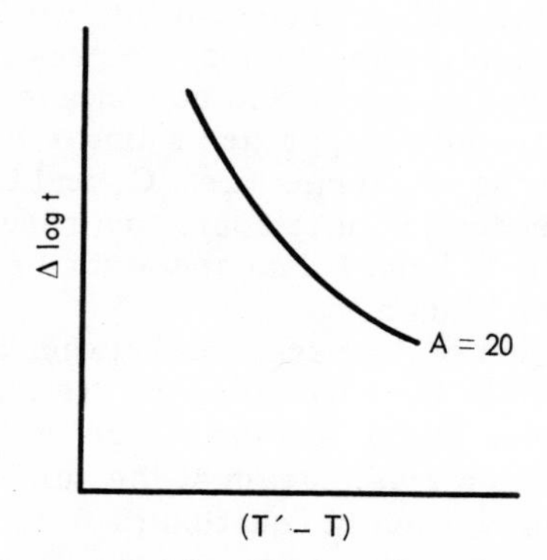

Figure 5-3 — Plot of Δ log t from Figure 5-2

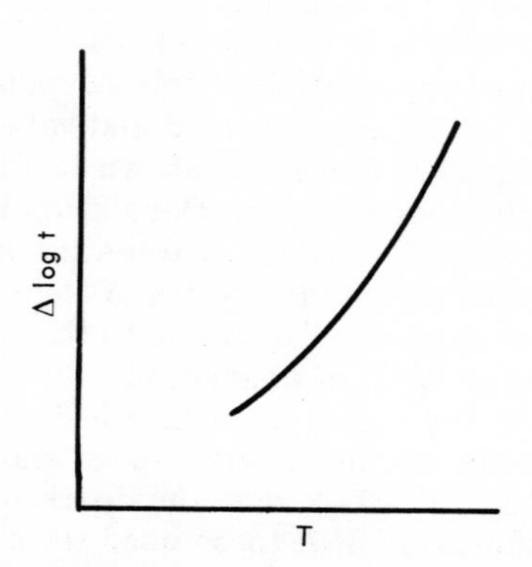

Figure 5-4 — Plot of Δ log t from experimental data

is then plotted against the highest (450) value of $(T' - T)$ which in this case would correspond to the lowest value of T. Repeating this procedure identifies the curve shown in Figure 5-3 for A = 20. Now a similar plot (using same ΔT as above) is made from the experimental data. Values of Δ log t are read from the experimental plot and plotted against the smaller of the two temperatures. Such a graph is shown in Figure 5-4. If Figure 5-3 is placed on top of Figure 5-4 (equal values on the ordinate and abscissa scales must coincide), the intersection of these lines locates a point on the T scale of Figure 5-4 and another just beneath it on the $(T' - T)$ scale of Figure 5-3. These two values lead then to the T' value. For example, if T = 550 and $(T' - T) = 550$ then obviously T' = 1100.

It will be clear from Figure 5-2 that the Δ log t and $(T_1 - T_2)$ combination can be satisfied on more than one curve. In other words, several different A values might result. This possibility was admitted in the Graham-Walles analysis when for some Nimonic data the following A and T' combinations led to good correlations:

A = 17.5 and T' = 1070°C
A = 22.5 and T' = 1175°C
A = 27.5 and T' = 1275°C

It is this behavior which is probably responsible for accepting A = 20 in the Graham-Walles parameter.

An illustration of the above procedure is given[69] by the Nimonic 80A data presented in Figure 5-5. This type of plot, it will be recognized, is similar to the type mentioned above in which the abscissa was the time to a given strain value. For rupture analyses, however, the time is that corresponding to rupture thus enabling the Graham-Walles parameter to be applied to data of this type. It was stated by Graham and Walles[69] that plots of log stress versus log time can be described by a series of connected short segments of straight lines each of slightly different slope. Detailed study of this behavior has shown[72] that the slopes of the segments, where these segments are clearly present, take values from the sequence:

$$-1, -1/2, -1/4, -1/8, -1/16\ldots \qquad (5\text{-}15)$$

Actually it might be expecting too much for exact linearity to be obtained and also for abrupt changes to be observed in going from one segment to another. Such an ideal case is seldom observed. More often the log stress versus log time graphs are continuous curves whose shapes approximate the connected linear segment concept. For cases where the k = 3 type of behavior is observed, the linear segment behavior is closely approached; with k = 1/3 or 1 the curvature is more gradual and may be regarded as being asymptotic to lines of standard slope at either end, An illustration of this curve shape is shown in Figure 5-6.[69]

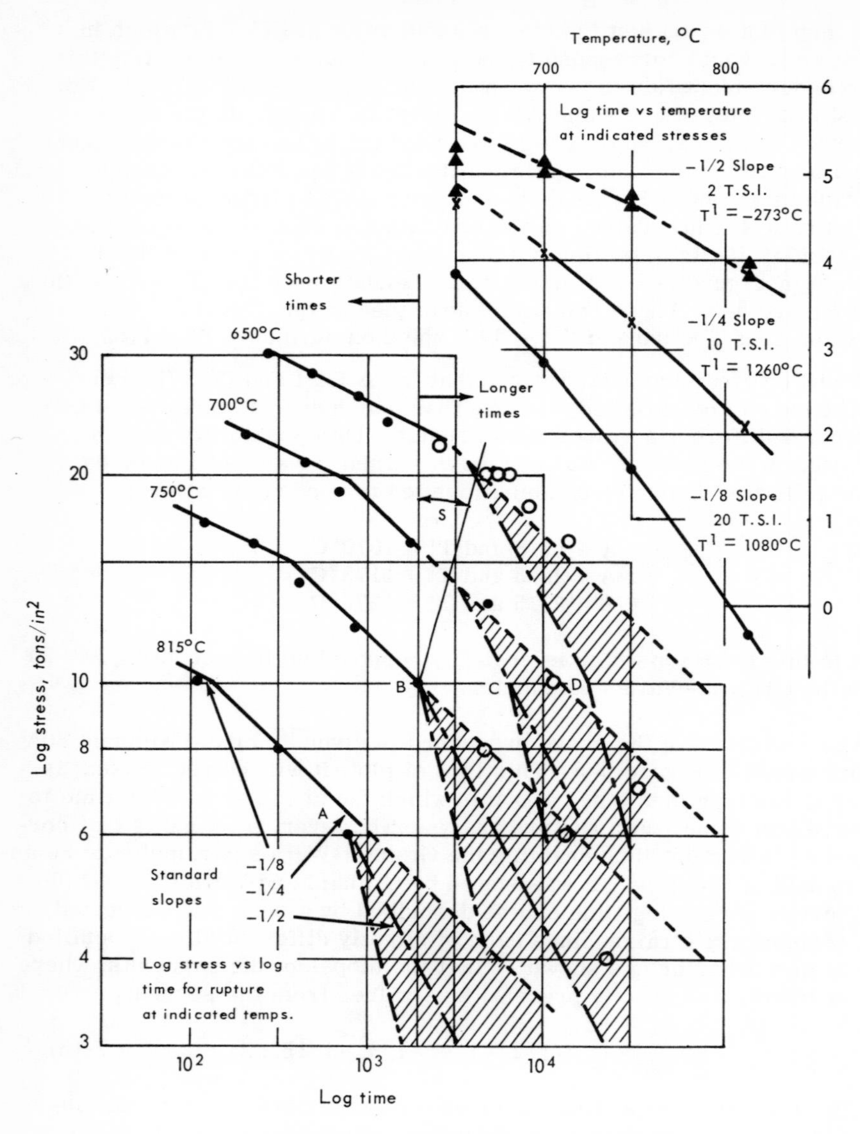

Figure 5-5 – Rupture data for Nimonic 80A(69).

In the experience of Graham and Walles the time to rupture corresponds closely to the time for the dominant component in equation (5-2) to reach a critical value. Materials which rupture after a pronounced stage of tertiary creep are usually found [73] to have times to rupture that are effectively determined by only the component of equation (5-2) for which the exponent is 3. On the other hand, materials which display a long stage of steady state creep and proceed to rupture without appreciable teritary creep have times to rupture which are effectively determined by the component whose exponent is unity.

Turning now to the data in Figure 5-5 Graham and Walles [69] made an arbitrary division of the data into two groups. Rupture times greater than 2,000 hours are shown as the open points while the solid points correspond to rupture in less than 2,000 hours. These latter points were employed in the analysis and these results then used to predict longer term behavior. In this way a direct comparison of the extrapolative capability could be made. In this figure the solid lines are based on the analysis of the shorter term data. Tentative lines were positioned with slopes (i.e., $-k/\beta$ values) of -1/8 and -1/4 on the log stress versus log rupture time plot in the region of the filled points. Then for segments having the same slope corresponding log σ and T values at a constant stress were obtained to prepare the plot in the upper portion of Figure 5-5. Some trial and adjustment may be necessary at this point to find the correct positions for the lines in both the upper and lower portions of this figure which afford the best fit for the experimental points. With the log $t(t_R$ in this case) versus T plot prepared in this manner, the Δ log t versus T plot described previously can be developed to allow the calculation of T'. Values of T' are shown in Figure 5-5 and are seen to vary with the k/β value. This situation introduces a complication into the Graham-Walles approach for if T' varies in this manner the use of this parameter becomes more complicated. Actually, if the stress-rupture isotherms are confined to a region of constant k/β, then one value of T' should be applicable and the analysis is a little more straightforward.

Once the upper part of Figure 5-5 is constructed it is not necessary to employ the graphical solution for T' that was described above. For example, if equation (5-8) is employed it follows that:[40]

$$\left(\frac{t_2}{t_1}\right)^{1/20} = \gamma = \frac{T' - T_2}{T' - T_1} \qquad (5\text{-}16)$$

which when solved yields:

$$T' = \frac{\gamma T_1 - T_2}{\gamma - 1} \qquad (5\text{-}17)$$

A similar expression for equation (5-9) is:

$$T' = \frac{\gamma T_2 - T_1}{\gamma - 1} \qquad (5\text{-}18)$$

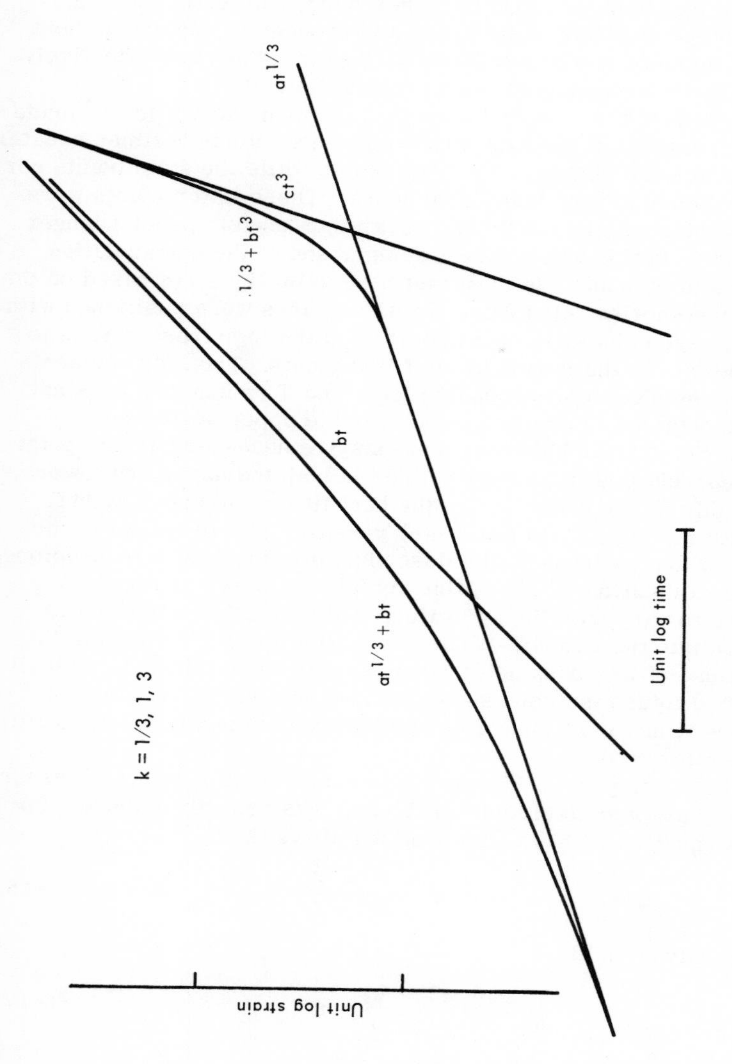

Figure 5-6 – Typical two-term log strain-log time master curves[69].

Hence once the constant stress lines in the upper part of Figure 5-5 are established it is a simple procedure to obtain T'. It is not necessary, therefore, to resort to the graphical procedure discussed in a previous section.* Referring to Figure 5-5 at 700° and 800°C the log rupture times at 10 tons in^2 are close to 14,100 and 210 hours, respectively. Substitution in equation (5-17) leads to T' = 1230°C which is seen to be very close to the value given in Figure 5-5.

Having established the solid lines in Figure 5-5 and having calculated T' a parameter plot can now be prepared. If only one value of T' is involved, the parameter plot will have the form of any other parameter plot discussed in previous chapters. When $\theta = t(T' - T)^{-20}$ is plotted as a function of stress or log stress, a single curve or line will develop. However, if several T' values are noted, each applicable to a different range (1/3, 1 or 3) of the data, then the parameter plot will have several segments each characterized by a different T' value. Such a situation is shown in Figure 9-24 where for both Nimonic 80A and 90 two distinct ranges of data are noted on the parameter plot each with a different value of T'. In the higher stress region of the Nimonic 80A data a value of T' = 1150°C was indicated whereas T' =1350°C in the lower stress region. Also in these stress regions the slopes were -1/8 and -1/4, respectively, in accordance with the Graham-Walles assumptions.

If the data analysis based on the type of plot shown in Figure 5-5 reveals different T' values for the 1/3, 1 and 3 ranges of the data, then this information can be employed in conjunction with equation (5-10) to identify the appropriate equation constants. For example, if T' for the 1/3 range is known, then a parameter plot of log σ versus θ will be linear with a slope of $-k_1/\beta_1$. Slope measurement will yield β_1 and the intercept value will yield C_1. In this way all the constants in equation (5-10) would be identified. Of course, for the two-term coefficient given in equation (5-5) the parameter plot would not be linear. However, as already indicated such plots become asymptotic to linear segments and if this condition is noted both C_3 and C_4 constants will evolve.

If during the course of the data analysis it can be deduced that within a certain range of the data only one T' value is indicated, then it will be possible to analyze these data in terms of the least squares procedures discussed in previous chapters. Applying the Manson and Mendelson [5] approach, it is possible to write an expression involving equation (5-1) as:

$$\log t - 20 \log(T' - T) = a_0 + a_1 x + a_2 x^2 + \ldots + a_m x^m \quad (5\text{-}19)$$

*A similar method was employed by Tilly [75] in analyzing data for an alloy steel and a nickel-chromium alloy. A plot was made of $t^{1/20}$ versus T at constant stress to yield a linear relation. At $t^{1/20} = 0$ the intercept yields T' (see equation (5-8)). Similarly, for equation (5-9) the value of T' can be obtained from a plot of $t^{-1/20}$ versus T. The above calculation procedure has been attributed to W. J. Harris by Walles. [76]

or

$$y = \log t = 20 \log(T' - T) + a_0 + a_1 x + a_2 x^2 \; . \; . \; . + a_m x^m \qquad (5\text{-}20)$$

where, as in previous chapters, $y = \log t$ (t_R if rupture data are being considered) and $x = \log \sigma$. An equation similar to equation (4-50) is seen to have developed where now y_a is replaced by 20 log (T' - T) and $(T - T_a) = 1$. Since equation (5-20) is non-linear in T', just as equation (4-35) was non-linear because of T_a, the solution procedure followed in this latter case can be employed to solve equation (5-20). Such an approach based on a trial and error or an iterative solution (see Chapter 10) will yield least squares values for T' and the polynomial coefficient In this way the parameter plot can be established.

It is worth noting that in connection with the upper part of Figure 5- the shape of the constant stress curves are a function of T'. Taking logarithms of equation (5-8) with A = 20 and then differentiating with respect to T leads to:

$$\frac{d \log t}{dT} = \frac{-20}{(T' - T)} \qquad (5\text{-}21)$$

Hence, as the value of T' is increased, the slopes of these constant stre lines at the same temperature assume lower negative values. In other words, the lines become less steep. Such a situation is shown schemati cally in Figure 5-7. It can also be shown that when $T' < T$ the constant stress lines become steeper as T' increases. Such behavior is shown schematically in Figure 5-8. Having prepared this type of plot from the experimental data, it is easy to establish whether T' is greater or less than T. Another useful plot for use in this connection is shown in Figure 5-9. The value of this plot lies in the linearity which results when $T' = 0$. Also noted are the shapes which result when T' is greater than or less than T.

Some mention should be made of a special condition which arises when T' is negative. In this instance the plot shown in Figure 5-9 will be concave downward. Since this type of curvature is typical of the case when $T' > T$, it requires a moment of reflection to differentiate these two types of behavior. In other words, if the plot shown in Figure 5-9 is concave downward, the behavior could be either $T' > T$ or $T' < T$ with $T' < 0$. However, a plot of the type shown in Figure 5-8 will resolve this issue for if this plot yields a concave upward behavior then a concave downward relationship in Figure 5-9 identifies the fact that $T' < T$ with $T' < 0$.

An advantage assigned to the Graham-Walles approach is that different shapes of the log t versus T plots at constant stress can be handled by the simple expedient of adjusting the T' value. As already mentioned these plots are concave downward when $T' > T$ and concave upward when the reverse is true. Several of the common parameters discussed previously can accommodate the concave upward case but not that in which the constant stress lines are concave downward.

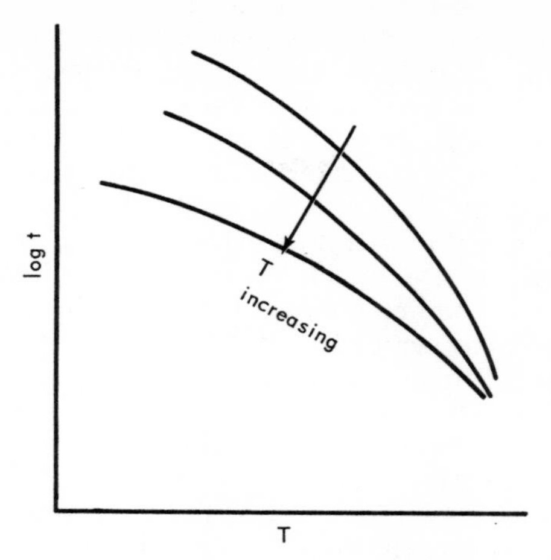

Figure 5-7 – Schematic of log t versus T constant stress curves for T′ > T.

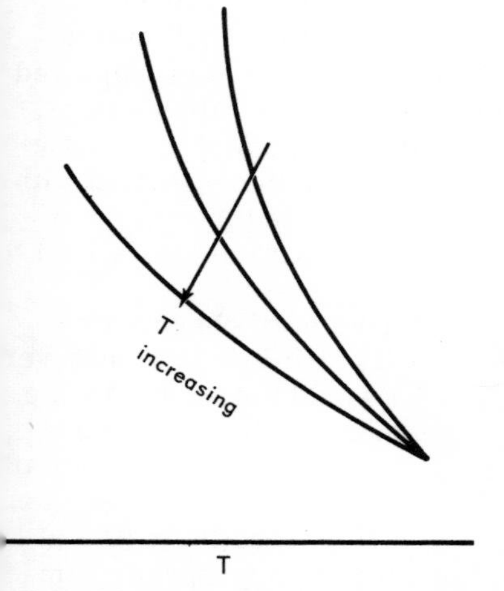

e 5-8 – Schematic of log t versus T constant stress curves for T′ < T.

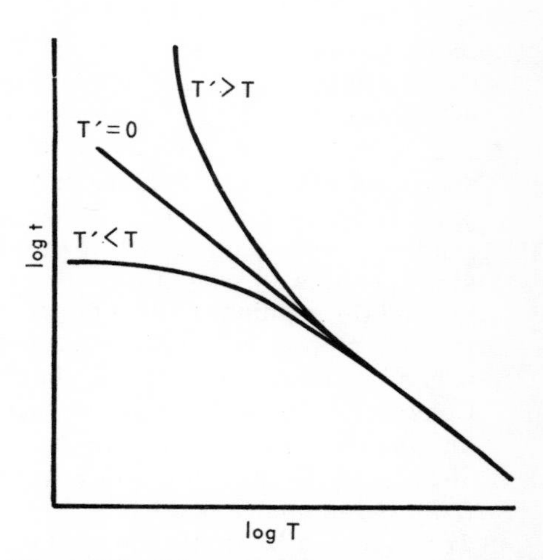

Figure 5-9 – Schematic of log t versus log T plot at constant stress.

Extrapolation beyond the 2000-hour range in Figure 5-5 can be made once the Graham-Walles type of analysis has established the solid lines shown. A direct extension of these lines (shown dashed) provides extrapolated results which are viewed as optimistic values to the extent that these extrapolated rupture times will be greater than the actual data if a slope change occurs beyond the 2000-hour dividing line. According to the Graham-Walles approach the next segment has a slope of -1/2 but it is not known just where this will take place. This is so in all cases of extrapolation where no experimental points are available to correctly locate the transition point where the next (-1/2) segment begins. If a segment of -1/2 slope is drawn originating from the last experimental point in the experimental (less than 2000 hours) range, a pessimistic estimate of material behavior is obtained. Such lines are drawn for the 815° and 750°C isotherms in Figure 5-5 and will be seen initiating at points A and B, respectively. In this way a shaded area in the extrapolated region is defined by a line (-1/4 slope) of optimistic behavior and a line (-1/2 slope) corresponding to pessimistic behavior.

In the case of the 700° and 650°C isotherms the positioning of the segments of -1/2 slope was based on a relationship defined by equation (5-21). Written in incremental form this is:

$$\frac{\Delta \log t}{\Delta T} = \frac{20}{|T' - T|} \tag{5-22}$$

which defines the minimum spacing of parallel segments. According to Graham and Walles, based on a study of more than 40 alloys, the value of T' lies between 0°K and the melting point. Hence if the value of T', which is the more remote from T, is used, equation (5-22) will define the minimum spacing which can exist. This consideration was employed in positioning the -1/2 segments for the two lowest temperatures in Figure 5-5. Shaded areas, as above, are bounded by lines of optimistic and pessimistic extrapolations. These considerations in connection with point B define a sector, S, to the right of which is located the region of shaded areas. To the left of this line through B the extrapolations lead to single values.

While segment slopes corresponding to -1 have been observed no steeper slopes have been encountered. For the Figure 5-5 data, however it has been concluded that a segment slope of -1 would not be applicable. Considering point B, it might happen that a segment of slope -1 would originate at this point. This could also be applicable for point A. But at 700°C and 650°C minimum spacing considerations prevent the -1 segment from being positioned to the left of points C and D, respectively (C and D were located by minimum spacing calculations for the appropriate temperature and measured off from point B). If -1 segments are drawn in this case, the extrapolations would be more optimistic than those obtained with the -1/2 segments. Since the rule for pessimistic extrapolation is to use the most unfavorable slope, the use of the -1 segments in this analysis is not appropriate.

Another example[69] of rupture data analysis is given in Figure 5-10. These data represent behavior for a 4-6% chrome-molybdenum steel in which the creep curve exhibits no tertiary stage. In this case the creep process is governed by the terms in equation (5-4) for which $k = 1$. The data have been divided into two groups with the dividing line at 10 hours. It will be noted that in this instance the isotherms no longer approximate a series of linear segments. This follows because with $k = 1$ the curvature of the transitions is more gradual and they extend over much of the experimental range. Rupture behavior in this example is described by at least two terms with $k = 1$ in equation (5-4) and the shape of the curve is governed by the values of β. Several examples of master curves involving two terms are given in Figure 5-11 for several values of k and β. When more than two terms are involved, the situation becomes a little more complicated. Usually the positions of the asymptotes which represent the basic terms must be established by the method of successive approximations.

Once the k and β values are established, for the data in Figure 5-10, the rest of the analysis proceeds as in Figure 5-5. A series of shaded areas results based on optimistic and pessimistic extrapolations.

Graham and Walles have stated that in the analysis of rupture data the form shown in equation (5-11) is applicable with each θ value involving a different value of T'. When $k = 3$ or more, linear segments on log stress versus log rupture time plots are obtained and the T' values indicate that the displacements of the different segments are not the same as the temperature is changed. In general, it was stated, rupture analyses usually involve two to four different T' values.

When only one term of the Graham-Walles parameter equation is involved, equation (5-11) written for rupture is:

$$t_R(T' - T)^{-20} = f(\sigma) \qquad (5\text{-}23)$$

In such a case the stress-rupture isotherms have a shape identical to that given by the master-rupture plot relating the Graham-Walles parameter and stress. For example, if a linear relationship is obtained in the form:

$$\log t_R(T' - T)^{-20} = a - b \log \sigma \qquad (5\text{-}24)$$

then linear isotherms will be obtained on the log stress versus log rupture time plot. It will also be noted that all isotherms are parallel with a slope equal to b which is really the k/β value. Furthermore, the value of T' determines the spacing of the linear isotherms. An illustration of this behavior is presented in Figure 5-12 for an assumed stress dependency of the type given in equation (5-24). For this example, a value of b (i.e., k/β) was chosen equal to 1/4 from the Graham-Walles sequence. It will be noted that for $T' > T$ the isotherm spacing corresponding to equi-spaced temperatures increases as T increases. Also as T' decreases the spacing between two given isotherms increases. When $T' < T$ the results shown in Figure 5-13 apply using the same stress dependency as employed in Figure 5-12. In this case, the isotherm spacing decreases with increasing temperature, and as T' decreases the spacing between any two given isotherms decreases.

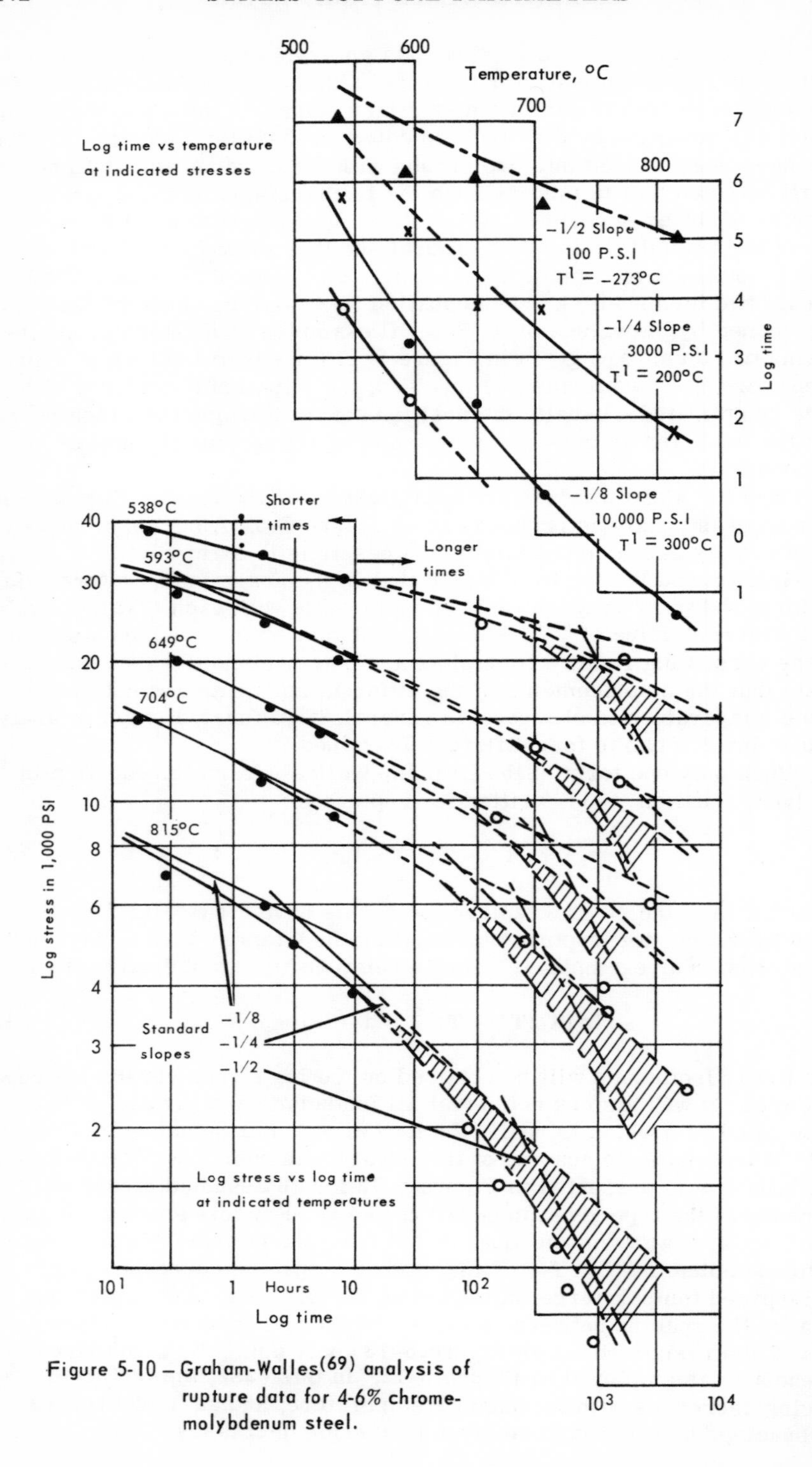

Figure 5-10 – Graham-Walles(69) analysis of rupture data for 4-6% chrome-molybdenum steel.

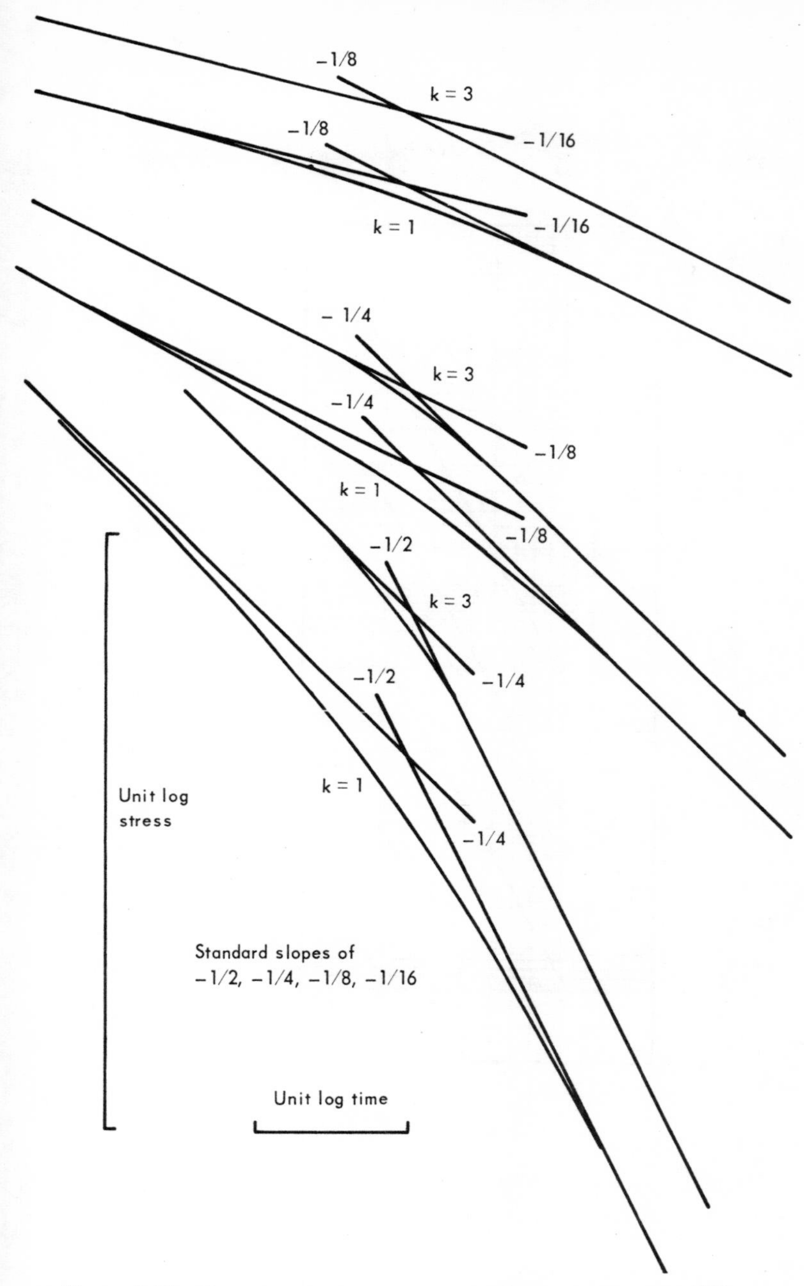

Figure 5-11 – Typical two-term master curves for several k values[69].

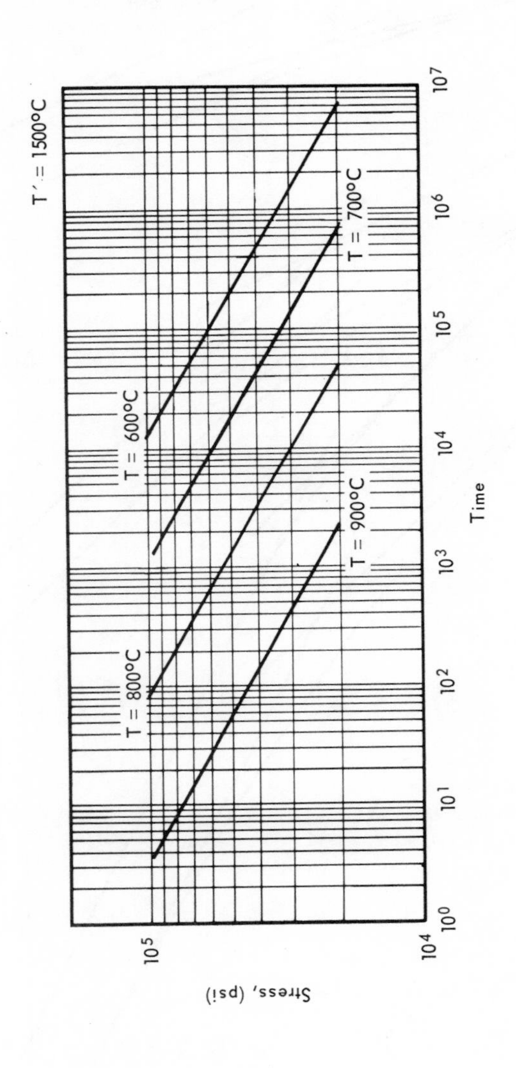

T′ = 1500°C
T = 600°C
T = 700°C
T = 800°C
T = 900°C
Stress, (psi)
10^5
10^4
Time
10^0
10^1
10^2
10^3
10^4
10^5
10^6
10^7

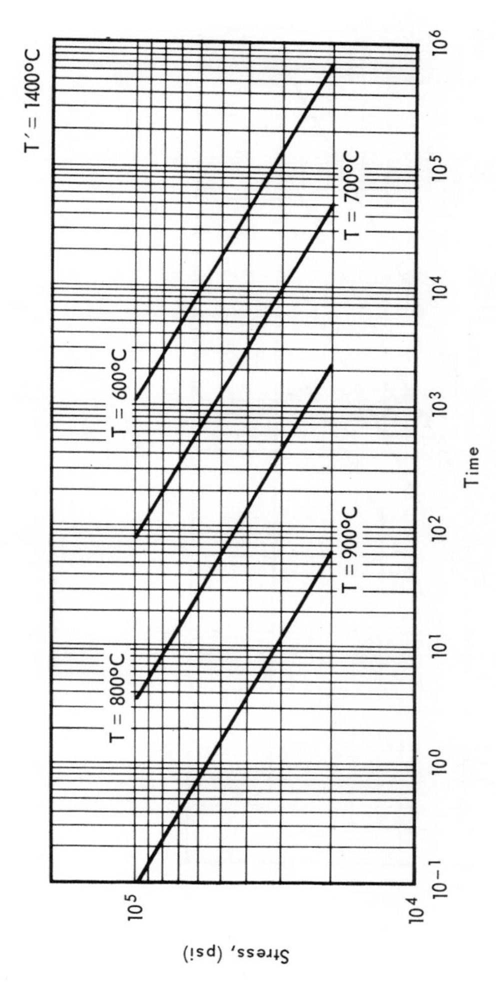

Figure 5-12 – Stress-rupture isotherms calculated from equation (5-24) for $T' > T$ using assumed stress dependency.

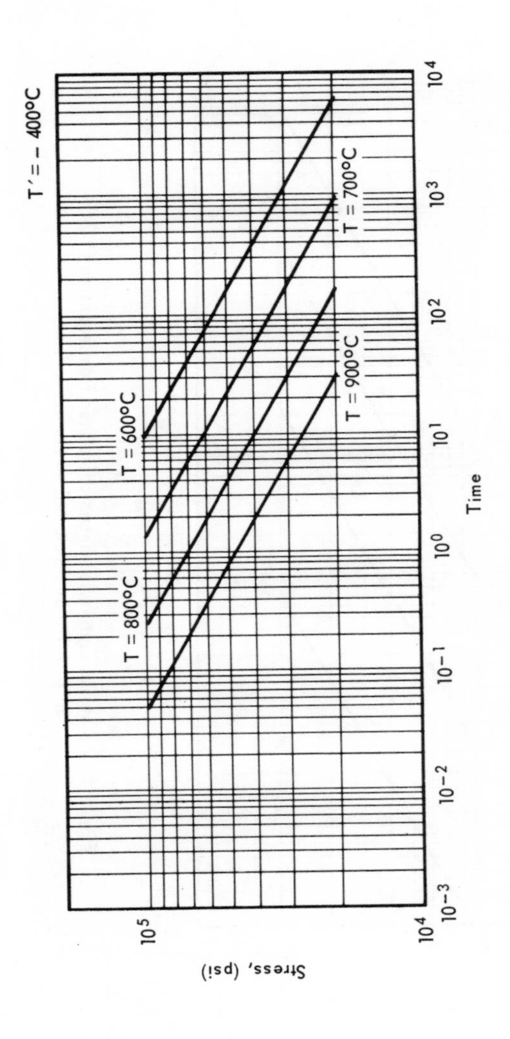

T′ = − 400°C
T = 600°C
T = 700°C
T = 800°C
T = 900°C
Stress, (psi)
10^5
10^4
Time
10^-3
10^-2
10^-1
10^0
10^1
10^2
10^3
10^4

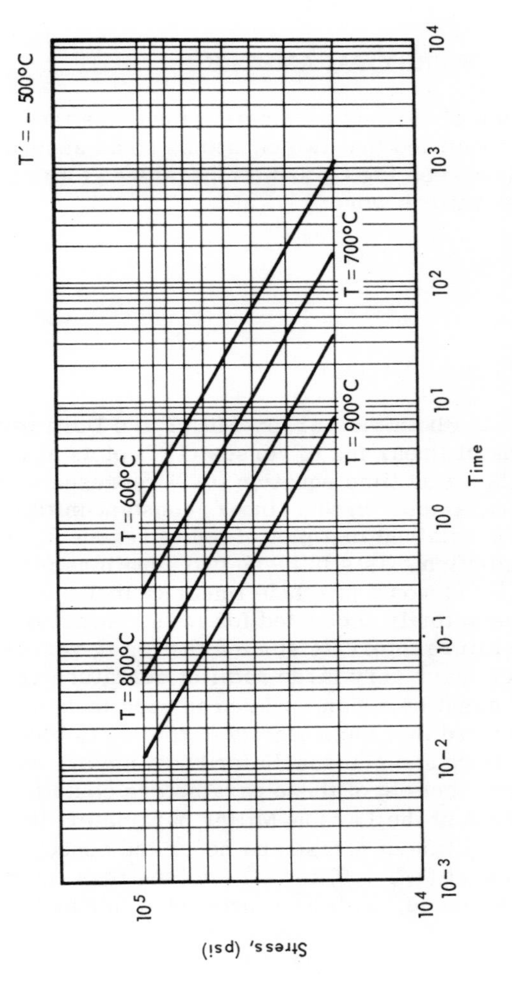

Figure 5-13 – Stress-rupture isotherms calculated from equation (5-24) for $T' < T$ using assumed stress dependency.

CHAPTER 6

MURRY PARAMETER

In a detailed examination of various parametric formulae (see Chapters 2, 3 and 4), Murry[31] concluded that two equations could accurately express the relationship between log t_R and temperature at a constant initial stress. These equations were:

$$\log t_R = \frac{F_1(\sigma_0)}{T} - F_2(\sigma_0) \tag{6-1}$$

and

$$\log t_R = f_2(\sigma_0) - T\, f_1(\sigma_0) \tag{6-2}$$

Equation (6-1) represented both the Larson-Miller and Dorn parametric approaches in admitting of linear log t_R versus (1/T) plots at constant initial stress, σ_0. At the same time equation (6-2) represented the form of the Manson-Haferd parameter in that linear, constant initial stress, relationships were to be obtained in a plot of log t_R versus T. It was noted that some contradiction exists in these two equations for it would seem that linearity in (1/T) would preclude linearity in T and vice versa However, this was satisfactorily accounted for in the observation that over the narrow temperature intervals studied the log t_R versus (1/T) and log t_R versus T plots have very large radii of curvature and hence both types of behavior might be accommodated in such instances.

While Murry concurred that the linearity of the log t_R plots dictated by the Larson-Miller, Dorn and Manson-Haferd parameters was readily observed a second characteristic of these parameters could not be substantiated. In the case of the Larson-Miller parameter, the constant C, was thought to be a function of stress and hence the concept of a common point of intersection at (1/T = 0) for all the isostress lines was considered not to be applicable. This is represented in equation (6-1) by the term $F_2(\sigma_0)$. Similarly, in the case of the Dorn parameter, the concept of parallel constant stress lines was not substantiated, hence, the $F_1(\sigma_0)$ term in equation (6-1). Finally, no common point of intersection for the constant stress lines on a log t_R versus T plot seemed to be justifiable as required by the Manson-Haferd approach. Hence the stress function, $f_2(\sigma_0)$, in equation (6-2) was employed to suggest this deviation from the Manson-Haferd assumption.

Having proposed the form of equations (6-1) and (6-2) for use in the correlation of stress-rupture behavior, Murry recognized the convenience which would result if the coefficients (stress functions) in these two expressions were simply related. In such a case it would probably be possible to evaluate these quantities from experimental data. Only one parameter varying with σ_0 would then be needed in applying these expressions and a new parametric approach would be defined.

In a study of the coefficients in equations (6-1) and (6-2), it was found that they varied with σ_0 in much the same way. However, it was also noted that the curves representing the variations of one coefficient in terms of the other did not suggest a simple relationship. Additional analyses were then performed which revealed linear relations between the slopes of the coefficient versus σ_0 plots. In other words, the quantity $\partial f_2(\sigma_0)/\partial\sigma_0$ or as a first approximation $\Delta f_2(\sigma_0)/\Delta\sigma_0$ was found to be linear in $\partial f_1(\sigma_0)/\partial\sigma_0$ or $\Delta f_1(\sigma_0)/\Delta\sigma_0$. A similar situation was observed for the coefficients in equation (6-1). This behavior is indicated graphically in Figure 6-1 and suggested to Murry the existance of the following relationships:

$$\frac{F_2(\sigma_0)}{\sigma_0} = n\,\frac{F_1(\sigma_0)}{\sigma_0} + p \qquad (6\text{-}3)$$

and

$$\frac{f_2(\sigma_0)}{\sigma_0} = m\,\frac{f_1(\sigma_0)}{\sigma_0} - r \qquad (6\text{-}4)$$

Results of analyses based on these expressions are presented in Figures 6-2 and 6-3 indicating quite excellent linearity. A least squares analysis of these linear plots led to the values of n, p, m and r for each material. These data are presented in Table 6-1.

Rearrangement of equations (6-3) and (6-4) yields:

$$F_2(\sigma_0) = n\,F_1(\sigma_0) + p\sigma_0 \qquad (6\text{-}5)$$

and

$$f_2(\sigma_0) = m\,f_1(\sigma_0) - r\sigma_0 \qquad (6\text{-}6)$$

Substitution of these expressions into equations (6-1) and (6-2) leads to:

$$\log t_R = F_1(\sigma_0)(1/T - n) - p\sigma_0 \qquad (6\text{-}7)$$

and

$$\log t_R = f_1(\sigma_0)(m - T) - r\sigma_0 \qquad (6\text{-}8)$$

which on simple rearrangement yield:

$$F(\sigma_0) = \frac{\log t_R - p\sigma_0}{\frac{1}{T} - n} \qquad (6\text{-}9)$$

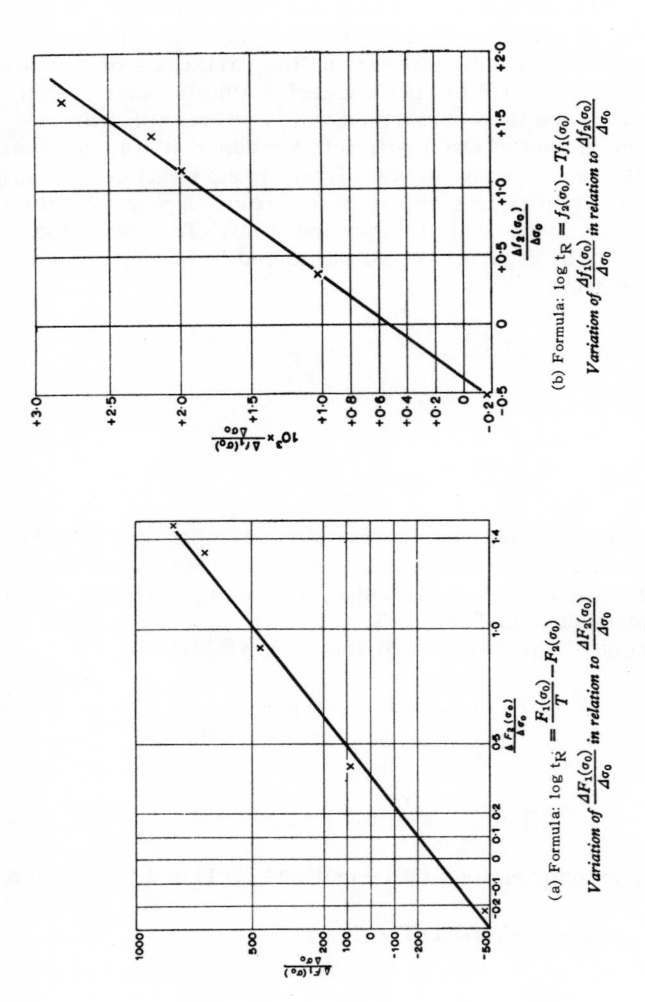

(a) Formula: $\log t_R = \frac{F_1(\sigma_0)}{T} - F_2(\sigma_0)$

Variation of $\frac{\Delta F_1(\sigma_0)}{\Delta\sigma_0}$ *in relation to* $\frac{\Delta F_2(\sigma_0)}{\Delta\sigma_0}$

(b) Formula: $\log t_R = f_2(\sigma_0) - Tf_1(\sigma_0)$

Variation of $\frac{\Delta f_1(\sigma_0)}{\Delta\sigma_0}$ *in relation to* $\frac{\Delta f_2(\sigma_0)}{\Delta\sigma_0}$

Figure 6-1 – Murry[31] analysis of data for A37 steel.

and

$$f(\sigma_0) = \frac{\log t_R - r\sigma_0}{m - T} \tag{6-10}$$

These two equations define two new parametric expressions for use in the analysis of stress-rupture behavior and represent the Murry parameters.

In both equations (6-9) and (6-10) the temperature, T, appears in such a way as to identify (1/n) and m as characteristic temperatures. Murry further noted that when T exceeds these values then log t_R will be a negative quantity and hence 1/n and m may be regarded as limit temperatures beyond which the creep strength is negligible. It was also observed that different equations give very similar values for 1/n and m for the same type of steel as indicated in the following:

Steel	1/n, °K	m, °K
A 37	1087	1103
2-1/4% Cr - 1% Mo	1071	1085
17-22 As	1088	1087
422	1054	1060
18% Cr - 12% Ni - Ti	1331	1344

Murry also noted that for all four α steels the 1/n and m values are very nearly equal and within the range 1054° to 1103°K (781° to 830°C). This temperature interval was recognized as corresponding to the start of the $\alpha \rightarrow \gamma$ transformation whereas the temperatures for the austenitic form are close to 1340°K or 1067°C. For the same four steels the coefficients p and r exhibit the same trend on going from the A37 steel to the 422 steel (see Table 6-1). Also the magnitude of these constants is inversely related to creep strength with the highest values being associated with the lowest creep strength (A37) and the lowest values associated with the highest creep strength (17-22AS and 422).

Plots of the parameter values shown in equations (6-9) and (6-10) have been prepared by Murry and are presented in Figure 6-4 expressed as a function of log σ_0. In general, these parameter plots seem to exhibit in the vicinity of 10 kfg/mm No claim was made that these parameters were capable of general application. Further study would seem to be in order before the real usefulness of the Murry approach can be assessed.

One minor shortcoming associated with the Murry parameters concerns the occurrence of T_R, T and σ_0 in the parameter value itself. Hence no direct solution is available to yield the stress corresponding to a certain rupture time at a given temperature. A trial and error solution can be employed in such a calculation but the approach is not as direct as that made available by the more widely used parametric approaches.

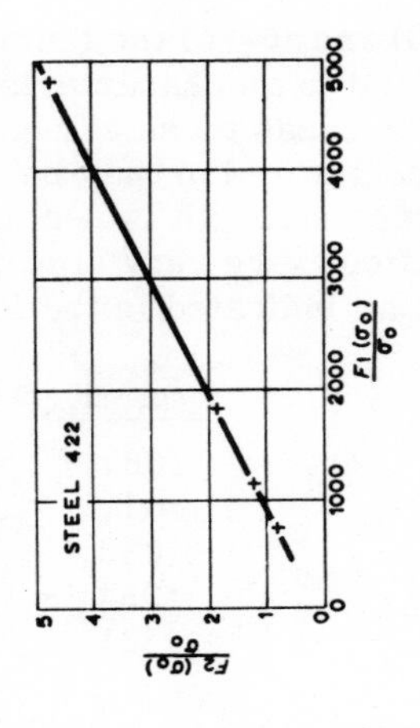
STEEL 422
$\frac{F_2(\sigma_0)}{\sigma_0}$
$\frac{F_1(\sigma_0)}{\sigma_0}$
0
1000
2000
3000
4000
5000
1
2
3
4
5

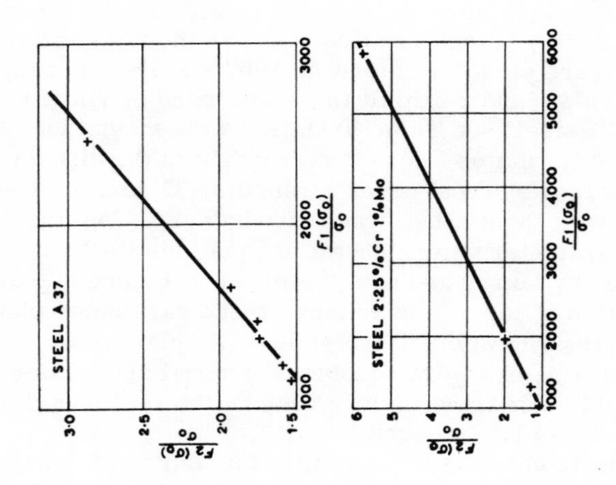
STEEL A 37
$\frac{F_2(\sigma_0)}{\sigma_0}$
$\frac{F_1(\sigma_0)}{\sigma_0}$
1000
2000
3000
1·5
2·0
2·5
3·0
STEEL 2·25%Cr 1%Mo
$\frac{F_2(\sigma_0)}{\sigma_0}$
$\frac{F_1(\sigma_0)}{\sigma_0}$
1000
2000
3000
4000
5000
6000
1
2
3
4
5
6

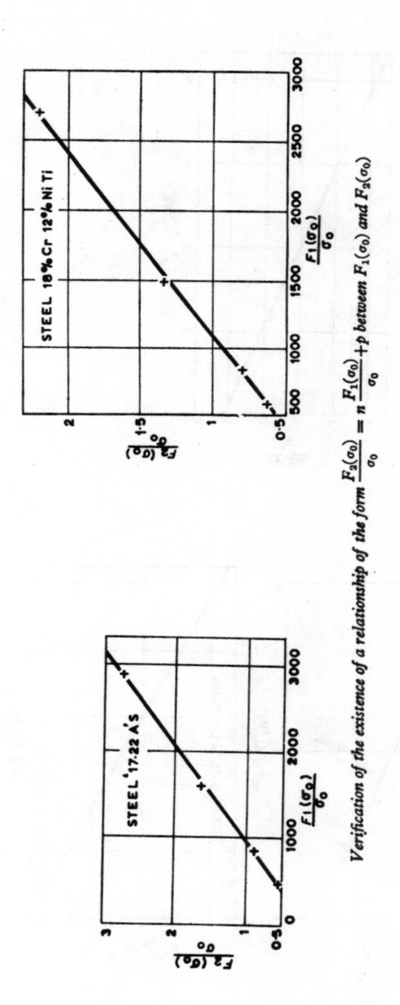

Verification of the existence of a relationship of the form $\frac{F_2(\sigma_0)}{\sigma_0} = n\frac{F_1(\sigma_0)}{\sigma_0} + p$ *between* $F_1(\sigma_0)$ *and* $F_2(\sigma_0)$

Figure 6-2 – Confirmation plot for equation (6-3).

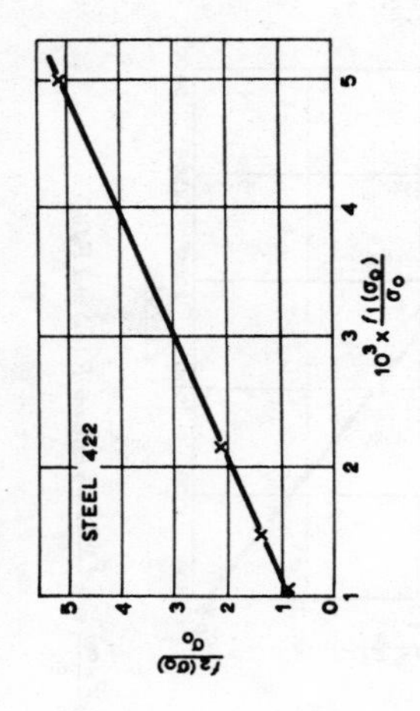
STEEL 422
$\frac{f_2(\sigma_0)}{\sigma_0}$
$10^3 \times \frac{f_1(\sigma_0)}{\sigma_0}$

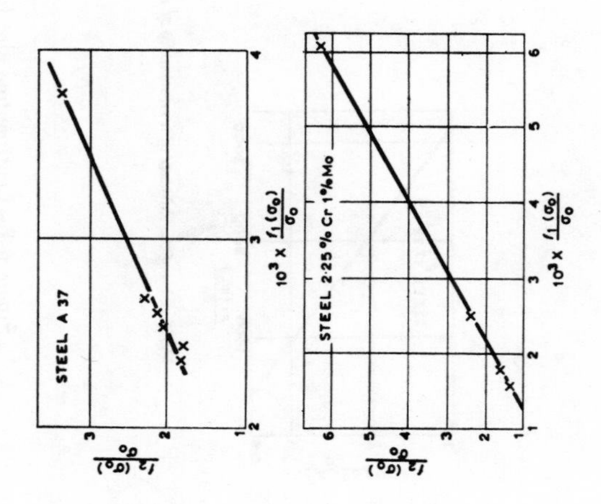
STEEL A 37
$\frac{f_2(\sigma_0)}{\sigma_0}$
$10^3 \times \frac{f_1(\sigma_0)}{\sigma_0}$
STEEL 2·25 % Cr 1 % Mo
$\frac{f_2(\sigma_0)}{\sigma_0}$
$10^3 \times \frac{f_1(\sigma_0)}{\sigma_0}$

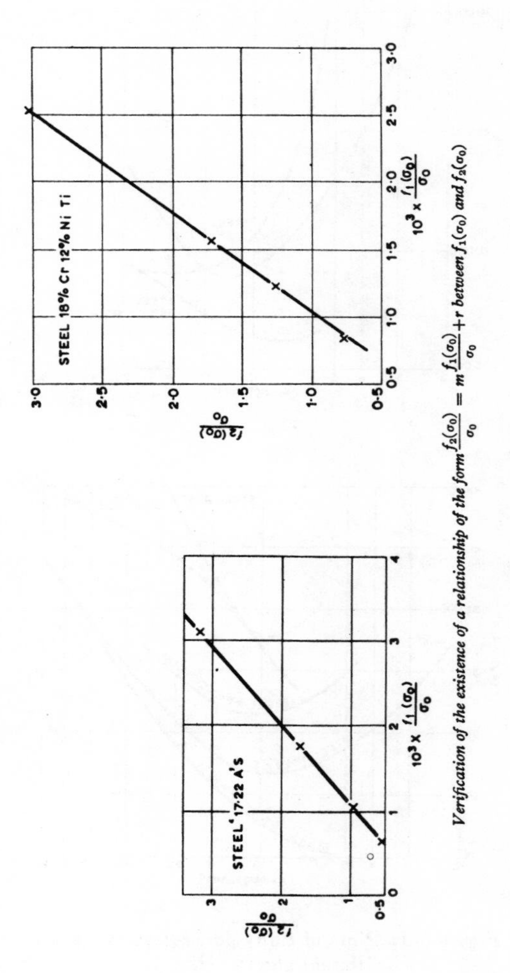

Verification of the existence of a relationship of the form $\frac{f_2(\sigma_0)}{\sigma_0} = m\frac{f_1(\sigma_0)}{\sigma_0} + r$ *between* $f_1(\sigma_0)$ *and* $f_2(\sigma_0)$

Figure 6-3 – Confirmation plot for equation (6-4).

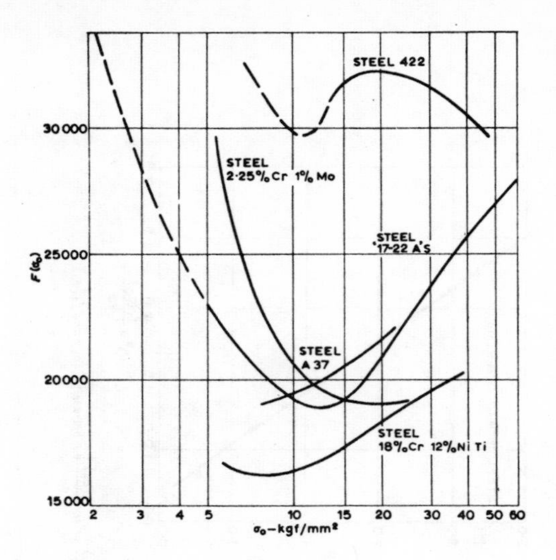

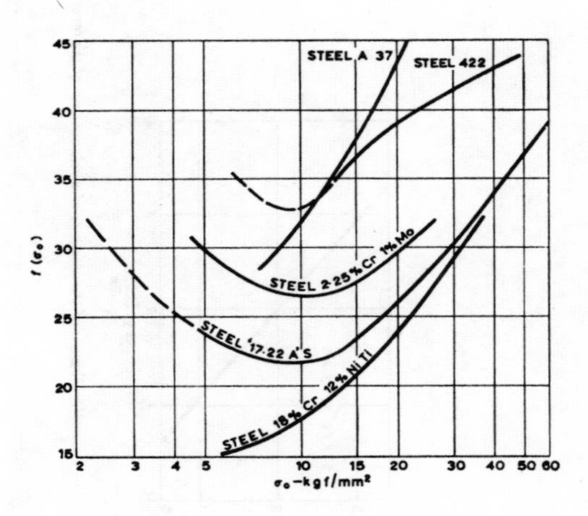

Figure 6-4 – Plots of Murry parameters for several different steels(31).

TABLE 6-1
SUMMARY OF COEFFICIENTS FOR EQUATIONS (6-3) AND (6-4)[31]

Formula: $\log t_R = \frac{F_1(\sigma_0)}{T} - F_2(\sigma_0)$

Determination of coefficients of the equation

$$\frac{F_2(\sigma_0)}{\sigma_0} = n\frac{F_1(\sigma_0)}{\sigma_0} + p$$

Steel	p	n	$\frac{1}{n}$ °K	Linear correlation coefficient
'A 37'	0·444 21	$0{\cdot}9200 \times 10^{-3}$	1087	> 0·99
'2·25% Cr–1% Mo'	0·198 28	$0{\cdot}9333 \times 10^{-3}$	1071	> 0·99
'17–22 A'S . .	0·126 24	$0{\cdot}9194 \times 10^{-3}$	1088	> 0·99
'422'	0·146 62	$0{\cdot}9492 \times 10^{-3}$	1054	> 0·99
'18% Cr–12% Ni–Ti'	0·190 55	$0{\cdot}7512 \times 10^{-3}$	1331	> 0·99

Formula: $\log t_R = f_2(\sigma_0) - Tf_1(\sigma_0)$

Determination of coefficients of the equation

$$\frac{f_2(\sigma_0)}{\sigma_0} = m\frac{f_1(\sigma_0)}{\sigma_0} - r$$

Steel	r	m °K	Linear correlation coefficient
'A 37'	0·766 53	1103	> 0·99
'2·25% Cr–1% Mo' .	0·315 64	1085	> 0·99
'17–22 A'S	0·160 36	1087	> 0·99
'422'	0·198 91	1060	> 0·99
'18% Cr–12% Ni–Ti'	0·386 68	1344	> 0·99

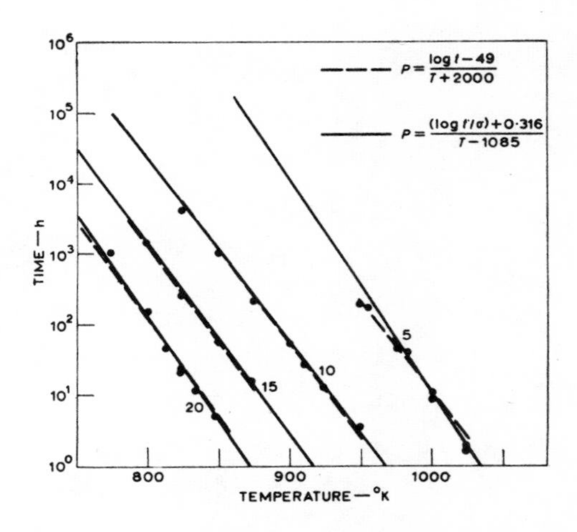

Figure 6-5 – Comparison of linear and Murry parameters for 2-1/4% Cr – 1% Mo steel[61].

In a discussion of the Murry parameters Manson[61] pointed out that a slight rearrangement of the Murry parameter in equation (6-10) leads to:

$$\frac{f(\sigma_0)}{\sigma_0} = \frac{\dfrac{\log t}{\sigma_0} - r}{m - T} \qquad (6\text{-}11)$$

which is identical in form to one variation of the general parameter prepared by Manson[56] and given in equation (4-34). A consideration of both these forms suggests linearity in log t_R / σ_0 versus T instead of log t_R versus T as follows from the linear parameter.

It was pointed out by Manson that the Murry conclusion, that the stress-modified parameter leads to a more effective correlation especially in the case of the data for 2-1/4% Cr - 1% Mo steel, is subject to some doubt. Manson felt that the increase in effectiveness was only marginal. Using optimized constants in both cases the comparison in Figure 6-5 reveals that the linear and stress-modified parameters yield results which are not too different.

CHAPTER 7

BROZZO PARAMETER

It is generally accepted that the parametric approaches discussed in previous chapters provide various techniques for use in summarizing, correlating and comparing stress-rupture results. It is also fairly well accepted that these procedures afford satisfactory methods in making at least approximate extrapolations of short-term data. Unfortunately, none of these parametric approaches has been found to be completely accurate in every instance. There is also some question regarding the range of test variables over which these extrapolation procedures can be applied satisfactorily. Each parametric approach is based on certain basic assumptions and only when a given set of data exhibits behavior which is consistent with these assumptions will a given parametric approach be completely applicable.

Since some questions still arise regarding the general applicability of parametric formulae to the extrapolation of experimental data, some alternate approaches to be used in data extrapolation continue to be proposed. One such procedure worthy of consideration is that of Brozzo; and while this is not a parametric approach, it is included in this text because it is related to the type of extrapolation usually performed by stress-rupture parameters.

Citing the work of Grant,[37] a complexity in certain stress-rupture data was emphasized. Based on studies dealing with materials ranging from pure aluminum to the S590 and S816 alloys, Grant and his co-workers observed a transition in stress-rupture behavior at certain test conditions. When the familiar log σ versus log t_R plot was employed, the stress-rupture isotherms were as presented in Figure 7-1. At certain different stress levels, depending on the temperature, a definite change in slope of the stress-rupture isotherms was noted. It was established that this transition represented a change in the deformation behavior with the fracture being transcrystalline at the higher stresses and intergranular at the lower stresses. A similar transition in behavior was observed in a plot of log stress versus log minimum creep rate. In the rupture plot of Figure 7-1 the line or curve S'S defines the locus of transition points and represents the dividing line between transcrystalline and intergranular behavior.

It is important to note that the type of behavior represented in Figure 7-1 would pose some particularly difficult problems in any parametric approach. Such changes in slope represent changes in material behavior and it is almost impossible for stress-rupture parameters thus

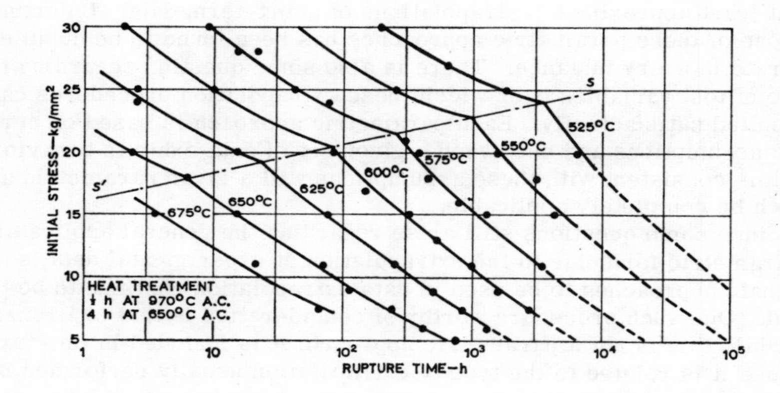

Figure 7-1 – Rupture time versus initial stress for a 2-1/4% Cr – 1% Mo steel[28].

far proposed to cope with this complicated behavior. That these different modes of deformation would introduce complications was specifically emphasized by Brozzo in concluding that:

(a) From the point of view of the correlation of creep and stress-rupture data, each range must be taken into consideration individually. In particular, it may be easily predicted that, when a given correlation has been found reliable in one range, any attempt to extend the use of this correlation into the other range may result in considerable error.

(b) Since the transition points appear to be located at different stress levels, which depend on temperature, the results obtained from a series of constant stress tests may be heterogeneous in nature. In fact the higher temperature data (i. e. those located on the left of the separating line) will belong to the transcrystalline range while the other data will fall into the intergranular region. This can clearly constitute a primary cause of curvature in the plots of isostatic data versus the reciprocal of the absolute temperature.

In the Brozzo approach to the extrapolation of stress-rupture data, the relation between stress, temperature and the log of the rupture time was assumed to be represented by:

$$\log t_R = F(\sigma, T) \tag{7-1}$$

Considering for the moment the intergranular range of Figure 7-1, it was noted that the absolute value of the slope of each isotherm continuously decreases with decreasing stress.* Furthermore, no matter what the stress level, the slopes of two given isotherms appear to be nearly in the same ratio which is characteristic of the chosen pair of temperatures. Based on these observations, it was inferred by Brozzo that within the intergranular range being considered the partial derivative of equation (7-1) with respect to stress can be generally expressed as the product of two distinct continuous functions, one of stress, the other of temperature. Thus:

$$\frac{\partial \log t_R}{\partial \sigma} = f(\sigma) \cdot g(T) \tag{7-2}$$

It thus follows that the ratio of the slopes at σ_1 for T_1 and T_2 will be:

$$\frac{\left(\dfrac{\partial \log t_R}{\partial \sigma}\right)_1}{\left(\dfrac{\partial \log t_R}{\partial \sigma}\right)_2} = \frac{f(\sigma_1) \cdot g(T_1)}{f(\sigma_1) \cdot g(T_2)} = \frac{g(T_1)}{g(T_2)} \tag{7-3}$$

*Other cases can be cited in which the isotherms exhibit a constant slope over a certain range of stress but they are never concave downward. These characteristics have been observed by Grant and Bucklin[38] and Betteridge[39] for a number of different materials.

At σ_2 for T_1 and T_2

$$\frac{\left(\frac{\partial \log t_R}{\partial \sigma}\right)_1}{\left(\frac{\partial \log t_R}{\partial \sigma}\right)_2} = \frac{f(\sigma_2) \cdot g(T_1)}{f(\sigma_2) \cdot g(T_2)} = \frac{g(T_1)}{g(T_2)} \tag{7-4}$$

Hence the ratio of the slopes for a given pair of isotherms will be the same independent of stress and will be determined by T_1 and T_2.

In some concluding remarks Brozzo noted that:

(a) It is very probable that the pattern of isothermal lines traced in Figure 7-1 is somewhat idealized and therefore equation (7-2) is only approximated. In fact, some details of the plots, such as local variations of slope which can give rise to discontinuities, might well remain unrevealed unless the number of tests is greatly increased. However, this should not introduce serious error in extrapolation, even if present, due to the limited dispersion of the experimental points around the traced curves.

(b) By examini Figure 7-1, as well as those that will be presented later, it is clearly suggested that in the intergranular range the separation between two given isothermals can never increase with decreasing stress. This feature, although not essential for extrapolation purposes, can be helpful in plotting short-time data. In fact, it implies that, if all data belong to the intergranular range, at a given stress level, the slope of the isothermal lines can never increase with increasing temperature. Such a rule, moreover, applies "a fortiori" to a given test time, since the isothermals are concave upward.

(c) In connection with the latter point, it must be recalled that the observed trend of the separation between two given isothermals is in accordance, in a qualitative sense, to the well-known Manson-Haferd parameter.[36] This parameter, however, cannot account for the discontinuous behavior of the above separation which is associated with the transition in the appearance of fracture. Moreover, an appreciable error may arise from its application for extrapolation purposes since the isostatic plots of log time versus temperature are not generally straight, as already noted. Further evidence is shown in Figure 7-2 where data from Figure 7-1 have been replotted to obtain six isostatic lines. In particular, it is noteworthy that in a given range of temperature, namely from 525°C to 625°C, a quite different trend is exhibited by the isostatics at 30 and 25 kg/mm^2 in comparison with those at lower stress. This is apparently due to the fact that the high stress curves are well within the transcrystalline range, whereas the other curves belong, either wholly or in part, to the intergranular region.

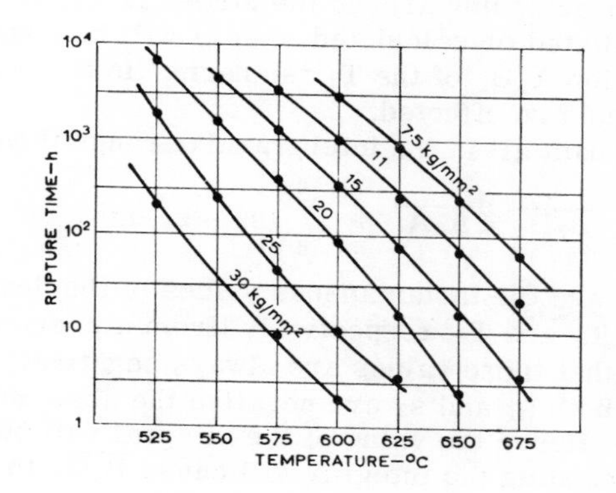

Figure 7-2 – Isostatic plots of rupture time versus temperature for a 2-1/4% Cr – 1% Mo steel(28).

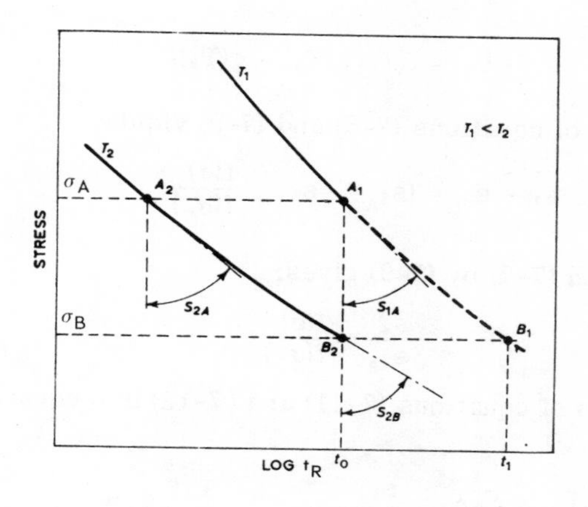

Figure 7-3 – Illustration of Brozzo extrapolation procedure(28).

An explanation of the Brozzo extrapolation procedure is provided by reference to Figure 7-3 where data at two temperatures, T_1 and T_2, are indicated up to a rupture time of t_0. On this plot of stress versus log time it is to be further noted that the stress ranges covered at T_1 and T_2 are slightly overlapping around the stress level σ_A. Now, if the leng $\overline{B_2B_1}$ can be predicted or calculated, then it will be possible to establish the unknown portion A_1B_1 of the T_1 isotherm. In this way extrapolation of the T_1 data would be effected.

Considering data all in the intergranular range then:

$$\overline{B_2B_1} = \overline{A_2A_1} - \int_{\sigma_B}^{\sigma_A}(s_1 - s_2)d\sigma \tag{7-5}$$

where s_1 and s_2 are the instantaneous values of the derivative (∂ log t_R/ at temperatures T_1 and T_2, respectively (from a previous remark it will be remembered that these values are always negative). It will be recog- nized that while both s_1 and s_2 are negative the absolute value of s_1 is smaller than s_2. Hence the value of the integral will be positive and the negative sign preceding the integral will cause $\overline{B_2B_1}$ to be less than $\overline{A_2A}$

Using equation (7-2) it is possible to write:

$$s_1 = f(\sigma) \cdot g(T_1) \tag{7-6}$$

$$s_2 = f(\sigma) \cdot g(T_2) \tag{7-7}$$

and

$$s_{1_A} = f(\sigma_A) \cdot g(T_1) \tag{7-8}$$

$$s_{2_A} = f(\sigma_A) \cdot g(T_2) \tag{7-9}$$

Therefore:

$$s_1 - s_2 = f(\sigma)\,[g(T_1) - g(T_2)] \tag{7-10}$$

and substitution of equations (7-8) and (7-9) yields:

$$s_1 - s_2 = (s_{1_A} - s_{2_A})\,\frac{f(\sigma)}{f(\sigma_A)} \tag{7-11}$$

Dividing equation (7-7) by (7-9) gives:

$$\frac{s_2}{s_{2_A}} = \frac{f(\sigma)}{f(\sigma_A)} \tag{7-12}$$

Now substitution of equations (7-11) and (7-12) into equation (7-5) result in:

$$\overline{B_2B_1} = \overline{A_2A_1} - \frac{s_{1_A} - s_{2_A}}{s_{2_A}} \int_{\sigma_B}^{\sigma_A} s_2\, d\sigma \tag{7-13}$$

which allows the T_1 isotherm to be extrapolated to time t_1. If for sim- plicity it is supposed that the derivative s_2 varies linearly with stress between σ_A and σ_B then the integral in equation (7-13) can be written as:

$$\int_{\sigma_B}^{\sigma_A} s_2 \, d\sigma = \frac{s_{2_A} + s_{2_B}}{2} (\sigma_A - \sigma_B) \qquad (7\text{-}14)$$

Therefore:

$$\overline{B_2 B_1} = \overline{A_2 A_1} - \left(\frac{s_{1_A} - s_{2_A}}{2}\right)\left(1 + \frac{s_{2_B}}{s_{2_A}}\right)(\sigma_A - \sigma_B) \qquad (7\text{-}15)$$

where only the values of the derivative at points A_1, A_2 and B_2 are required in order to make the extrapolation.*

A special case quite frequently encountered involves the situation when there is no appreciable difference between s_{1_A} and s_{2_A}. This, of course, corresponds to parallel isotherms in which case equation (7-15) specifies:

$$\overline{B_2 B_1} = \overline{A_2 A_1} \qquad (7\text{-}16)$$

It will be recognized that no extrapolation below σ_B in Figure 7-3 is possible since no value for the new stress (say σ_C) would be obtainable for the T_2 isotherm. Hence, the term s_{2_B} (now s_{2_C} though for extrapolation below σ_B) in equation (7-15) could not be evaluated. Of course, the linearity mentioned in connection with equation (7-14) could be employed to obtain s_{2_C} but then the $\overline{B_2 B_1}$ (now $\overline{C_2 C_1}$) value would have to be referenced to an extended portion of the T_2 isotherm. Integration of the s_2 equation, assumed linear in stress, could be employed to extend this isotherm but little confidence can be placed in this type of extension of this procedure. Naturally, if another isotherm was available to the left of T_2, this could be used to extend the T_2 curve which could then be used to extend the T_1 curve, etc.

Several examples of the extrapolation method just described were presented by Brozzo and are presented now. It was pointed out that the intergranular range of data has particular commercial significance simply because in most instances the design life is rather large and hence the stress levels are comparatively low. This combination causes attention to be focused on the intergranular range of material behavior. In the extrapolation approach, therefore, it is important to restrict consideration to those experimental data which fall in this regime. In this way, the extrapolations will have the best accuracy. Any experimental program, therefore, designed to provide data for use in extrapolation to longer term results should be so organized to first of all identify the transition area identified as line S'S in Figure 7-1; following this identification, it is then necessary to generate enough data in the intergranular

*It was noted by Brozzo that the second term on the right-hand side of equation (7-15), is always fairly small and represents merely a correction for the first term. Thus, only small error is expected in this method even if appreciable error is made in evaluating the correction.

range to allow for meaningful extrapolation within this region. An important observation was made pertinent to the fact that the transition behavior occurs at relatively short times for certain materials (fcc alloys for instance) and hence the test program does not involve lengthy tests to generate intergranular data. In the case of the bcc alloys, however, the transition is realized after longer time periods and the generation of the type of data required involves a time consuming test program.

In the illustrations given (including Figure 7-1), the portions of the isotherms based on experimental results are drawn as solid lines or curves (positioned visually rather than statistically using least squares) while the extrpolated portions are represented by a dashed curve or line Also, long term experimental points, when available, have been positione on these plots to provide an indication of the effectiveness of the extrapolation procedure.

Examples of several cases in which all data are located in the intergranular range are presented in Figures 7-4, 7-5 and 7-6. Since the slope of the isothermals exhibited no appreciable temperature dependenc it was possible to make use of equation (7-16). In this way the dashed (extrapolated) portions of the isotherms were positioned. For the data given in Figure 7-7, the use of equation (7-16) was not warranted. Instead the more exact equation (7-15) was employed. It was necessary to disregard the 650°C isotherm momentarily since this behavior was not consistent with the decreasing slope concept discussed previously under item (b). This example provides an illustration of the use of this extrapolation procedure in connection with other than rupture data.

A very particular case is presented in Figure 7-8. In the stress range from 6 to 30 tons/in.^{2}, the short-term isothermals appear to be straight. In this case, the usual straight line extrapolation is justified and is so indicated.

An example of some data in which the transition region is clearly evident is presented in Figure 7-9. Very good agreement between extrapolated and experimental results is easily recognized.

In Figure 7-10, an example is given in which the transition occurs at fairly long times at the lowest temperature and as a result few data are available for this isotherm. As a result the value for s_{1_A} (see Figure 7-3) to be used in equation (7-15) is difficult to obtain. Aside from obtaining additional tests at this temperature, it is possible to employ an approximate procedure. It is assumed that at constant stress and within a limited temperature range, the value of the derivative ($\partial \log t_R/\partial \sigma$) is linearly related to temperature. This procedure was actually employed in Figure 7-10 as well as at the lowest temperature of Figure 7-7 and as will be noted the accuracy seems quite satisfactory

In the example shown in Figure 7-11 the intergranular range in the region of the lower temperature was not defined experimentally. In this case the transition behavior at the higher temperature was assumed to apply in the lower temperature region and the line S'S was extended to define the intergranular region at the lower temperatures. Then equation (7-16) was assumed applicable in both the transcrystalline

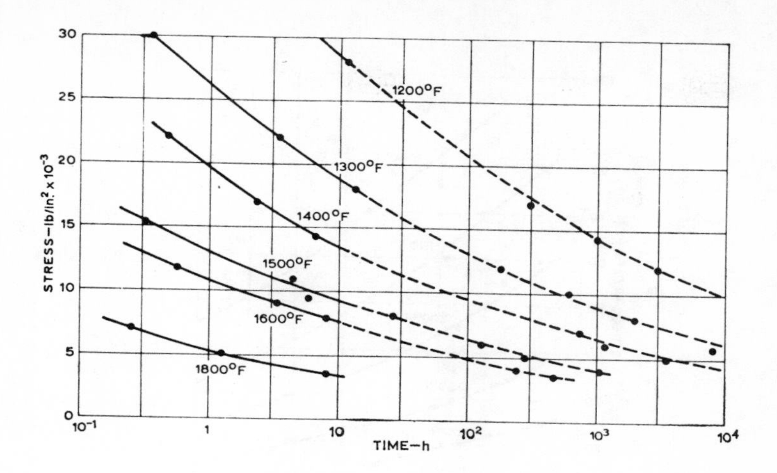

Figure 7-4 – Extrapolation of stress-rupture data for 18-8 stainless steel(28).

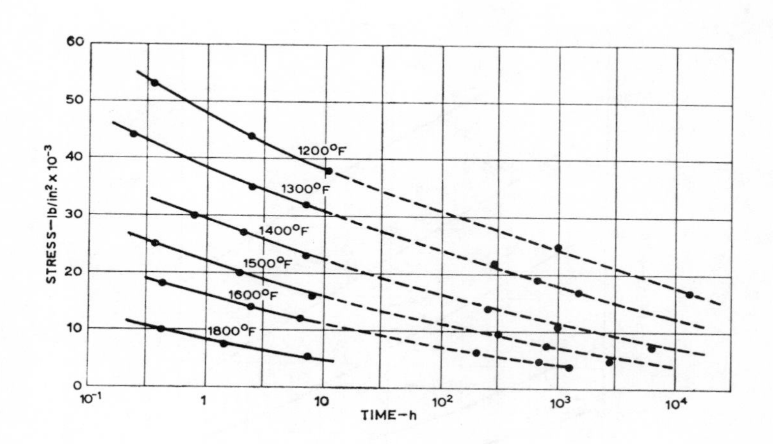

Figure 7-5 – Extrapolation of stress-rupture data for 16-13-3 stainless steel(28).

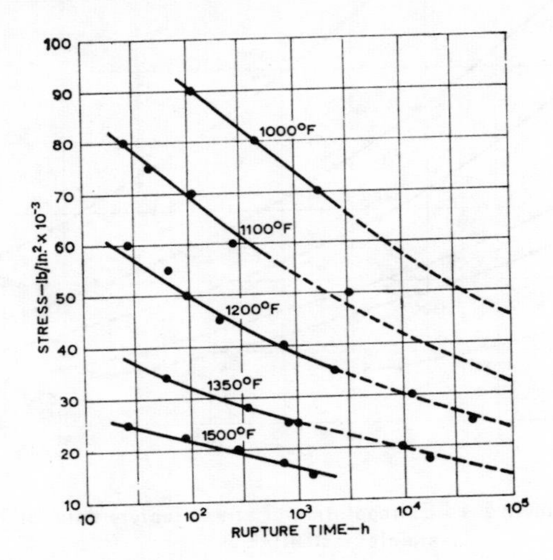

Figure 7-6 – Extrapolation of stress-rupture data for S590 alloy(28).

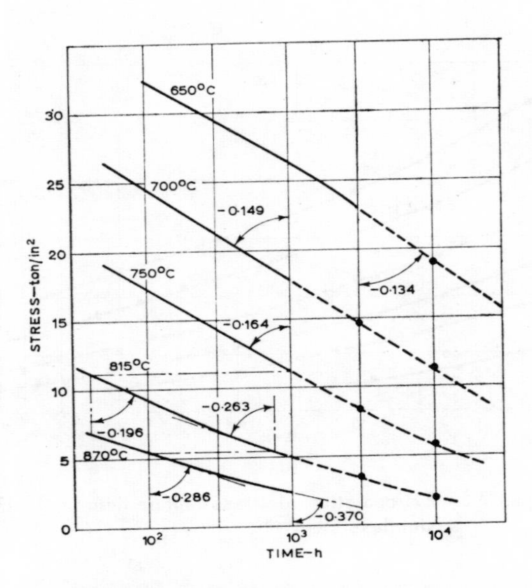

Figure 7-7 – Extrapolation of 0.2 percent elongation data for Nimonic 90 alloy(28).

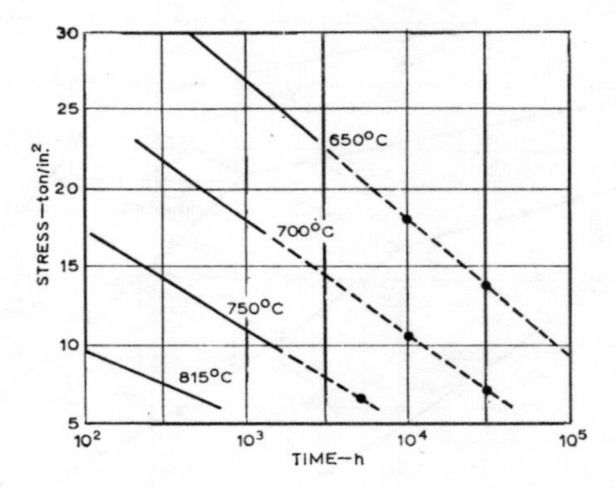

Figure 7-8 – Extrapolation of 0.5 percent elongation data for Nimonic 80A alloy[28].

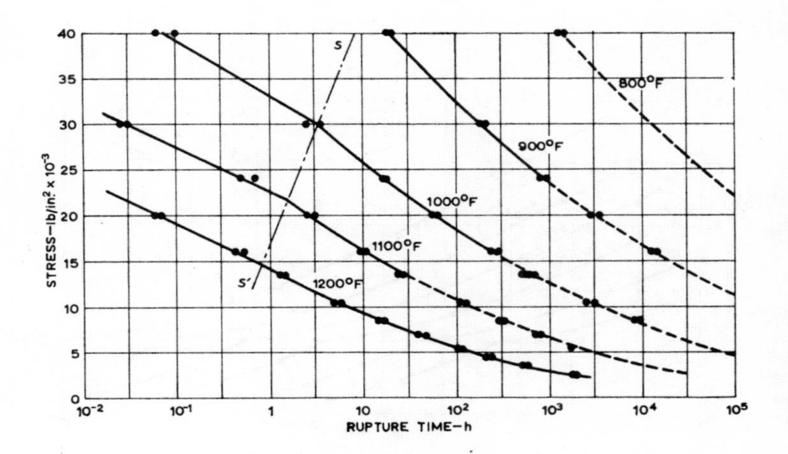

Figure 7-9 – Extrapolations of stress-rupture data for killed carbon steel[28].

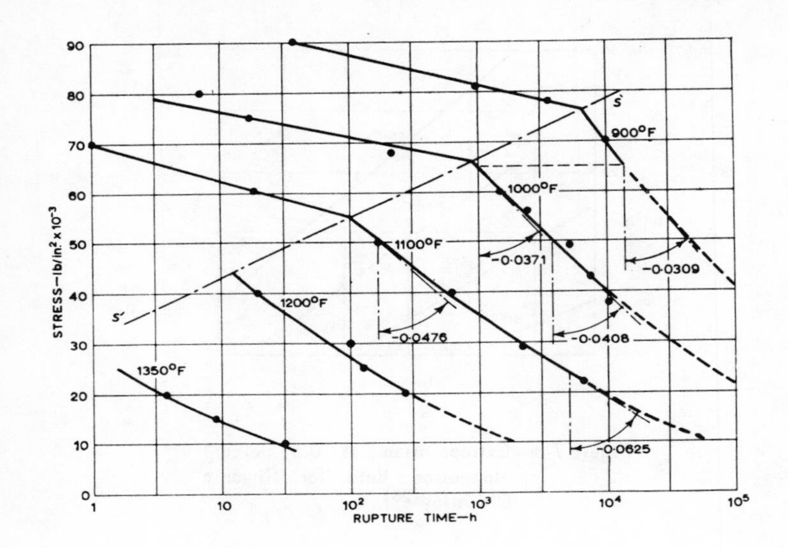

Figure 7-10 – Extrapolation of stress-rupture data for 1% Cr – 1% Mo – 1/4% V steel(28).

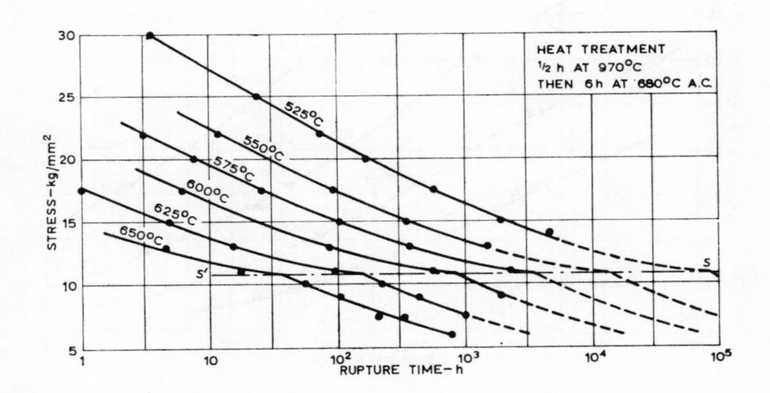

Figure 7-11 – Extrapolation of stress-rupture data for 2-1/4% Cr – 1% Mo steel(28).

and intergranular regions to define the extrapolated portions of the isotherms not established experimentally. Some reservation, of course, is to be attached to this approach in view of the uncertainity of the assumptions employed.

CHAPTER 8

CHITTY-DUVAL PARAMETER

While the correlation approach proposed by Chitty and Duval[63] has not been widely used and has not been generally referred to as a stress-rupture parameter, it does have parametric form and hence has been in cluded in the present discussions.

In studying the rupture data for steam pipe and tube steels, Chitty and Duval concluded that neither the Larson-Miller, Dorn or Manson-Haferd parameter was completely applicable. Although plots of log t_R versus T or (1/T) yielded straight lines, it did not appear that these lines exhibited a common point of intersection (see Figure 8-1c). Since such a condition is specified by all the parameters considered, it was felt that the use of these in the analysis would lead to only approximate results. Instead a new approach was proposed which it was felt gave a more realistic representation of the material behavior.

Referring to the data presented in Figure 8-1a, Chitty and Duval noted the linearity shown in Figure 8-1c. No common point of intersection, however, seemed to be indicated. Expressing the behavior in Figure 8-1c as:

$$T = m \log t_R + d \tag{8-1}$$

it followed directly that at constant stress:

$$\left(\frac{\partial T}{\partial \log t_R}\right)_\sigma = m \tag{8-2}$$

and then:

$$d = T - \left(\frac{\partial T}{\partial \log t_R}\right)_\sigma \log t_R \tag{8-3}$$

where the quantity, d, can be considered to be a stress-rupture parameter.

For the data analyzed by Chitty and Duval, it was observed that a plot of the slope of the constant stress lines in Figure 8-1c as a function of stress yielded a linear relationship on logarithmic coordinates as shown in Figure 8-1d (linearity here, while convenient, is not necessary to the use of this approach). Such line..rity requires that:

$$\left(\frac{\partial T}{\partial \log t_R}\right)_\sigma = a\sigma^b \tag{8-4}$$

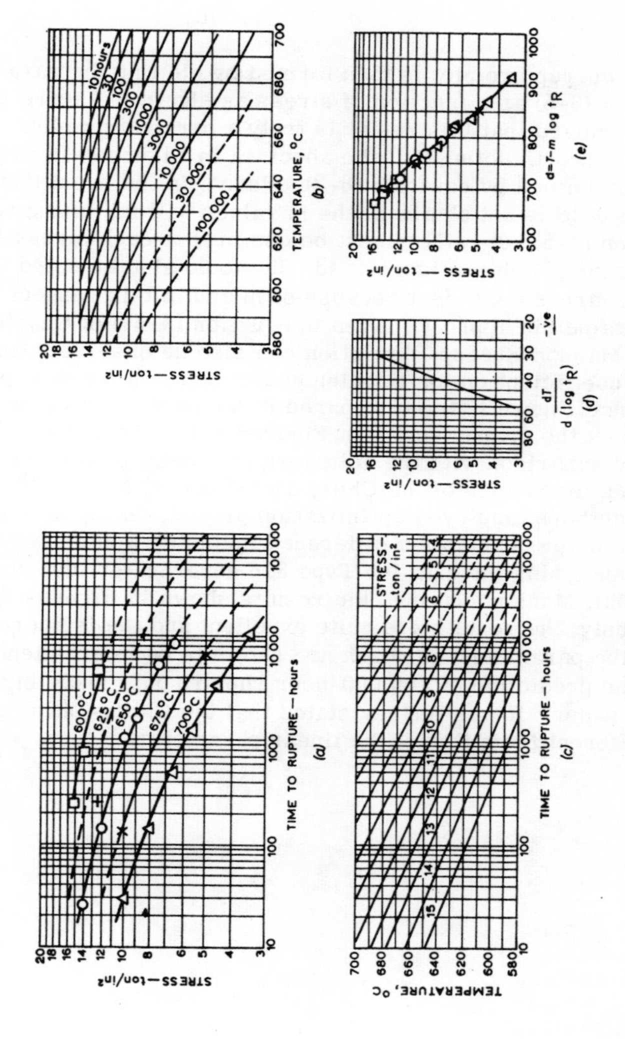

Figure 8-1 – Chitty-Duval analysis of data for 316 steel(63)

and substitution in equation (8-3) yields:

$$d = T - a\sigma^b \log t_R \tag{8-5}$$

A master-rupture plot is then formed by plotting the parameter in equation (8-5) as a function of stress as shown in Figure 8-1e. It will be recognized that this result is truly a parametric plot.

It is worth noting that the abscissa in Figure 8-1e is given in terms of m as defined by equation (8-2). Hence, in the event that linearity in Figure 8-1d is not obtained, the m values will not be expressed as in equation (8-5) but rather must be obtained at each stress level by consulting the graph in Figure 8-1d. It should also be noted that this parameter is stress dependent because of m and in this respect is similar to the parametric approach given in equation (4-34) of Chapter 4. Similarity to the Manson-Succop[46] relation can also be observed except that instead of the coefficient on log t_R being constant it is a function of stress.

Once Figure 8-1e is prepared it can be used in the usual fashion to construct the graphs shown in Figures 8-1a, -1b and 1c. In this way the usual comparison with the actual experimental points is allowed.

In a discussion of the Chitty-Duval paper, Manson[61] felt that had these authors employed optimization procedures in their determination of parameter constants a different conclusion would have been reached. In re-analyzing the data for Type 316 superheater tube and steam pipe material, Manson obtained the results shown in Figures 8-2 and -3. Obviously, the results are quite excellent and the isotherms constructed from the parameter approach are shown to be in excellent agreement with the prediction of 100,000-hour rupture data made in the Chitty-Duval paper. It was further stated that the Chitty-Duval approach is not too different from that of the linear parameter.

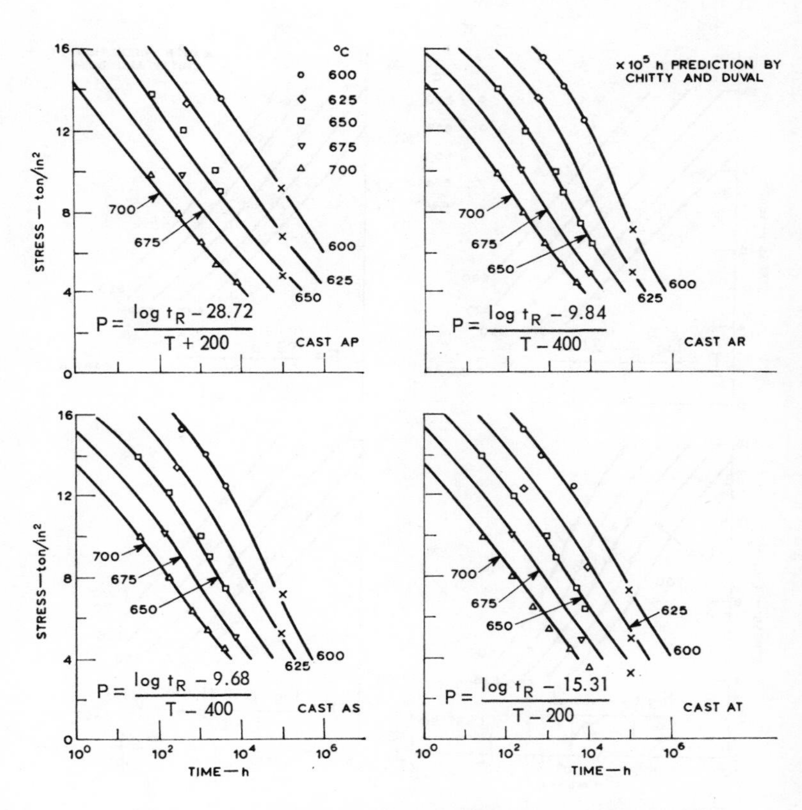

Figure 8-2 – Manson-Haferd analysis of Type 316 superheater tube material(61).

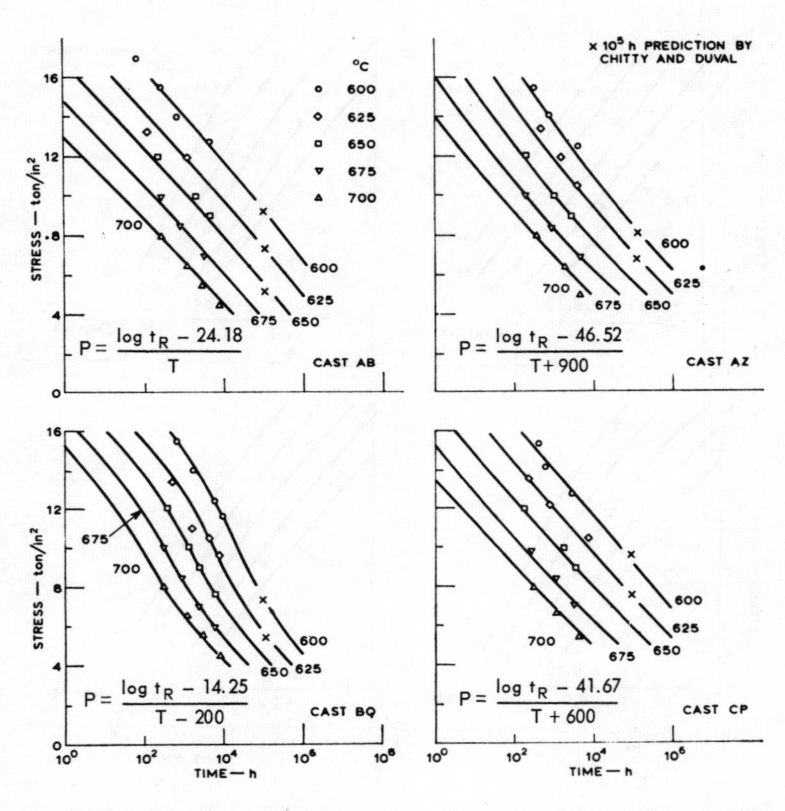

Figure 8-3 – Manson-Haferd analysis of Type 316 steam pipe material[61].

CHAPTER 9

COMPARISON OF PARAMETER EFFECTIVENESS

Following the previous discussions of the various parameters, it seems in order at this point to discuss the relative effectiveness of these devices. In this section, however, consideration is limited to the Dorn, Larson-Miller and Manson-Haferd parameters because these are the most widely used in this country. It might also be said that these three parameters have been studied in more detail and for this reason have been developed to a greater degree.

In comparing parameter effectiveness, a good starting point should be a clarification of just what is meant by "parameter effectiveness." As might be expected, no simple answer can be given to this question. In general it can be said, however, that the parameter which provides the best accuracy in achieving the objective of the analysis of the available experimental data, whether it be stress-rupture, creep rate or creep strain data, must be considered the most effective. In other words, parameters can be judged in terms of how well they:

(1) Correlate experimental data; this applies to the development of a consistent relationship between the variables of stress, temperature and rupture time (at least for stress-rupture data); such a relationship might take the form of a graph in which data at various stresses and temperatures plot to yield a smooth curve or line; similar plots for other materials could then be combined or compared to allow the relative strengths of the materials to be assessed.

(2) Interpolation of data; this implies the generation of data at temperatures intermediate between those for which data are available; to the extent that this operation is effective additional experimental measurements are eliminated.

(3) Time extrapolations at given temperatures; this operation actually involves the extension of established isotherms using short-term results to estimate long-term behavior; considerable test time is saved if, for example, 10,000-hour rupture data can be accurately predicted from tests involving 100- and 1000-hour results.

(4) Time extrapolation at lower temperatures; since reduced operating temperatures at the same stress lead to increased rupture life, it is sometimes desirable to employ existing data in a temperature range to predict the rupture life if a certain reduction is made in the operating temperature.

(5) Temperature extrapolation; when experimental data are available in a certain temperature range some additional testing can be avoided if these can be used to predict stress-rupture behavior at temperatures slightly higher than the data range.

Experience has shown that if the objective stated in (1) is achieved then satisfactory results will follow in (2). For example, if the correlation is based on a certain parameter, P, involving a combination of rupture time and temperature, and if a plot of this parameter as a functi of stress yields a single line or curve for all the test temperatures, ther a proper correlation results and accurate interpolation is assured. On the other hand, excessive scatter in the type of parameter plot just mentioned would lead to only approximate results in any interpolation of the data. Particularly objectionable in this correlation procedure would be an instance in which instead of having the data define a single line or curve the data for each temperature would define an individual line or curve characteristic of that temperature (see Figure 2-23). Of course, in this case too, interpolation would lead to only very approximate and perhaps even erroneous results.

Ordinarily the use of stress-rupture parameters does not have as its principal objective the type of effort described in items (1) and (2). Instead these parameters are employed, for the most part, to extrapolate existing data in accordance with (3) or (5). While it is probably true that item (1) prompted the development of stress-rupture parameters, it is probably just as true that, at present, most parametric analyses are concerned with items (3) and (5).

Which parametric approach will yield the best results, in terms of the items or objectives listed above, is difficult to say. Even now some 14 years after the introduction of the Larson-Miller parameter (considered to be the first attempt at the parametric analysis of rupture data) no general consensus of opinion has formed in favor of any one parameter at least to the exclusion of others. Based on the many articles which have been written on the subject it does appear, however, that in terms of yielding the best results with the greater number of materials the Manson-Haferd approach would seem to be preferred. Such preference might appear to follow from the fact that this parametric approach involves one more constant than employed in the Dorn or Larson-Miller parameters. On the other hand some disadvantage is assigned to the Manson-Haferd approach due to this single fact; the added constant causes a slightly more complicated analysis and the parameter is just a little more difficult to employ. Considerable convenience, on the other hand, follows from use of the Dorn and Larson-Miller parameters due to their simplicity. Despite such considerations of convenience the major objective of the parametric approach should not become secondary to the level of complexity involved in the data analysis. And if one parameter clearly leads to more accurate extrapolation, then obviously, this one factor and this factor alon should determine which parametric approach is to be employed. Of the three mentioned above, the Manson-Haferd seems to have earned the distinction of being the most effective in this respect. Now, of course, instances can be cited in which the Dorn or Larson-Miller approaches are more exact but in general the literature seems to prove that in the majority of cases the Manson-Haferd parameter will be found to lead to more effective results.

It is certainly true that the approach which will yield the best results is that one whose basic underlying assumptions are most closely satisfied by a given set of experimental data. Conversely, if a given set of data exhibits behavior which is not consistent with the basic premise on which a given parameter is based, then accurate results cannot be expected. This is not to say that this particular parameter cannot be applied for it can. It is only to be recognized that the best accuracy will not be achieved. As a matter of fact, of the three parameters being compared in this section it might well happen that a given set of data would not completely support the underlying assumptions for any of the parameters. An accurate analysis would not then be possible and the best parameter to use would be the one whose underlying assumptions come closest to being satisfied.

Unfortunately it is not possible to view a set of stress-rupture data, complete with several isotherms, and tell at a glance which parametric approach would be the best to use. Some assistance in this selection is provided by the analyses of Clauss[20] and Larke and Inglis[30] but these are somewhat idealized systems. Usually it is difficult to decide which parametric approach to employ. In a study by Mullendore, et al.,[42] some consideration of this problem was presented. Employing the concepts of Chapters 2, 3 and 4 the recommended first step in any analysis of this type is the preparation of the type of plot shown in Figure 9-1, for both rupture time and minimum creep rate data. It is clear, for example, that if a common point of intersection is obtained at $(1/T) = 0$ for linear isostress lines on the log t_R versus $(1/T)$ plot then the Larson-Miller parameter is indicated. A series of parallel straight lines on this type of plot would indicate use of the Dorn parameter. Finally, if linearity on a log t_R versus T plot is demonstrated and if, further, a common point of intersection of the non-parallel isostress lines is identifiable, then the Manson-Haferd parameter is suggested. Since some type of linearity is a basic assumption for all these parameters, any non-linearity noted in a Figure 9-1 type of plot would lead to non-conformity and hence to approximate or even completely erroneous results.

Employing the type of plot shown in Figure 9-1, Mullendore, et al., presented rupture and creep rate data for L-605 and Udimet 500. Based on Figure 9-2, for example, it was concluded that the application of the Larson-Miller parameter should be satisfactory since for the rupture data only the 23,000 psi line (40,000 psi line for creep rate data) departs markedly from the concept of a common point of intersection at $(1/T) = 0$. It would appear that the Dorn assumption of parallel isostress lines is less accurately satisfied in Figure 9-2 and hence a slight preference for

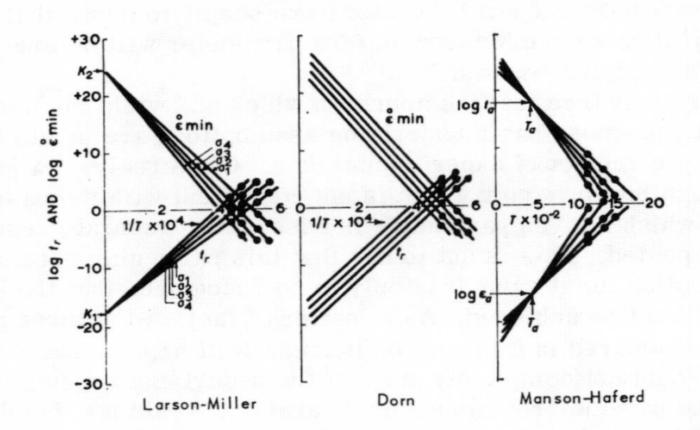

Figure 9-1 – Graphical representation of rupture time-temperature variations for various parametric approaches[42].

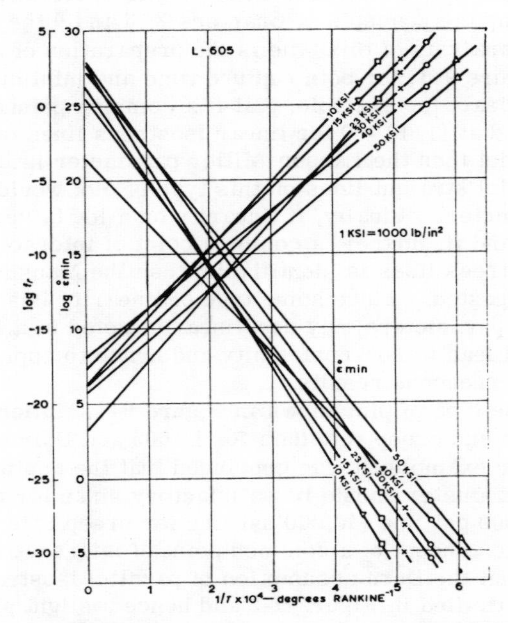

Figure 9-2 – Plot of log t_R (and ϵ_{min}) versus (1/T) for L-605[42].

the Larson-Miller approach is indicated. In Figure 9-3 the degree to which the Manson-Haferd assumptions are satisfied is illustrated. It was concluded that this plot revealed that the Manson-Haferd approach would be applicable only for the low stress data (below 30,000 psi). Furthermore, the Manson-Haferd approach was concluded to be only approximately applicable to the minimum creep rate data for L-605.

A similar consideration of data for Udimet 500 is presented in Figs. 9-4 and 9-5. It was concluded that the Larson-Miller approach would yield fair results for rupture and creep rate; the Dorn approach would be suitable for a creep rate correlation as would the Manson-Haferd approach.

A Larson-Miller parameter plot for L-605 is presented in Figure 9-6. As was predicted from Figure 9-2 a fairly good correlation is indicated. Some slight separation of data at the various temperatures is detected but this is probably due to the fact that at $(1/T) = 0$ an exact common point of intersection was not obtained. For the creep rate data the correlation is less impressive as indicated by a noticeable deviation of the low temperature data away from an average curve. At 35,000 psi and 1200°F the value for the creep rate departs from the average curve by an amount which would give one order of magnitude error in the prediction of the creep rate using the average curve. It was indicated that extrapolation to lower stresses at 1200°F would produce even greater errors. Similarly, at 1500°F, extrapolation to lower stresses would seem to incur considerable error.

For L-605 the Manson-Haferd correlation was interpreted to be less satisfactory than that provided by the Larson-Miller approach. This is shown in Figure 9-7. By altering the constants good correlation is obtained for stresses below 25,000 psi but the scatter at higher stresses becomes substantial.

For the Udimet 500 data a slightly different result was obtained. As shown in Figure 9-8 the Larson-Miller correlation of the minimum creep rate data is better than that obtained for the rupture data. This is opposite to that observed in the case of the L-605 analysis. It was observed that this behavior confirms the lack of a strict proportionality between creep rate and rupture life.

When both minimum creep rate and rupture data are available, Mullendore, et al.,[42] suggested an alternative extrapolation procedure. Use is made of a parametric approach based on which quantity ($\dot{\epsilon}_{min}$ or t_R) leads to the best correlation. If this happened to be $\dot{\epsilon}_{min}$, then the corresponding extrapolated value of t_R could be read from the type of plot shown in Figure 9-9 prepared from the original data.

Manson-Haferd and Dorn parameter plots for the creep data of Udimet 500 are presented in Figure 9-10. Both produced a good correlation but neither was very effective in the analysis of rupture data.

In a discussion of the Mullendore, et al., analysis Manson[61] emphasized the need for using optimized parameter constants if valid indications of parameter effectiveness were to be achieved. Reference was made to the L-605 data (shown in Figure 9-3) for which Mullendore, et al., chose $T_a = -610°C$ and $\log t_a = 20$ for the rupture results. Referring to

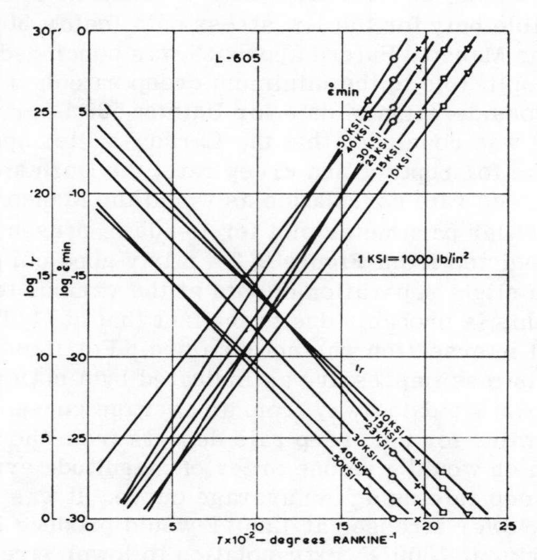

Figure 9-3 – Plot of log t_R (and ϵ_{min}) versus T for L-605[42].

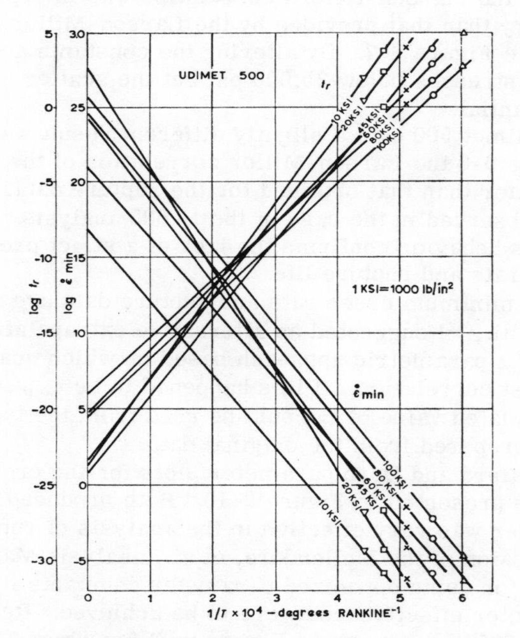

Figure 9-4 – Plot of log t_R (and ϵ_{min}) versus (1/T) for Udimet 500[42].

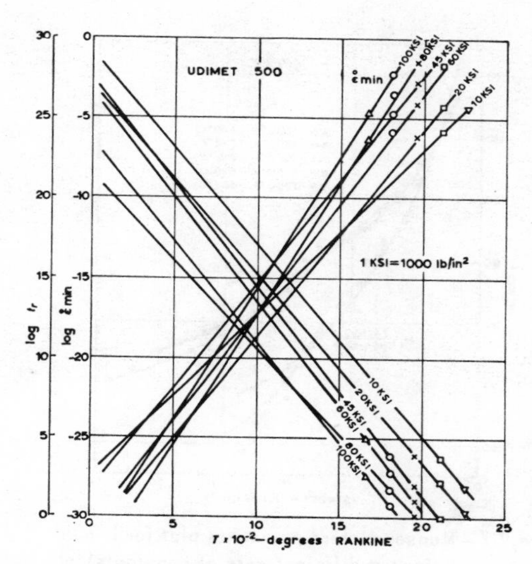

Figure 9-5 – Plot of log t_R (and ϵ_{min}) versus T for Udimet 500(42).

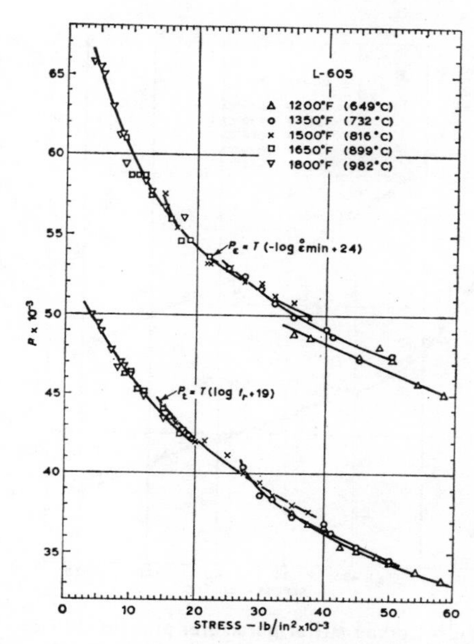

Figure 9-6 – Larson-Miller parameter plot for L-605; P_t for rupture, P_ϵ for creep rate[42].

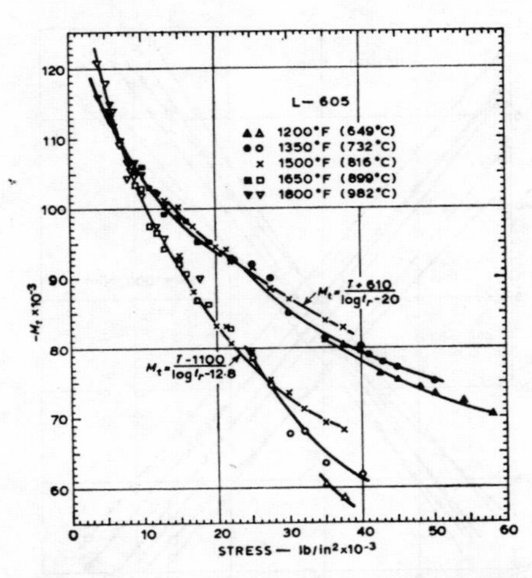

Figure 9-7 – Manson-Haferd parameter plot for L-605 using two different sets of constants[42].

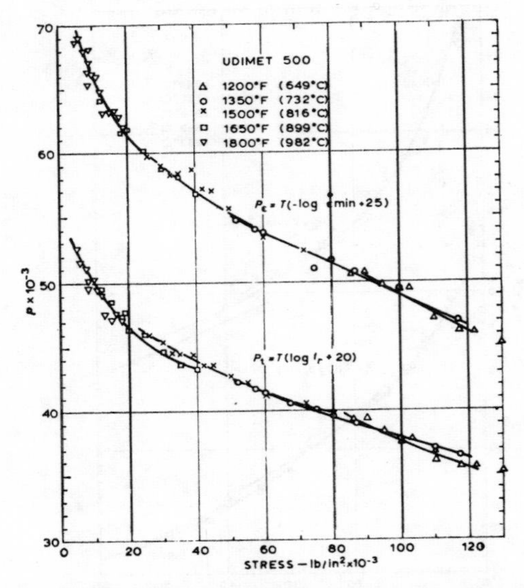

Figure 9-8 – Larson-Miller parameter plot for Udimet 500[42]; P_t for rupture and P_ϵ for creep rate.

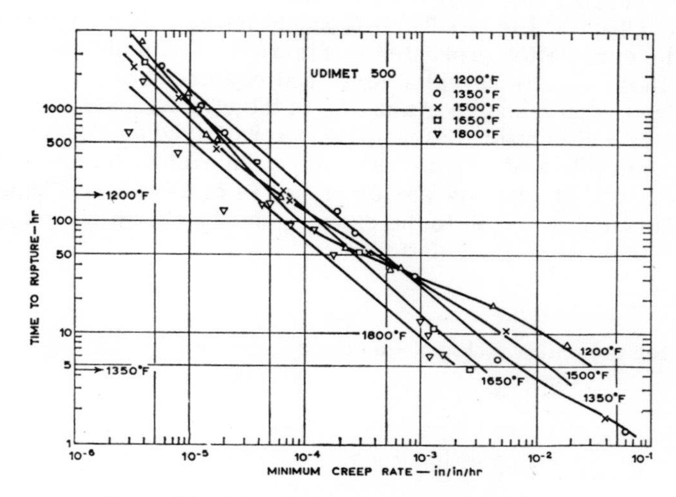

Figure 9-9 – Plot of log t_R versus log $\dot{\epsilon}_{min}$ for Udimet 500[42].

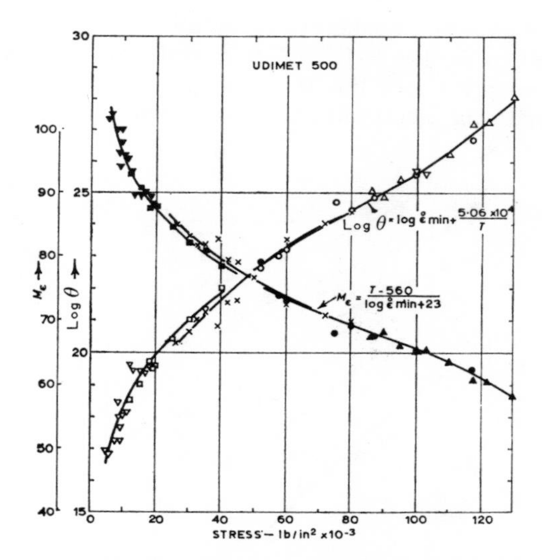

Figure 9-10 – Manson-Haferd and Dorn parameter plot for the creep data of Udimet 500[42].

the data in Figure 9-3, Manson could not agreee that the point of intersection is well represented by these values. Hence the ineffectiveness of the Manson-Haferd parameter in representing these data is not unexpected. A re-analysis using the optimized calculation procedures discussed in Chapter 4 led to $T_a = -7000$ and $\log t_a = 91.6$. Using these constants the correlation presented in Figure 9-11 was obtained. Obviously, these results reveal a very good representation.

In a very comprehensive evaluation of the effectiveness of the Dorn, Larson-Miller and Manson-Haferd parameters Larke and Inglis[30] analyzed the rupture data of 14 different alloys. In each case, the least squares method[5] of analysis was employed as discussed in Chapters 2, 3, and 4. This approach led to the expression of the parameters as simple polynominals in log σ as follows:

Larson-Miller

$$T(C + \log t_R) = a_0 + a_1 \log \sigma + a_2(\log \sigma)^2 + a_3(\log \sigma)^3 \qquad (9\text{-}1)$$

Dorn

$$\log t_R - \frac{Q}{2.3RT} = a_0 + a_1 \log \sigma + a_2 (\log \sigma)^2 + a_3(\log \sigma)^3 \qquad (9\text{-}2)$$

Manson-Haferd

$$\frac{\log t_R - \log t_a}{T - T_a} = a_0 + a_1 \log \sigma + a_2 (\log \sigma)^2 + a_3 (\log \sigma)^3 \qquad (9\text{-}3)$$

A summary of the equation constants calculated in the Larke and Inglis study is presented in Tables 9-1, 9-2, 9-3, and 9-4. For each material the range of stress corresponding to the available experimental data is presented along with the maximum observed rupture time.

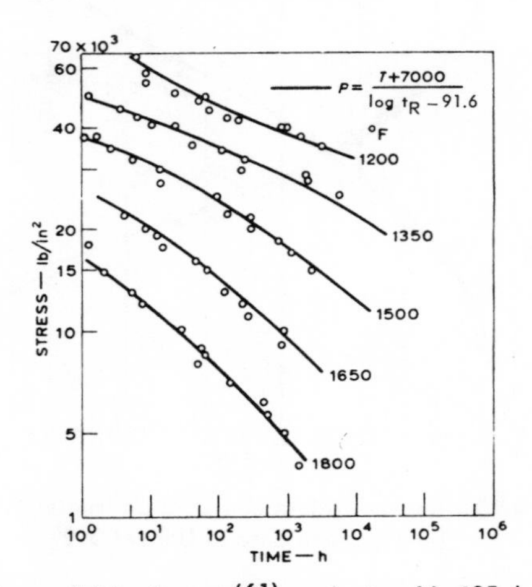

Figure 9-11 – Manson[61] analysis of L-605 data.

TABLE 9-1

CONSTANTS OBTAINED IN LARSON-MILLER ANALYSIS[30].

$$\phi = a_0 + a_1 \log \sigma + a_2 (\log \sigma)^2 + a_3 (\log \sigma)^3 = T(C + \log t_R)$$

Temperature T in °K

Material	a_0	a_1	a_2	a_3	C	Limits of σ, ton/in²		Maximum time, h
						min.	max.	
68/30/1/1, Cu–Ni–Fe–Mn	39793·03	−50815·04	56966·52	−23394·25	26·8405	4·0	21·0	2637
76/22/2, Cu–Zn–Al	9970·15	2385·45	−4709·84	1054·92	14·2384	4·0	22·0	1350
80/10/5/5, Cu–Al–Ni–Fe	15138·35	−5469·75	1228·38	−277·47	14·8691	1·0	32·5	3401
1/0·7/0·6 Si–Mg–Mn–Al alloy HE30 fully heat treated	15579·44	−7787·46	9518·28	−5892·72	23·2389	2·0	20·0	1726
2½% Mg–Al alloy. NE4	14665·06	−18491·48	28249·90	−16971·97	18·2699	1·8	10·2	2567
1% Ni/½% Fe–Al alloy	9601·40	−3408·90	−3720·99	1490·21	15·2817	1·3	5·1	43
Nimonic 80A	24682·35	−8110·65	5721·70	−2509·17	16·0895	6·0	30·0	1857
Nimonic 90	26815·23	−10430·33	9115·06	−3961·22	17·2130	3·0	35·0	2547
2¼/1 Cr–Mo steel	23031·40	8271·55	−16038·69	6044·29	22·7619	3·0	14·0	3005
18/12/1 Cr–Ni–Nb steel	2058·73	55741·50	−56121·72	16579·04	16·4751	6·0	25·2	1842
13/½ Cr–Mo steel	42537·99	−31359·87	30988·87	−12282·53	32·7985	4·9	25·0	2598
½/0·13 Mo–C steel	37478·66	−19706·92	23309·51	−10817·75	33·8266	3·1	20·7	1717
16/26/1½/2/0·3 Cr–Ni–Mo–Ti–V steel (A-286)	30977·70	−20248·46	17535·51	−6293·04	19·0022	4·5	35·7	983
20/20/20/4/4 Co–Ni–Cr–Mo–W–Nb +Fe alloy (S-590)	24893·40	204·17	−6375·55	1547·33	16·7280	4·5	44·6	15 335

TABLE 9-2

CONSTANTS OBTAINED IN DORN ANALYSIS[30].

$$\log \phi = a_0 + a_1 \log \sigma + a_2(\log \sigma)^2 + a_3(\log \sigma)^3 = \log t_R - \frac{B}{T} = \log t_R - \frac{Q}{RT} \log_{10} e$$

Temperature T in °K

Material	a_0	a_1	a_2	a_3	B	Q calories/mole $= 2{\cdot}303RB$ $R = 1{\cdot}986$
68/30/1/1, Cu–Ni–Fe–Mn	7·5495	−97·8901	110·9912	−43·9416	19771·6	90 431
76/22/2, Cu–Zn–Al	−9·9157	−0·5053	−1·8438	−0·8937	8118·5	37 132
80/10/5/5, Cu–Al–Ni–Fe	−9·5748	−5·7055	1·1729	−0·9509	10727·2	49 064
1/0·7/0·6 Si–Mg–Mn–Al alloy. HE30 fully heat treated	−12·6905	−25·6675	36·9918	−21·0117	11020·0	50 403
2¼% Mg–Al alloy. NE4	−4·6321	−46·1087	76·7732	−46·5490	8329·6	38 098
1% Ni/½ Fe–Al alloy	−12·8846	−1·9850	−15·7412	4·7373	8026·2	36 710
Nimonic 80A	−9·3238	−12·3205	10·8561	−4·3827	18813·1	86 047
Nimonic 90	−10·6653	−12·7473	12·7870	−5·4328	20300·7	92 850
2¼/1 Cr–Mo steel	−21·5416	8·6945	−16·1485	5·5793	21856·6	99 967
18/12/1 Cr–Ni–Nb steel	−29·7376	49·7752	−49·1494	13·8796	17067·6	78 063
13/½ Cr–Mo steel	−14·4050	−42·2075	42·8696	−16·8484	28003·1	128 079
½/0·13 Mo–C steel	−23·2700	−27·1927	32·9069	−15·0311	29238·5	133 730
16/26/1½/2/0·3, Cr–Ni–Mo–Ti–V steel (A-286)	−7·7930	−23·8490	22·2282	−8·0309	20343·4	93 046
20/20/20/4/4 (S-590) Co–Ni–Cr–Mo–W–Nb + Fe alloy	−8·8410	−4·7267	0·2815	−0·9749	17661·3	80 779

TABLE 9-3

CONSTANTS OBTAINED IN MANSON-HAFERD ANALYSIS[30] FOR $T_a < T$

$$\frac{1}{\phi} = a_0 + a_1 \log \sigma + a_2(\log \sigma)^2 + a_3(\log \sigma)^3 = \frac{\log t_R - \log t_a}{T - T_a}$$

Temperature T in °C

Material	Values to be multiplied by 10^{-4}				$\log t_a$	T_a, see footnote, p. 6–46
	a_0	a_1	a_2	a_3		
68/30/1/1, Cu–Ni–Fe–Mn	−389·1509	−8·1796	9·4665	−4·0883	2569·7087	−65 000
76/22/2, Cu–Zn–Al	−247·4654	−27·4075	6·0358	−25·0701	24·4674	−500
80/10/5/5, Cu–Al–Ni–Fe	−152·2957	−94·1118	26·8501	−28·0728	13·3916	−100
1/0·7/0·6 Si–Mg–Mn–Al alloy, HE30 fully heat treated	−558·6490	−2·6098	3·4141	−2·2620	3232·7005	−57 500
2½% Mg–Al alloy. NE4	−439·6530	−5·8911	9·1166	−5·7199	2548·5072	−57 500
1% Ni/½% Fe–Al alloy	−234·1804	−53·9810	−338·3138	−283·9129	9·2759	−50
Nimonic 80A	−184·1370	−3·4819	2·4736	−1·1568	386·1205	−19 800
Nimonic 90	−125·5843	−135·1794	139·7536	−60·7464	20·1572	−150
2¼/1 Cr–Mo steel	−285·6794	101·2775	−177·9230	61·7510	31·6866	−400
18/12/1 Cr–Ni–Nb steel	457·3370	−1772·7154	1971·2391	−802·3197	6·0200	450
13/½ Cr–Mo steel	−400·5045	−7·8492	7·9051	−3·0658	2289·1176	−56 094
½/0·13 Mo–C steel	485·6681	−2897·7266	3682·5642	−1606·8602	7·9844	400
16/26/1½/2/0·3 Cr–Ni–Mo–Ti–V steel (A-286)	−215·7897	−3·7092	3·2893	−1·1824	1295·9785	−58 750
20/20/20/4/4 (S-590) Co–Ni–Cr–Mo–W–Nb+Fe alloy	−122·2824	−37·2342	1·9994	−17·3869	17·9236	−100

TABLE 9-4

CONSTANTS OBTAINED IN MANSON-HAFERD ANALYSIS[30] FOR $T_a > T$

$$\frac{1}{\phi} = a_0 + a_1 \log \sigma + a_2 (\log \sigma)^2 + a_3 (\log \sigma)^3 = \frac{\log t_a - \log t_R}{T_a - T}$$

Temperature T in °C

Material	Values to be multiplied by 10^{-4}				$\log t_a$	T_a, °C
	a_0	a_1	a_2	a_3		
68/30/1/1, Cu–Ni–Fe–Mn	−549·6943	338·3597	−378·7496	175·1187	−39·0626	1500
76/22/2, Cu–Zn–Al	−307·9046	−0·2528	0·6990	−0·0321	−2093·0988	68 400
80/10/5/5, Cu–Al–Ni–Fe	−240·2829	0·6974	−0·1010	0·0176	−2386·0560	100 000
1/0·7/0·6 Si–Mg–Mn–Al alloy. HE30 fully heat treated	−3063·3815	7391·6909	−7500·9400	2568·0269	−30·0070	700
2¼% Mg–Al alloy. NE4	−5162·5797	16 940·6683	−21 038·6737	8785·0033	−22·3696	600
1% Ni/½% Fe–Al alloy	−307·1943	1·8444	1·6542	0·0518	−1070·5873	35 200
Nimonic 80A	−188·7951	2·5526	−1·7497	0·8311	−499·2553	27 600
Nimonic 90	−194·1025	1·5081	−1·3315	0·6024	−1171·7934	61 563
2¼/1 Cr–Mo steel	−293·1819	−3·3486	6·1067	−2·2804	−949·6319	33 100
18/12/1 Cr–Ni–Nb steel	−204·9988	−9·5524	9·5006	−2·7931	−1412·0950	68 750
13/½ Cr–Mo steel	−504·6436	−963·3482	1007·3094	−134·0088	−4·9687	700
½/0·13 Mo–C steel	−428·3487	4·6167	−5·5715	2·5453	−2494·0736	59 063
16/26/1½/2/0·3 Cr–Ni–Mo–Ti–V steel (A-286)	−441·9404	386·3085	−286·5128	94·8869	−9·8050	1250
20/20/20/4/4(S-590) Co–Ni–Cr–Mo–W–Nb+Fe alloy	−200·1464	−0·4976	1·1566	−0·2644	−1542·4345	78 125

In the above analysis, certain data were not included in the group of data used in the calculation of the constants presented in Tables 9-1 through 9-4. These few points which were withheld are listed in columns 2 and 3 and 8 of Table 9-5. These data were used to enable a comparison to be made of the effectiveness of the various parametric approaches in terms of how well these data points could be predicted. (It is well to note that these points correspond to the longest rupture times and thus the operation involved represents the type of calculation indicated by item (3) discussed previously.) For example, a point at 450°C, 10.1 tons/in.^{2} and t_R = 5582 hours was withheld and the ability to predict first the stress at this temperature and rupture time and then the rupture time at the given temperature and stress was evaluated in terms of the data in the above tables. Results of this comparison study are presented in columns 4, 5, 6, and 7 and also in columns 9, 10, 11, and 12 where the percentage differences between calculated and predicted values are referenced to the actual values of stress and rupture time. Worthy of note are the extremely large errors in the predicted rupture values in certain instances. For example, a 636 percent error is involved for one material in the prediction of a rupture time corresponding to a measured value of 3486 hours.

In comparing the effectiveness of the parametric approaches employed Larke and Inglis calculated standard deviations, μ, in the form:

$$\mu = \left[\frac{\Sigma(R)^2}{n} - \left(\frac{\Sigma R}{n} \right)^2 \right]^{1/2} \qquad (9\text{-}4)$$

where:

$$R = 100 \frac{\sigma_p - \sigma_a}{\sigma_a} \qquad (9\text{-}5)$$

and

n = number of R values

with σ_p and σ_a corresponding to the predicted and actual stress values respectively. A summary of these results is presented in Figure 9-12 where the range of percentage deviations associated with a 95 percent confidence level is shown. Despite the fact that the least satisfactory results were obtained for the copper alloys when the Manson-Haferd approach was employed the opinion expressed by Larke and Inglis was that taking the results for all 14 materials into consideration the error in a predicted stress will be approximately the same whichever parametric approach is employed.

Referring to Figure 9-12, the over-all height of any of the 20 blocks indicates the range of percentage error which the analysis indicated should be associated with predicted stress values and it will be observed that, in general, the heights of the four blocks relating to the copper alloys--and those for the aluminum alloys--are greater than the heights of the blocks representing the Nimonic alloys and the steels. However,

TABLE 9-5

COMPARISON[30] BETWEEN PREDICTED AND MEASURED RUPTURE DATA BASED ON RESULTS IN TABLES 9-1, -2, -3, AND -4

Material	Temp., °C	Actual stress, ton/in²	$\left[\frac{\text{Predicted stress} - \text{actual stress}}{\text{Actual stress}}\right]$, %				Observed fracture time, h	$\left[\frac{\text{Predicted time} - \text{actual time}}{\text{Actual time}}\right]$, %			
			See note (1)					See note (1)			
			L	D	$M(T_a < T)$	$M(T_a > T)$		L	D	$M(T_a < T)$	$M(T_a > T)$
68/30/1/1 Cu–Ni–Fe–Mn	450	10·1	13	7	14	14	5582	263	88	290	417
	450	9·1	19	12	20	22	9746	440	125	487	796
76/22/2 Cu–Zn–Al	200	12·9	−6	−8	−10	−9	2746	−40	−44	−51	−41
	200	11·4	−6	−9	−12	−10	7960	−40	−50	−59	−54
	250	7·0	1	−4	−2	1	2671	9	−21	−14	7
	250	5·5	11	2	2	9	6951	75	4	7	52
80/10/5/5 Cu–Al–Ni–Fe	350	6·0	−12	−18	−30	−17	8535	−55	−66	−72	−64
	350	5·5	−29	−40	−53	−36	70 301	−90	−93	−95	−93
	450	2·0	−5	−15	−20	0	10 556	−18	−60	−66	−14
1/0·7/0·6 Si–Mg–Mn–Al alloy. HE30 fully heat treated	100	15·9	−4	−4	−8	0	2563	−70	−63	−84	−6
	100	15·0	−2	−2	−7	2	7302	−49	−39	−78	57
	150	9·0	14	12	13	0	3486	636	466	503	−15
	200	5·0	14	12	20	6	2114	176	73	309	683
	200	4·0	30	20	35	30	4653	394	104	614	8×10^6

Table 9–5 (continued)

2¼% Mg–Al alloy. NE 4	100	9·1	−7	−7	−10	−2	7168	−85	−85	−91	−57
	150	6·0	3	0	0	0	5833	41	−7	0	−7
	200	3·5	−9	−23	−6	20	4290	−46	−69	−31	2×10^6
	200	3·2	−13	−25	−9	28	8902	−58	−80	−47	$6·6 \times 10^8$
1% Ni/½% Fe–Al alloy	150	3·2	−6	−6	−6	−13	97	−57	−43	−55	−73
	150	2·9	−7	−3	−10	−10	331	−47	−31	−57	−73
	200	1·9	0	0	−5	−5	321	−9	−20	−47	−32
Nimonic 80A	650	22·0	1	2	−1	−1	2655	6	14	−7	−7
	650	20·0	0	1	−3	−3	5270	1	8	−15	−16
	650	18·0	4	4	0	0	8171	26	31	0	0
	650	16·0	8	8	3	3	13 386	54	53	16	16
	700	13·0	2	1	1	1	4836	10	4	4	5
	700	10·0	12	8	10	10	10 896	61	34	46	48
	700	7·0	21	13	17	20	34 053	121	50	84	91
	750	8·0	−1	−5	0	0	4450	−3	−17	1	2
	750	6·0	See note (2)			0	13 089	−4	−26	−2	1
Nimonic 90	650	26·0	−4	−3	−5	−6	4111	−29	−23	−35	−41
	650	24·0	−1	0	−3	−4	6443	−8	0	−21	−28
	650	23·0	6	7	3	3	5375	57	71	30	20
	650	20·0	7	8	3	2	15 294	65	74	20	13
	700	13·0	15	14	12	12	12 094	109	88	60	80
	700	12·5	9	6	3	6	20 399	50	32	12	28
	750	10·0	−3	−10	−6	−1	7593	−9	−20	−17	−4
	750	7·0	4	−7	−7	6	22 159	16	−18	−19	22
	815	5·5	−5	−13	−11	0	3342	−16	−31	−26	−4
	815	4·0	5	−5	−3	10	6830	17	−14	−9	33

TABLE 9-5 (Cont.)

COMPARISON[30] BETWEEN PREDICTED AND MEASURED RUPTURE DATA BASED ON RESULTS IN TABLES 9-1, -2, -3, AND -4

Material	Temp., °C	Actual stress, ton/in²	[(Predicted stress − actual stress)/Actual stress], % See note (1)				Observed fracture time, h	[(Predicted time − actual time)/Actual time], % See note (1)			
			L	D	$M(T_a < T)$	$M\ T_a > T)$		L	D	$M(T_a < T)$	$M(T_a > T)$
2¼/1 Cr–Mo steel	538	8·0	10	10	8	5	8335	94	90	60	60
	593	5·0	8	6	8	10	4238	59	41	47	63
18/12/1 Cr–Ni–Nb steel	550	17·8	−10	−9	−12	−12	7247	−57	−53	−49	−65
	600	11·9	3	1	−10	2	5371	23	8	−40	11
	600	10·7	11	8	−7	9	6769	137	90	−24	104
	650	8·2	2	−1	−23	2	6579	18	−4	−57	19
13/½ Cr–Mo steel	525	14·7	−11	−12	−12	−5	4108	−72	−74	−76	−57
	575	6·4	3	−2	2	5	4343	19	−3	3	27
	575	5·4	15	9	11	15	6532	138	85	104	77
½/0·13 Mo–C steel	510	10·5	30	30	26	30	3877	1069	928	299	855
	540	7·1	31	30	15	32	3848	331	251	42	314

Table 9–5 (continued)

16/26/1½/2/0·3 Cr–Ni–Mo–Ti–V steel (U.S.A.) A-286	538	35·7	−3	2	−8	−14	4554	−29	34	−63	−85
	593	35·7	−1	2	−1	−4	123	−3	27	−12	−40
	593	33·5	−6	−3	−7	−10	517	−47	−32	−55	−70
	593	31·2	−5	−3	−8	−11	1081	−43	−28	−55	−69
	593	31·2	−9	−8	−13	−15	1861	−67	−58	−73	−82
	593	29·0	−1	1	−4	−7	1501	−6	16	−29	−51
	593	26·8	2	4	−2	−5	2550	27	50	−11	−35
	593	24·6	4	5	−1	−4	5244	43	61	−6	−28
	648	15·6	2	−1	−1	2	7131	10	−3	−7	11
	704	11·2	7	3	7	13	1435	35	12	39	92
	704	8·9	8	0	9	19	3538	38	−1	39	157
	734	8·9	−5	−11	−3	6	1232	−17	−32	−11	29
20/20/20/4/4 Co–Ni–Cr–Mo–W–Nb and Fe alloy (U.S.A.) (S-590)	593	22·3	−4	−5	−6	−6	3149	−33	−37	−42	−42
	648	26·8	0	−2	−2	1	26	−5	−20	−20	5
	648	24·6	−2	−3	−2	0	63	−12	−22	−20	−3
	648	22·3	4	3	4	5	93	45	30	36	57
	648	20·1	7	5	7	7	192	87	64	74	98
	648	17·9	3	1	2	3	756	40	17	24	45
	648	15·6	6	2	3	6	2243	61	21	26	60
	648	13·4	2	−4	−4	2	11 937	22	−22	−22	15
	648	11·2	5	−3	−4	4	43 978	67	−15	−23	43
	734	8·9	−6	−11	−10	−3	9529	−37	−56	−50	−26
	734	7·8	0	−8	−6	1	16 964	−2	−40	−33	12

Note (1) L = Larson and Miller.
D = Orr, Sherby and Dorn.
M = Manson and Haferd.
Note (2) Outside stress range of equations to master curves.

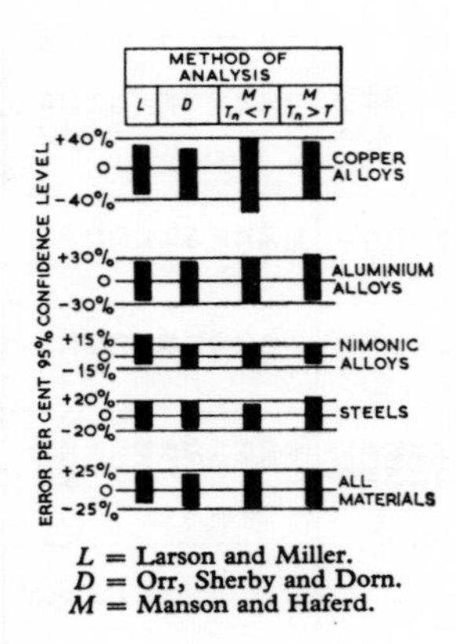

Figure 9-12 – Percentage error between predicted and actual stress values based on a 95 percent confidence level(30).

TABLE 9-6

DISTRIBUTION OF ERRORS BETWEEN PREDICTED AND OBSERVED FRACTURE TIMES(30)

Per cent error range, ±	Percentage of 74 comparisons within error range			
	L	D	$M (T_a < T)$	$M (T_a > T)$
10	19	13	15	16
20	30	28	31	31
30	38	40	43	41
40	47	55	53	46
50	59	63	63	54
60	69	70	76	66
70	77	77	78	73
80	80	84	85	78
90	84	92	88	81
100	85	93	91	87

in view of the difference between the numbers of results detailed in Table 9-5 for each of these latter two materials and those for the copper and for the aluminum alloys the authors consider that the evidence should only be accepted as an indication that the methods of analysis are more applicable to Nimonic alloys and steels than to copper or aluminum alloys. In other words, the 95 percent probability differences found between predicted and actual stress values of $\pm$ 40 percent for copper alloys and $\pm$30 percent for aluminum alloys should be accepted with caution; the difference of $\pm$25 percent, which relates to all the materials examined being, is considered a more reasonable expectation.

Larke and Inglis observed that the percentage differences between predicted and observed values did not seem to follow a normal distribution and hence the use of the standard deviation expression in equation (9-4) might not be justified. As a result, a different presentation was employed as shown in Table 9-6. Gross differences between predicted and observed fracture times are evident. In general, it was noted, that the number of entries in any one range of error is about the same for all parameter methods. Errors exceeding 100 percent are also noted to exist in accordance with the large deviations entered in Table 9-5. These errors were always in a direction greater than the measured values.

Referring to Table 9-1 Larke and Inglis noted the range of C values to be from 14 to 34 which was observed to represent a significant deviation from the value of 20 proposed by Larson and Miller. A reference was made to the work of Bandel and Gravenhorst[65] in which C values ranging from minus 8 to plus 57 were observed.

In connection with the T_a values listed in Table 9-3 it was observed that very large negative values were obtained in certain instances. Also, very large values were obtained for the log t_a values. Some explanation for these observations was offered in a previous section (see Manson and Succop discussion in Chapter 4).

In a conclusion by Larke and Inglis no preference for one parameter over another could be offered. Errors in method were found to be of the order of 25 percent when extrapolated rupture data were considered. As a matter of fact, it was stated that the use of these methods for predicting fracture time was not recommended.

It is particularly important at this point to consider the Manson discussion of the Larke and Inglis analysis. In the first place, it was felt that too few experimental points were available to allow for an accurate determination of the parameter constants and for this reason a true indication of parameter effectiveness might not have been obtained. In addition, Manson pointed out that while Larke and Inglis employed the optimization procedures[5] recommended for the calculation of parameter constants it did appear that some difficulties due to ill-conditioned optimization equations[57] were involved. Loss of precision seemed to occur and an accurate correlation did not result. For this reason, the analysis approach involving orthogonal polynomials was employed in an analysis by Manson of some of the data studied by Larke and Inglis.

These results are presented in Figure 9-13 and a careful study will indicate better results than those obtained in the Larke-Inglis evaluation. For example, the 68% Cu - 30% Ni - 1% Fe - 1% Mn data illustrate this point very well. According to Figure 9-13 the solid curves predict rupture times near 10,000 psi which are in very good agreement with the experimental data, whereas the prediction in Table 9-5 at this same stress level corresponds to errors close to 500 percent. For the 13% Cr - 0.5% Mo - 0.1% C steel data, the log t_a and T_a values were so large that the analysis in terms of the Manson-Succop[46] approach was indicated.

A widely referenced comparison of the effectiveness of the Larson-Miller, Dorn and Manson-Haferd parameters is that of Goldhoff.[43] Employing rupture data for S-590, A-286, Nimonic 80A and 1Cr-1Mo-1/4V alloy the extrapolative ability of these parametric approaches was studied in considerable detail. Prior to discussing the conclusions which evolved from this study it is considered important to first consider the procedures employed in the analysis of these data. In what follows the data for S-590 (see Figure 9-14) will be used in this illustration. Based on the data in Figure 9-14, a series of constant time plots was prepared as shown in Figure 9-15. In this construction, it was found necessary to extrapolate the isotherms in Figure 9-14 but never more than about one-half of a log cycle. Although this was done manually using personal judgment, it was not felt that any errors invovled would have any great effect on the plot shown in Figure 9-15. All the curves in Figure 9-15 (and this applies as well to Figure 9-14 and all subsequent figures) were faired through the points being careful in each case to minimize the horizontal deviation of the points from the faired curve. With Figure 9-15 established the constant stress plots referred to in previous chapters were prepared to assist in the calculation of the appropriate parameter constants. For example, in Figure 9-16 a plot of log t_R versus $(1/T)$ is presented. Applying the Larson-Miller criteria, a series of linear constant stress lines should result having a common point of intersection at $(1/T) = 0$. Actually, the points in Figure 9-16 fail to describe an exactly linear relation and hence the Larson-Miller parameter is not strictly applicable (it was shown that linearity was lacking in all three parameter plots and hence not one of these parameters was strictly applicable). However, a series of lines was drawn through the points (using the minimum deviation concept) and the common point of intersection at $(1/T) = 0$ was determined equal to 17.

For the Dorn analysis the plot in Figure 9-16 was prepared, and as required, a series of parallel constant stress lines is to be obtained. Though linear relations were not described a series of parallel lines was nevertheless constructed. Of course, the slope of these lines defines ΔH in the Dorn parameter and this value follows directly from this plot. In this evaluation though, the temperatures were first converted to °K to obtain ΔH in calories per mole.

In a third use of the Figure 9-15 data the plot shown in Figure 9-17 was prepared to aid in the identification of the Manson-Haferd constants.

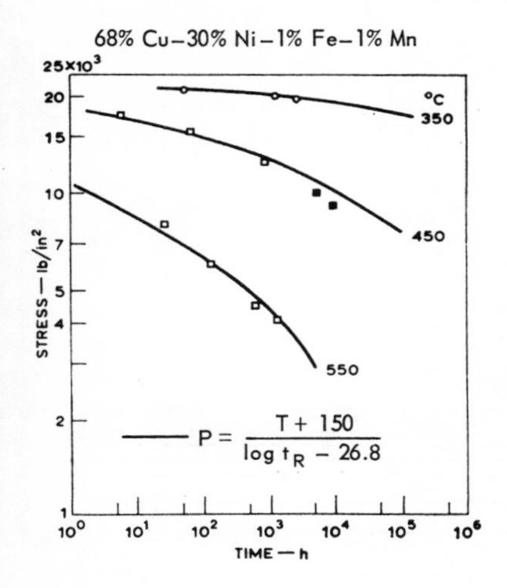

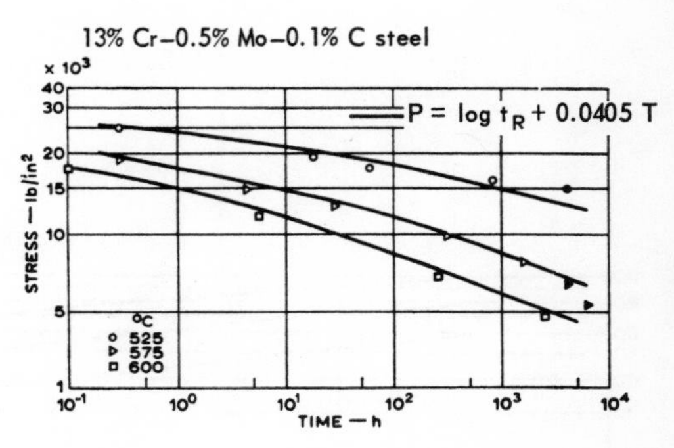

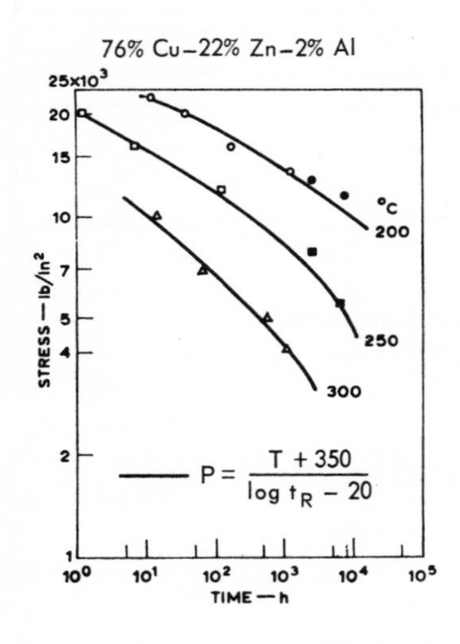

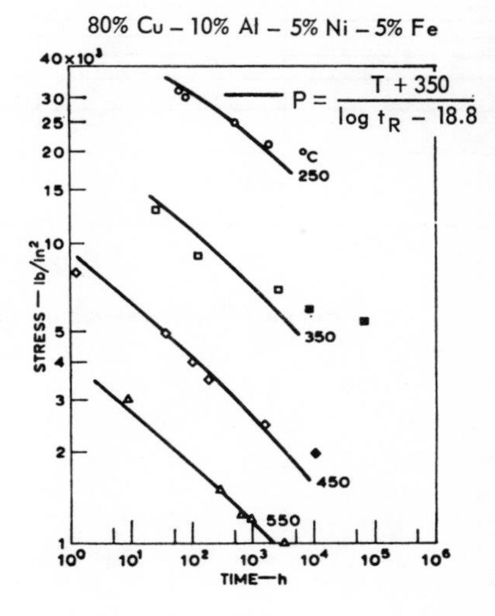

Figure 9-13 – Manson re-analysis of data for several steels(61).

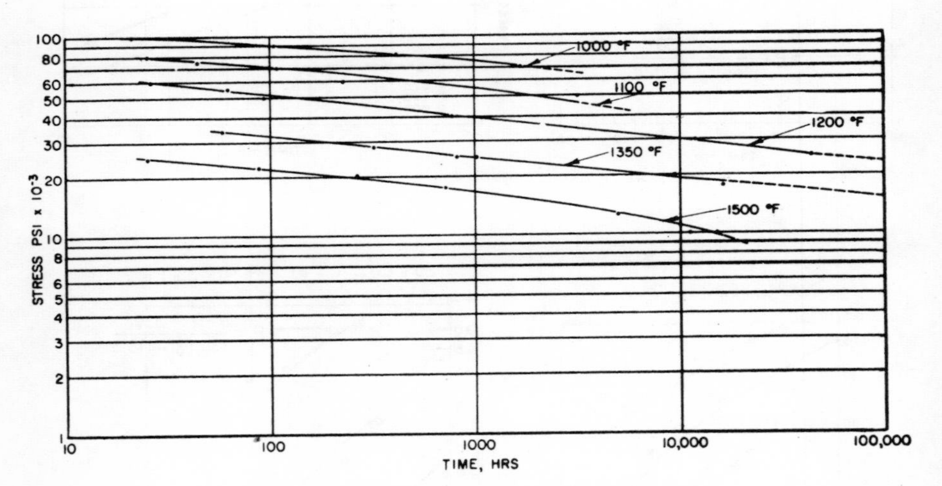

Figure 9-14 – Stress-rupture plot of S-590 data[43].

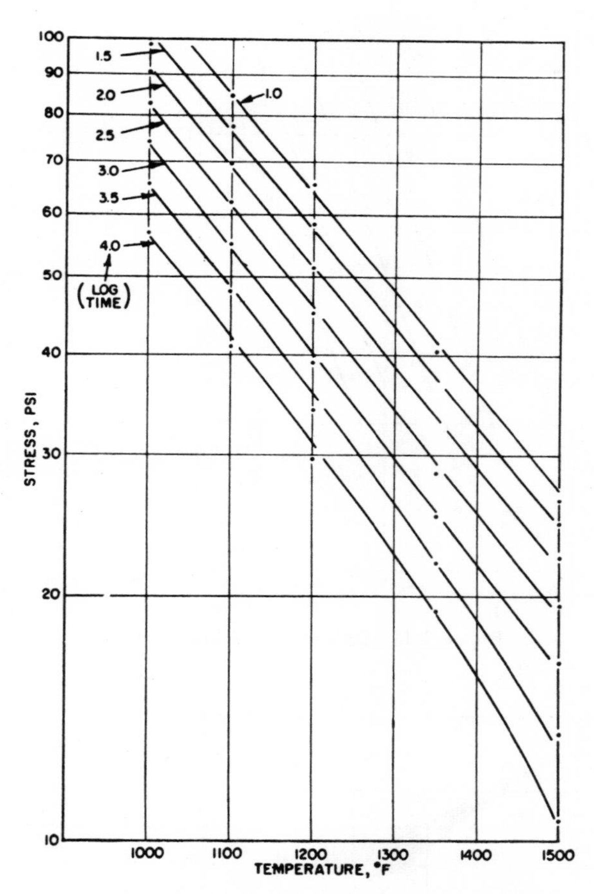

Figure 9-15 – Constant time lines for S-590 data[43].

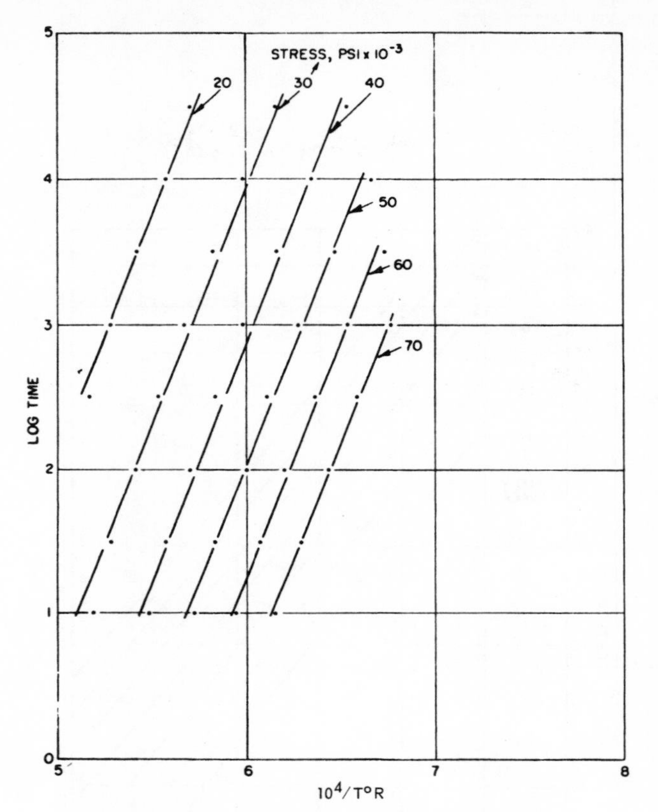

Figure 9-16 – Dorn plot for S-590 data[43].

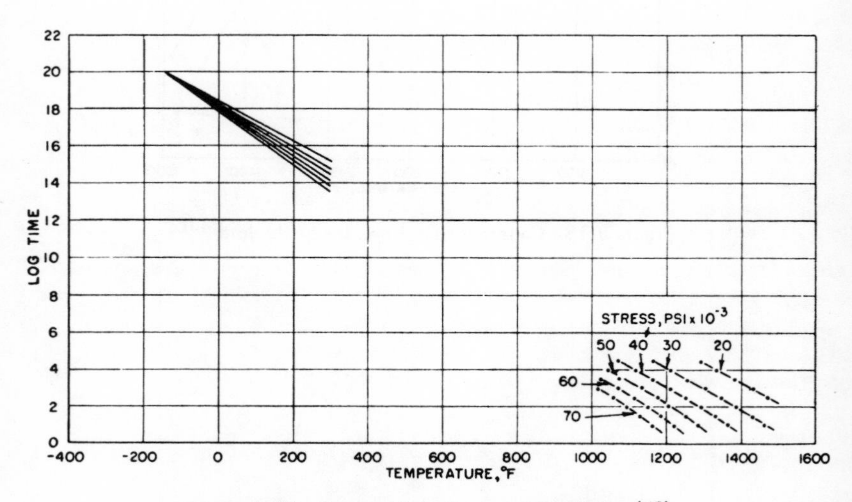

Figure 9-17 – Manson-Haferd plot of S-590 data[43].

These constant stress lines should be linear but definite curvature is clearly observed. However, a series of straight lines was employed and the common point of intersection determined to yield T_a = -150°F and log t_a = 20.

Using the above procedures the parameter constants summarized in Table 9-7 were developed. It is important to note that these constants were evaluated using all the experimental data available. This point is made because, in the usual extrapolations, the data in a certain range are used to calculate parameter constants and then this information is employed to extrapolate beyond the range of existing experimental data. Since this was not what was done in the Goldhoff analysis, the extrapolative effectiveness was not really being tested. A different approach to more clearly evaluate this effectiveness will be described below.

Having derived the parameter constants based on the entire range of experimental data, Goldhoff then prepared parameter plots using data within certain time ranges but always, of course, employing the constants in Table 9-7. These rupture time ranges were:

(1) data below 100 hours,
(2) data between 100 and 1000 hours,
(3) data between 1000 and 10,000 hours,
(4) combining all data to 1000 hours,
and (5) combining all data to 10,000 hours.

Table 9-7. Parameter Constants for Various Materials[43]

Alloy	Larson-Miller C	Dorn ΔH cal/mole	Manson-Haferd T_a, °F log t_a
S-590	17	102,500*	-150, 20
A-286	20	91,000	200, 16
Nimonic 80A	18	91,000	100, 16
1Cr-1Mo-1/4V	22	110,000	100, 18

*This value of ΔH is not reconcilable with Figure 9-16; slope calculations lead to a ΔH value closer to 85,000 cal/mole.

Typical Larson-Miller master-rupture plots for the S-590 alloy based on the above subdivision of the data are shown in Figure 9-18. Using the minimum deviation procedure smooth curves were faired through the plotted points.

With the master-rupture plots established, the extrapolative ability of the various parametric approaches was compared. In this comparison, the time values selected for use were:

(6) for S-590 using all data points exceeding 10,000-hour rupture (5 points; see Appendix B)

(7) for S-590 using (6) plus longest time point at two other temperatures which had no data exceeding 10,000 hours (7 points)

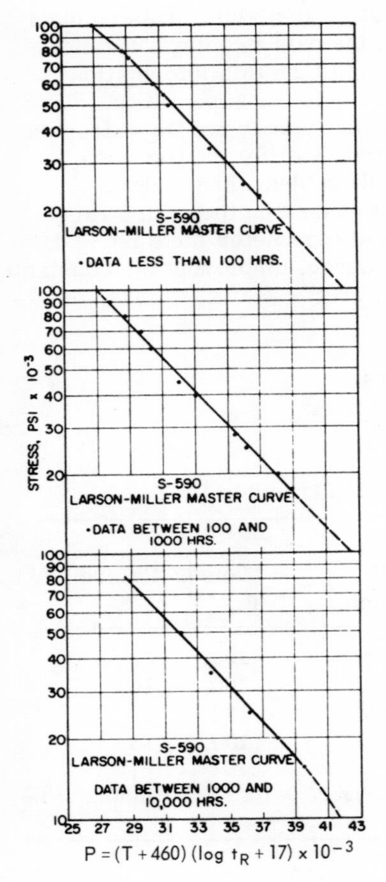

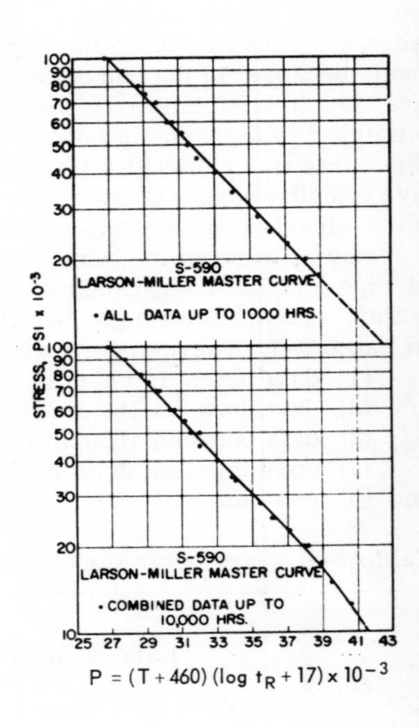

Figure 9-18 – Larson-Miller parameter plots for S-590[43].

(8) for A-286 using all data points exceeding 1000-hour rupture (10 points)

(9) for Nimonic 80A using all data points exceeding 10,000-hour rupture (11 points)

(10) for 1Cr-1Mo-1/4V steel using five longest rupture times (5108 to 10,447 hours)

In each case, the difference between the logarithm of the calculated rupture time and the logarithm of the measured rupture time was observed and used. These differences were then employed to calculate the standard deviation as:

$$\mu = \left(\frac{\Sigma d^2}{n} \right)^{1/2} \qquad (9\text{-}6)$$

where:

μ = standard deviation
n = number of points being compared
and d = difference in calculated and measured log t_R values

A summary of these results is presented in Table 9-8 where it will be noted that the Larson-Miller parameter was employed with both the commonly accepted value of C equal to 20 and with the calculated value of C. As can be noted, better results are obtained, in general, with the Larson-Miller parameter when the C value calculated from the data points is employed. This comparison in Table 9-8 also reveals rather conclusively that for general use in extrapolating high temperature stress-rupture data the linear parameter is superior to either the Larson-Miller or the Dorn parameter. In every case except one, the Manson-Haferd parameter led to a standard deviation which was smaller than that obtained with any other approach in this test of extrapolative ability.

It can also be noted in Table 9-8 that the Dorn parameter is inferior to the Larson-Miller parameter in the analysis of the S-590 and 1Cr-1Mo-1/4 V steel data whereas the reverse is true for the Nimonic 80A data. For A-286, these two parameters give comparable results.

In a re-evaluation of the Goldhoff analysis, Conway and Mullikin(41) were led to conclusions which were significantly different from those reached by Goldhoff. While only the S-590 data were employed, it is felt that similar results would have been obtained with the other materials. Employing optimization procedures, and assuming a second degree polynomial relating the parameter to log stress, master-rupture plots were prepared for the Larson-Miller, Dorn and Manson-Haferd parameters. In one case the analysis was based on data points below 10,000 hours while in a second evaluation only data points below 2,000 hours were included. After the master-rupture plots had been prepared, the isotherms were constructed with the results shown in Figures 9-19 and -20. Then standard deviations were calculated using the same expression employed in the Goldhoff study. Considering only those data points employed in the analysis, the standard deviations shown in Figures 9-19 and -20 were obtained. It will be noted that all three

Table 9-8. Comparison[43] of the Extrapolative Ability of the Dorn, Larson-Miller and Manson-Haferd Parameters. (Table entries represent standard deviations calculated in Equation (9-6)).

Parameters	(1) 100 hour Data	(2) 100 hour to 1000 hour Data	(3) 1000 hour to 10,000 hour Data	(4) All data to 1000 hours	(5) All data to 10,000 hours
		(6) S-590			
Larson-Miller (C = 17)	0.278	0.351	0.195	0.351	0.138
Larson-Miller (C = 20)	0.343	0.585	0.287	0.655	0.348
Dorn	0.646	0.481	0.268	0.430	0.309
Manson-Haferd	0.178	0.305	0.123	0.324	0.112
		(7) S-590			
Larson-Miller (C = 17)	0.235	0.295	0.182	0.293	0.131
Larson-Miller (C = 20)	0.293	0.464	0.235	0.510	0.282
Dorn	0.564	0.392	0.239	0.375	0.282
Manson-Haferd	0.174	0.250	0.115	0.260	0.100
		(8) A-286			
Larson-Miller (C = 20)	0.211	0.208		0.207	
Dorn	0.207	0.188		0.172	
Manson-Haferd	0.188	0.191		0.134	
		(9) Nimonic 80A			
Larson-Miller (C = 18)	0.493	0.342		0.385	
Larson-Miller (C = 20)	0.612	0.464		0.530	
Dorn	0.275	0.237		0.235	
Manson-Haferd	0.108	0.102		0.091	
		(10) 1Cr-1Mo-1/4V Steel			
Larson-Miller (C = 22)	0.386	0.431		0.339	
Larson-Miller	0.389	0.315		0.275	
Dorn	0.638	0.607		0.617	
Manson-Haferd	0.280	0.243		0.274	

parameters exhibit about the same effectiveness with a slight preference being indicated for the Larson-Miller parameter. This is a completely different conclusion from that reached in the Goldhoff study wherein strong preference for the Manson-Haferd parameter was indicated.

Since the analyses described above were based on 2,000-hour and then 10,000-hour data, a study of the extrapolation effectiveness of each parameter was made by comparing predicted (dashed lines in Figures 9-19 and -20) rupture times with experimental values. In each case the standard deviation was calculated based on only those points which were beyond the range of data used in the analysis (5 points for 10,000-hour data and 9 points for the 2,000-hour data). These results are given in Table 9-9. It will be noted that the Dorn parameter is the

Table 9-9. Comparison of Predicted with Experimental Rupture Times for S-590 Alloy for Larson-Miller, Dorn and Manson-Haferd Parameters[41]

a) Based on S-590 Data, t_R < 10,000 Hours

Stress (psi)	Temp. °C	Exper. Rupture Time, Hrs.	Predicted Rupture Times, Hrs. L-M	Dorn	M-H
25,000	1200	43,978	62,248	42,958	41,698
30,000	1200	11,937	11,999	9,977	10,085
17,500	1350	16,964	19,508	13,493	16,378
10,000	1500	15,335	34,465	17,436	21,870
10,000	1500	11,257	34,465	17,436	21,870
			μ = 0.278	0.105	0.151

b) Based on S-590 Data, t_R < 2,000 Hours

Stress (psi)	Temp. °C	Exper. Rupture Time, Hrs.	L-M	Dorn	M-H
50,000	1100	3,149	1,661	1,614	1,467
35,000	1200	2,243	2,582	2,206	2,304
20,000	1350	9,529	5,921	4,234	5,143
12,500	1500	5,052	6,428	4,076	5,084
25,000	1200	43,978	50,747	29,856	29,860
30,000	1200	11,937	10,069	7,518	7,715
17,500	1350	16,964	17,761	10,332	13,067
10,000	1500	15,335	35,918	13,873	19,445
10,000	1500	11,257	35,918	13,873	19,445
			μ = 0.244	0.195	0.190

most effective in the case of the 10,000-hour data with the Manson-Haferd just somewhat less effective. Rather poor results are seen for the Larson-Miller parameter. In the 2,000-hour analysis approximately equal effectiveness is seen for the Dorn and Manson-Haferd parameters with the Larson-Miller parameter again being somewhat less effective. These conclusions are again quite different from those of Goldhoff. A comparison of the results in Table 9-9(a) with those in (5) (6) of Table 9-8 will reveal the basis for these different conclusions. Apparently a different comparison results when optimization procedures are employed.

In a study of the stress-rupture behavior of a silicon-killed steel (see Appendix B for data), Wood and Wade[44] compared the extrapolative ability of the Larson-Miller, Dorn, Manson-Haferd and Graham-Walles parameters. Data for rupture times less than 10,000 hours were employed in the determination of parameter constants. Extrapolations beyond this range formed the basis of the comparison and included experimentally measured rupture times to 23,180 hours.

Parameters developed were as follows:

Larson-Miller $\quad T(23.8 + \log t_R)$

$$t_R e^{-\frac{80,000}{RT}}$$

Dorn

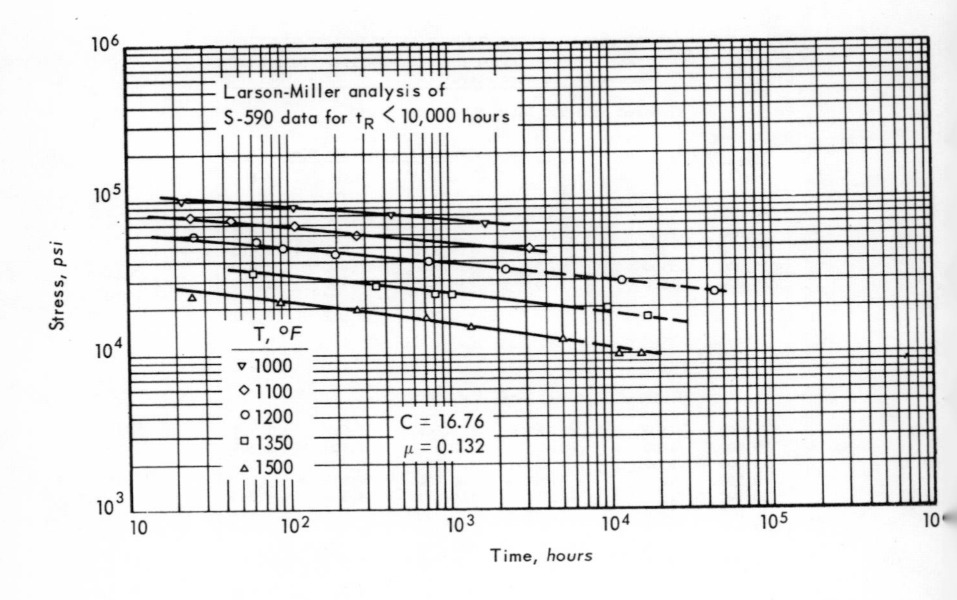

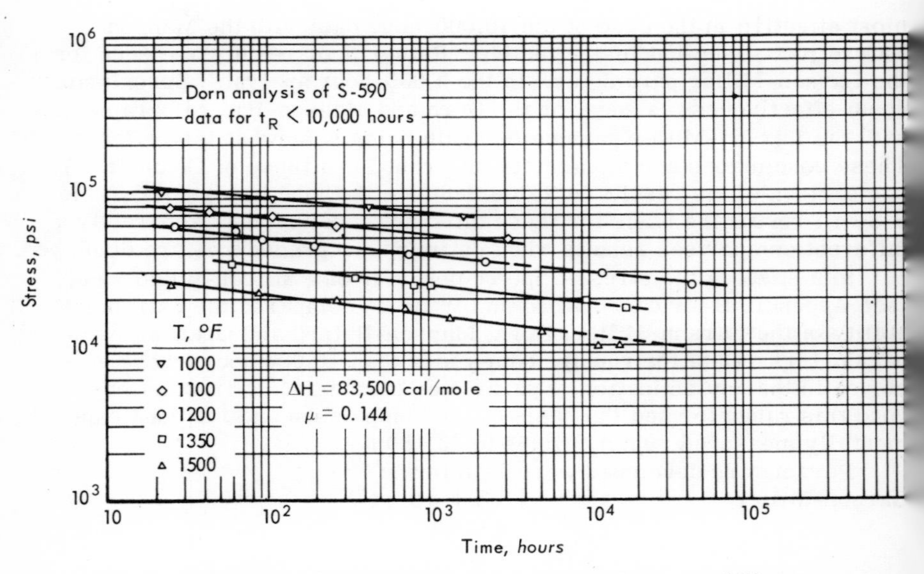

Figure 9-19 – Comparison of parameter results for S-590 data[41]; rupture times less than 10,000 hours employed in establishing parameter plot.

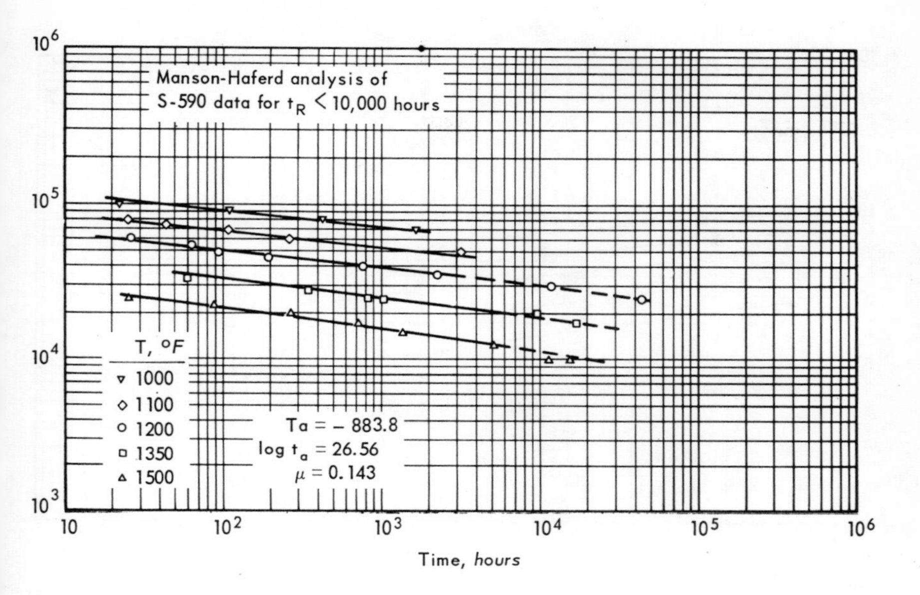

Figure 9–19 (continued)

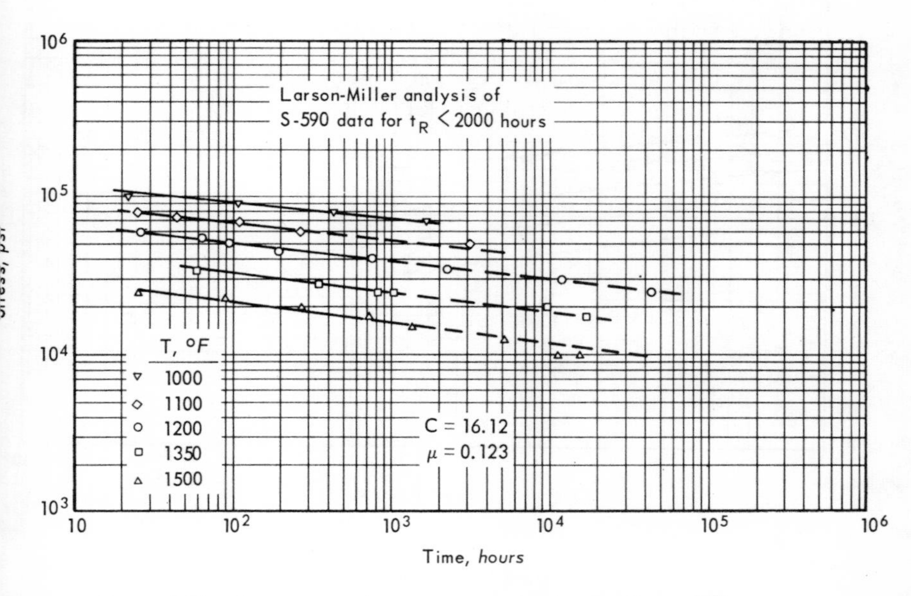

Figure 9-20 – Comparison of parameter results for S-590 data[41]; rupture times less than 2,000 hours employed in establishing parameter plot.

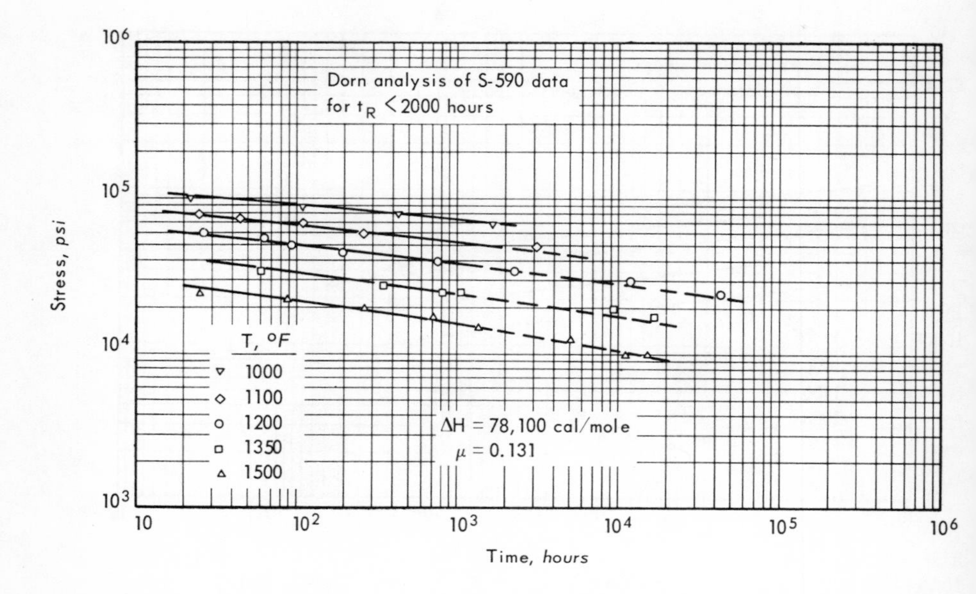

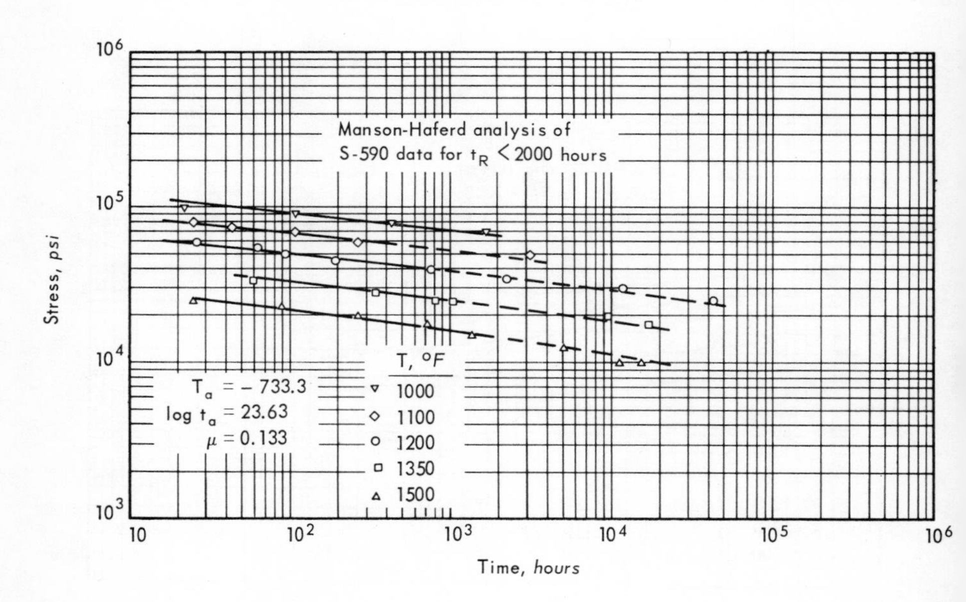

Figure 9-20 (continued)

Manson-Haferd $\frac{T + 62}{\log t_R - 21}$

Graham-Walles $t_R(T - 200°C)-20$

When the parameter plots were made and a smooth curve was drawn to represent the points, it was found that for every parameter the longer times points were in good agreement with the parameter curve. Never did the deviations exceed 6 percent based on stress.

In a graphical extrapolation of these same data, Wood and Wade plotted either stress or log stress and extrapolated these isotherms to 200,000 hours. It was noted that while this approach is the quickest, it is not likely to be the most accurate. Results beyond 10,000 hours were, however, observed to be within 7 percent of the extrapolated isotherms indicating that in this instance the graphical extrapolation led to fairly satisfactory results. This should not be expected in general, however, particularly for extrapolations involving one order of magnitude in rupture life.

Each of the methods described above was then employed to predict rupture conditions corresponding to 200,000-hour life for the silicon-killed steel. A summary of these results is presented in Table 9-10. It was noted that the accuracies for all the extrapolation procedures were essentially the same. It was not possible to assign any preference, therefore, to any one parameter. Also noted was the fact that the Dorn parameter led to results intermediate between the others and was, therefore, given some preference.

Table 9-10. Prediction of Rupture Conditions Corresponding to 200,000-Hour Life for Silicon-Killed Steel.[44]

	Stress, tons/in^2				
T°C	L-M	M-H	D	G-W	Graphical
400	11.0	10.0	10.6	10.8	11.0
375	14.0	13.2	13.6	14.0	15.0
350	17.0	16.4	16.7	17.9	--

In a study by Betteridge[47] of the rupture data for Nimonic 80A and Nimonic 90, the extrapolative effectiveness of various parameters was compared. Data up to 3,000 hours were employed to establish the parameter constants and to prepare the parameter plots; these results were then employed to obtain extrapolated data to compare with existing experimental data in the range from 3,000 to 34,000 hours. For the Larson-Miller analysis, C values for Nimonic 80A and Nimonic 90 were determined to be 16.9 and 19.2, respectively, with the parameter results shown in Figure 9-21. Obviously, the parameter values corresponding to the long-term tests fall consistently below the master curve.

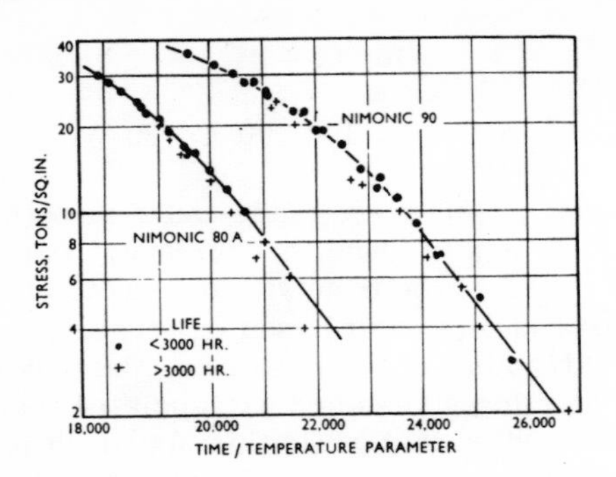

Figure 9-21 – Larson-Miller parameter plot for Nimonic 80A and Nimonic 90[47].

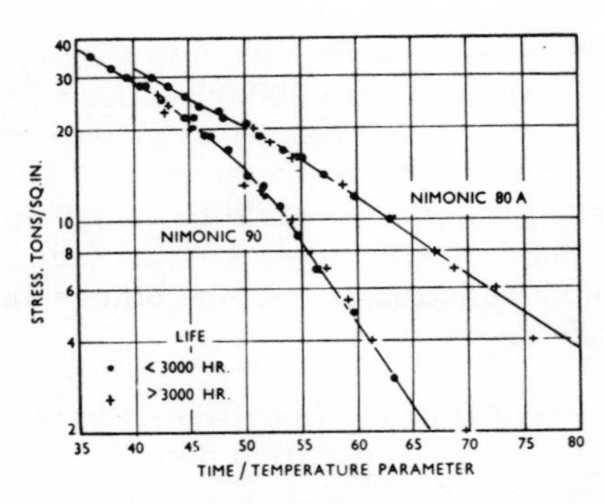

Figure 9-22 – Manson-Haferd parameter plot for Nimonic 80A and Nimonic 90[47].

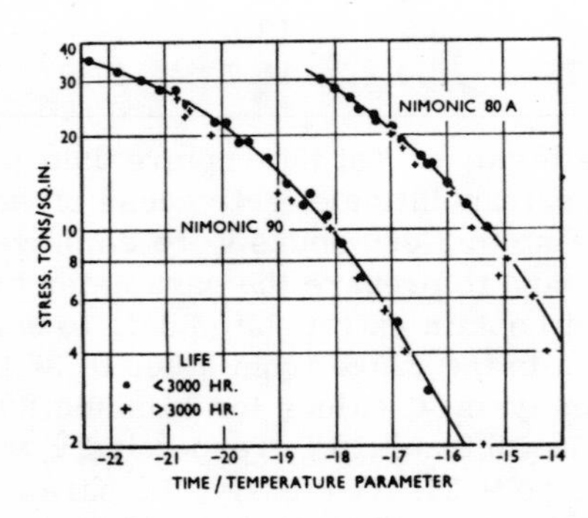

Figure 9-23 – Dorn parameter plot for Nimonic 80A and Nimonic 90[47].

Some error is then to be expected in extrapolations to longer term values based on the short-term data below 8,000 hours. In the Manson-Haferd analysis the constants for Nimonic 80A and Nimonic 90 were T_a = 850 °C, log t_a = 9.65 and T_a = 250°C and log t_a = 13.10, respectively. Parameter plots for these materials are presented in Figure 9-22. In this case the parameter points for the longer term data fall close to the master curve. For the Dorn parameter, ΔH was calculated to be 87,500 and 103,100 cal/mole for Nimonic 80A and Nimonic 90, respectively. Parameter plots are presented in Figure 9-23. In a Graham-Walles type of analysis, both materials required a change in the T' constant as the stress changed. For Nimonic 80A in the stress range from 20 to 30 tons/in^2, a value of T' = 1150°C was applicable; from 10 to 20 tons/in^2 a value of 1350°C was required. Of course, A was taken equal to 20 for both materials in accord with the Graham-Walles findings. Parameter values for this material are presented in Figure 9-24 in which the straight lines were drawn with standard slopes of 1/8 and 1/4 based on the Graham-Walles suggested approach. In the case of the Nimonic 90 data T' values of 1130°C and 1330°C were identified for the high and low stress ranges. Two changes of slope could be identified as shown in Figure 9-24; one of these occurs at 28 and the other at 15 tons/in^2. These segments of the parameter plot were drawn with slopes of 1/16, 1/8, and 1/4, but a T' value for the highest stress range could not be calculated so the adjacent T' value was used in the parameter calculations.

Using the results for the four parameters just described, Betteridge prepared the comparison shown in Tables 9-11 and -12. Based on a study of these results the Manson-Haferd parameter is definitely to be preferred for use in extrapolations of the Nimonic 80A data. An average deviation of 3 to 4 precent is noted compared to 10 to 12 percent for the other methods. In the case of Nimonic 90 the preference is not as decisive, although, if the single point at 2 tons/in^2 is eliminated, the Manson-Haferd parameter would once again seem to yield the best results. It was concluded, too, that this comparison suggests that extrapolation from 3,000 to 30,000 hours, i.e., one order of magnitude, is quite effective in that reliable results are obtained. If the stress corresponding to the extrapolated life is within the range of the parameter plot, estimates of stress corresponding to longer rupture life are likely to be within 10 percent of the true value.

A comparison of the Larson-Miller, Dorn and Manson-Haferd parameters was also provided by Manson and Succop[46] in a study of the Inconel 700 data (see Figure 4-9 and Appendix B). Graphical construction led to C = 28 and ΔH = 152,000 for the Larson-Miller and Dorn parameters, respectively. In these calculations the plot shown in Figure 9-25 was employed where the dot-dash lines represent the series of straight lines converging to a common point of C = 28 at $(1/T) = 0$; the dashed lines represent the Dorn series of parallel lines and the solid lines represent the lines from Figure 4-8. Differences between measured rupture times and those established by the various parameters were

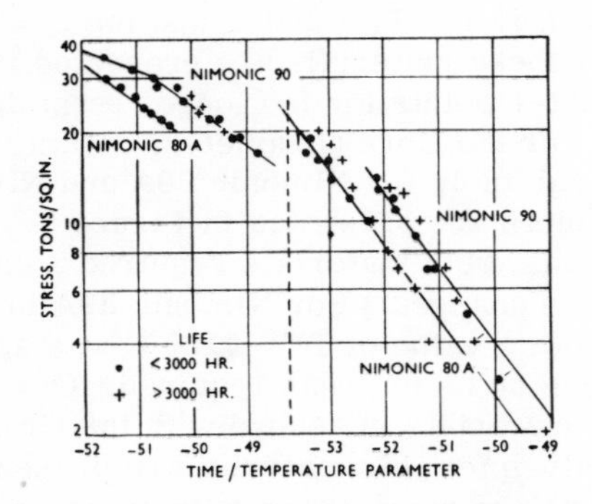

Figure 9-24 – Graham-Walles parameter plot for Nimonic 80A and Nimonic 90[47].

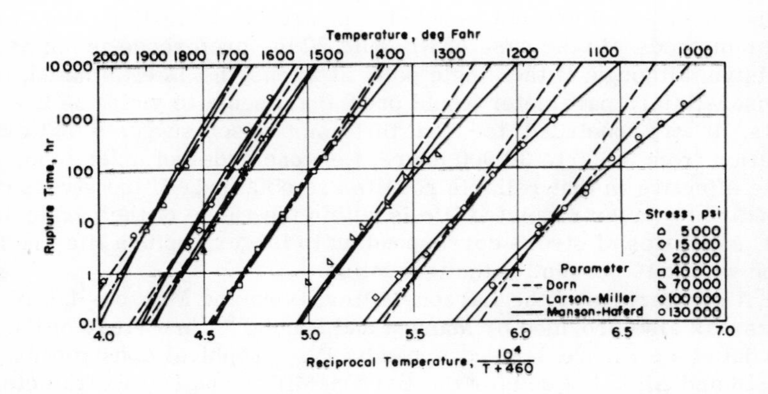

Figure 9-25 – Rupture time versus 1/T for Inconel 700[46].

TABLE 9-11

COMPARISON FOR NIMONIC 80A, OF LONG-TIME TEST RESULTS WITH THE PREDICTIONS OF DIFFERENT PARAMETERS FROM SHORT-TIME TESTS(47)

Temp., °C.	Test Result		Predicted Stresses to Give Observed Life							
			Larson and Miller		Manson and Haferd		Orr, Sherby, and Dorn		Graham and Walles	
	Stress, tons/in.^{2}	Life, hr.	Stress, tons/in.^{2}	Deviation, %	Stress, tons/in.^{2}	Deviation, %	Stress, tons/in.^{2}	Deviation, %	Stress, tons/in.^{2}	Deviation, %
650	20	5,270	20·4	+ 2	19·7	− 1½	20·3	+ 1½	16·5	−18
	18	8,171	19·0	+ 6	18·1	+ ½	18·9	+ 5	14·8	−18
	16	13,386	17·6	+10	16·0	0	17·6	+10	13·1	−18
700	13	4,836	13·6	+ 5	12·8	− 1½	13·9	+ 7	11·8	− 9
	10	10,893	11·6	+16	10·1	+ 1	11·6	+16	9·4	− 6
	7	34,065	8·8	+26	7·2	+ 3	8·7	+24	7·1	+ 1
750	8	4,450	8·0	0	7·9	− 1	7·9	− 1	7·9	− 1
	6	13,089	6·2	+ 3	5·6	− 7	6·0	0	6·0	0
	4	22,657	5·3	+33	4·6	+15	5·0	+25	5·2	+30
Average Deviation				11·2		3·4		10·0		11·2

TABLE 9-12

COMPARISON FOR NIMONIC 90, OF LONG-TIME TEST RESULTS WITH THE PREDICTIONS OF DIFFERENT PARAMETERS FROM SHORT-TIME TESTS[47]

Temp., °C.	Test Result		Predicted Stresses to Give Observed Life							
			Larson and Miller		Manson and Haferd		Orr, Sherby, and Dorn		Graham and Walles	
	Stress, tons/in.^{2}	Life, hr.	Stress, tons/in.^{2}	Deviation, %	Stress, tons/in.^{2}	Deviation, %	Stress, tons/in.^{2}	Deviation, %	Stress, tons/in.^{2}	Deviation, %
650	26	4,111	26·0	0	26·0	0	26·4	+ 2	24·2	− 7
	24	6,443	24·8	+ 3	24·4	+ 2	25·0	+ 4	23·0	− 4
	23	5,373	25·1	+ 9	25·0	+ 9	25·8	+12	24·0	+ 4
	20	15,294	22·5	+23	21·8	+ 9	23·0	+15	20·5	− 3
700	13	12,094	15·5	+19	14·6	+12	15·7	+21	11·8	− 9
	12·5	20,399	14·2	+14	13·0	+ 4	14·2	+14	10·3	−18
750	10	7,593	10·0	0	9·5	− 5	10·2	+ 2	8·6	−14
	7	22,159	8·0	+14	6·6	− 6	7·7	+10	6·6	− 6
815	5·5	3,342	5·7	+ 4	5·2	− 5	5·6	+ 2	5·9	+ 7
	4	6,830	4·7	+18	4·1	+ 2	4·3	+ 8	4·9	+23
870	2	16,292	1·8	−10	1·4	−30	1·5	−25	2·3	+15
Average Deviation				9·5		7·7		10·5		10·0

calculated at a stress of 100,000 psi. These results, expressed as percent, are plotted in Figure 9-26 and reveal a much better correlation in the case of the Manson-Haferd parameter. At a rupture time of 829 hours, for example, errors arising from the use of the Larson-Miller and Dorn parameters were 146 and 578 percent, respectively.

Use has been made of the Manson, Succop and Brown[52] analysis, presented in Figure 4-7 of Chapter 4, to construct the isotherms as shown in Figure 9-27 and compare these with the actual experimental data. One point at 940°F and 40,000 psi (24,000-hour rupture) is also shown in comparison with the predicted 940°F isotherms. Using these same data in both a Larson-Miller and a Dorn analysis led to the other constructed isotherms shown in Figure 9-27. In the plot shown in Figure 9-28 (same isostatic data as in Figure 4-6) the least squares lines do not appear parallel nor do they converge to a common point at $(1/T) = 0$. As a matter of fact, based on the Larson-Miller approach, $C = 18$ for the 10,000 psi data and 32 for the 80,000 psi results. In other words, the behavior is not consistent with either the Dorn or Larson-Miller concept. However, average values of $C = 25$ and $\Delta H = 108{,}000$ were employed to evaluate the type of results obtained with these parametric approaches. All experimental points were used in establishing master-rupture curves for each parameter.

A comparison of these results in presented in Figure 9-27 where isotherms at 900°, 940° and 1100°F have been positioned. To complete the comparison the case for $C = 20$ is also considered (parameter plots for the Dorn and Larson-Miller analyses are presented in Figures 9-29 and -30). It can be noted that the linear parameter leads to isotherms in Figure 9-27 which provide a more accurate representation of the experimental data. Particularly noteworthy is the fact that using this linear parameter the data corresponding to rupture in well over 1,000 hours have been fairly accurately predicted using data based on rupture times of less than 100 hours.

Considering the Larson-Miller results in Figure 9-27 it was noted that for $C = 20$ the 1100°F data were described fairly well within the experimental range but poor results were obtained at 900°F. At this temperature the rupture life predicted at 85,000 psi was in error by a factor close to five. If $C = 25$ the results at 900°F are seen to be improved; however, large errors result at 1100°F for the longer rupture times. At 940°F the predicted 24,000-hour rupture stress is found to be high by some 40 percent. Similar comments were made regarding the effectiveness of the Dorn parameter and, hence, a definite superiority in favor of the Manson-Haferd approach was identified.

In a comparison of the relative effectiveness of the Larson-Miller and Manson-Haferd parameters, Manson and Brown[50] considered the data for five different steels. Using all the experimental points the parameter constants were calculated and the master-rupture plot prepared. Isotherms were then constructed based on the master-rupture plot and a comparison of parameter effectiveness was provided by observing the agreement between the position of the calculated isotherms and the experimental points.

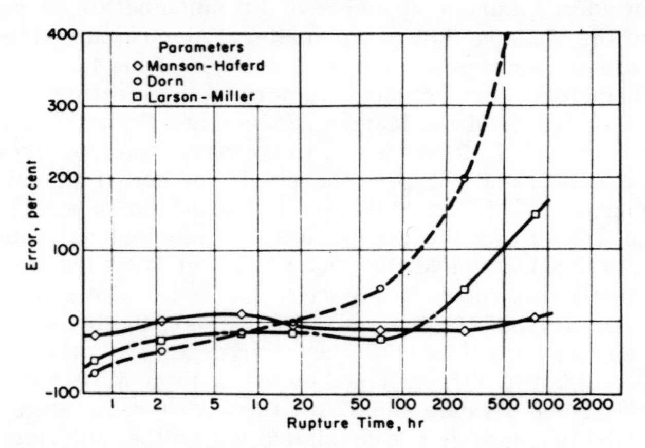

Figure 9-26 – Percent error in predicted life of Inconel 700 at 100,000 psi resulting from use of various parameters(46).

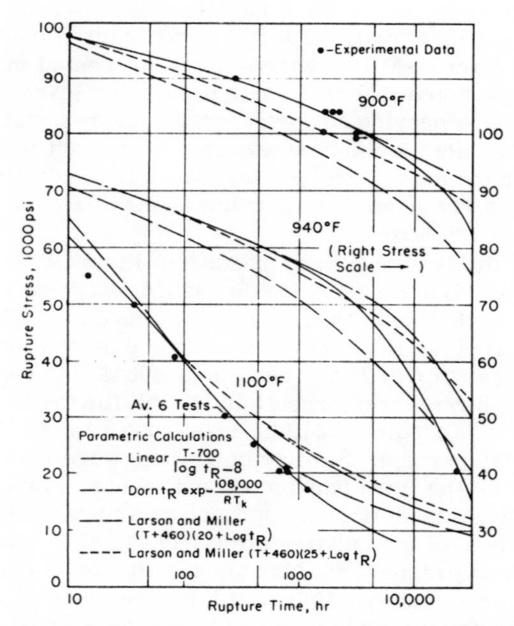

Figure 9-27 – Comparison of isotherms for "17-22-A"S based on Larson-Miller, Dorn and Manson-Haferd analyses(52).

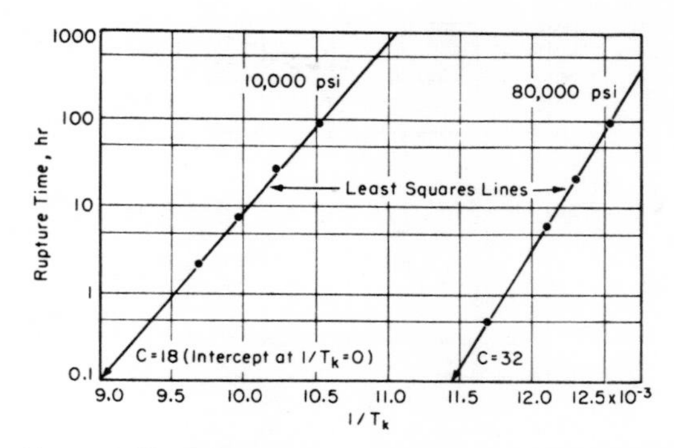

Figure 9-28 – Plot of log t_R versus 1/T for "17-22-A"S data[52].

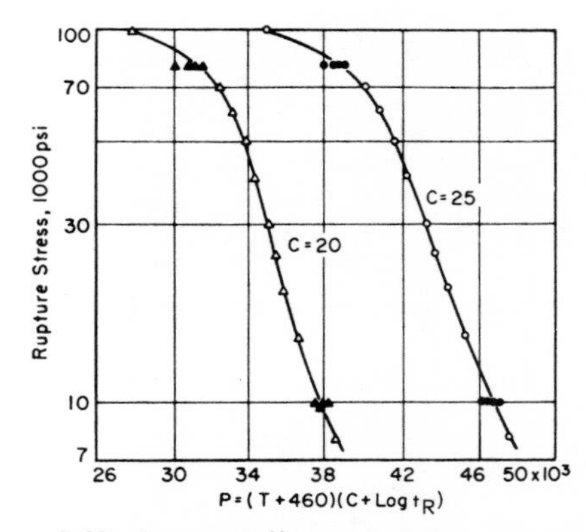

Figure 9-29 – Larson-Miller master-rupture curves for "17-22-A"S[52].

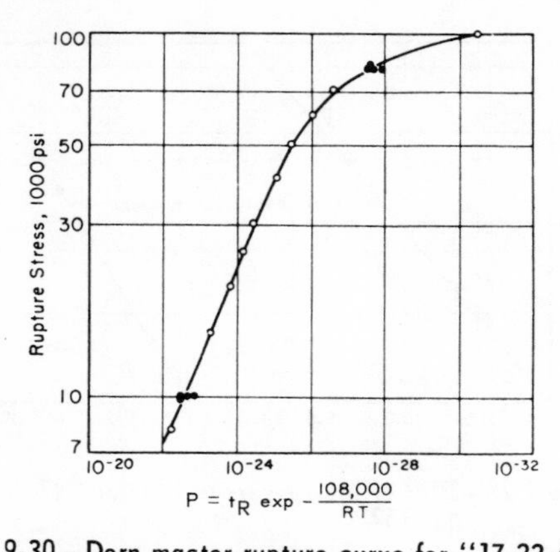

Figure 9-30 – Dorn master-rupture curve for "17-22-A"S[52].

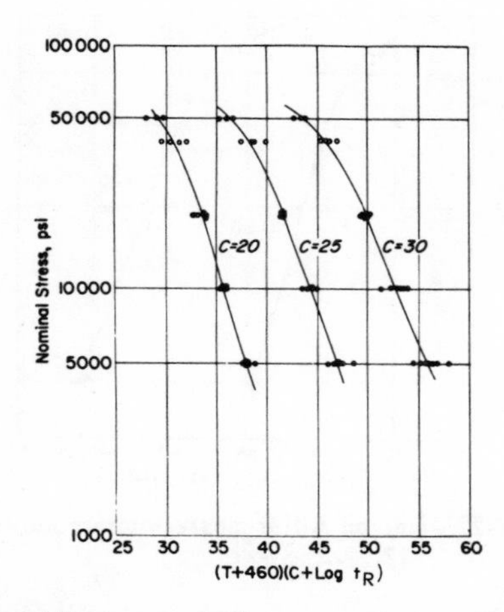

Figure 9-31 – Larson-Miller master-rupture plots for DM steel[50].

Calculations of the Larson-Miller constant were made graphically by Manson and Brown on a log t_R vs (1/T) plot. While noting that no common convergence point was observed, several different C values were investigated and the final value chosen was that which led to the best positioning of the calculated isotherms with respect to the experimental points. For the DM steel, several C values were considered leading to the master-rupture plots shown in Figure 9-31. Data for both C = 20 and C = 25 were eventually used for this material in this comparative study as shown in Figure 9-32.

Based on the comparative results presented in Figure 9-32 Manson and Brown concluded that in general the Manson-Haferd parameter gave the best results. As an extreme case, the Larson-Miller master-rupture plot gave a rupture time of 15 hours at 900°F and 50,000 psi compared to an experimental value of 400 hours. At 40,000 psi and 960°F, the calculated rupture time was 25 hours compared to an experimental value of 930 hours. In the Manson and Brown evaluation no comparison of the extrapolative ability of the two parameters was made. However, it should be clear that little success can be expected in making predictions based on some of the curves in Figure 9-32. For example, for the Larson-Miller (C = 20) results for DM steel at a temperature just about 1000°F the predicted rupture life is higher than the measured value whereas the reverse is true at the next lower stress.

An evaluation of the general form of the Manson-Haferd parameter given in equation (4-34) in Chapter 4 was described by Manson.(56,57) These discussions pertained to the German cooperative long-term creep program in which sufficient material was supplied to NASA Cleveland to enable measurements to be made of the short-term creep-rupture behavior. Using only these NASA data a parametric analysis was made to allow comparison with long-term results, predicted in this analysis, with the actual data obtained in the German test program. Three steels were employed, designated K, C and P (see original reference for composition). In the NASA test program rupture times to 13,140 hours were observed; in the German program times as long as 100,000 hours were encountered.

In the analysis of all three steels the stress exponent, Q, was found to be zero while the R value was different for each material being 1.0 for steel K, -1 for steel P, and 2.5 for steel C. A typical master-rupture plot for steel K is shown in Figure 9-33. Computed isotherms for all materials based on the optimized parameter approach are presented in Figure 9-34. In each case the range of the NASA data employed in the analysis is indicated and the plotted points represent the data obtained in the German test program. It can be seen that the predictions up to 10^6 hours based on the NASA analysis are in fairly good agreement with the German test data actually obtained.

In this same analysis the best linear parameter, the best Larson-Miller parameter and the best general parameter were employed to yield the comparison presented in Figure 9-35. Although for some of the steels fair agreement is obtained with one or the other of these

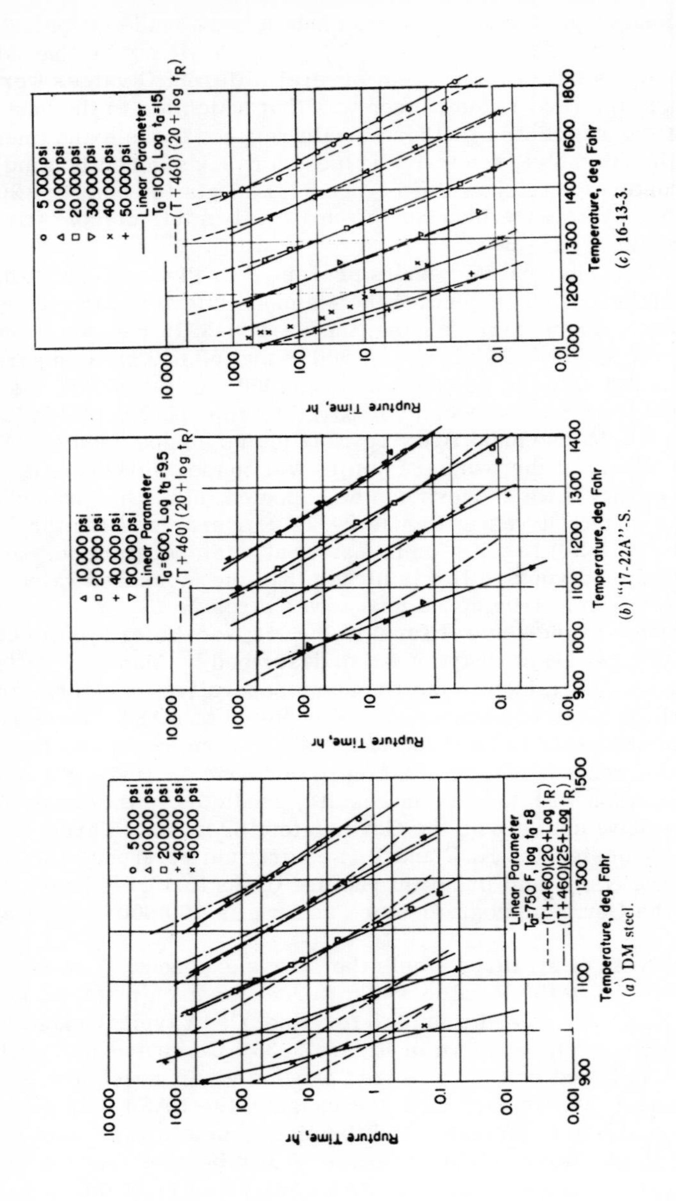

(a) DM steel.

(b) "17-22A"-S.

(c) 16-13-3.

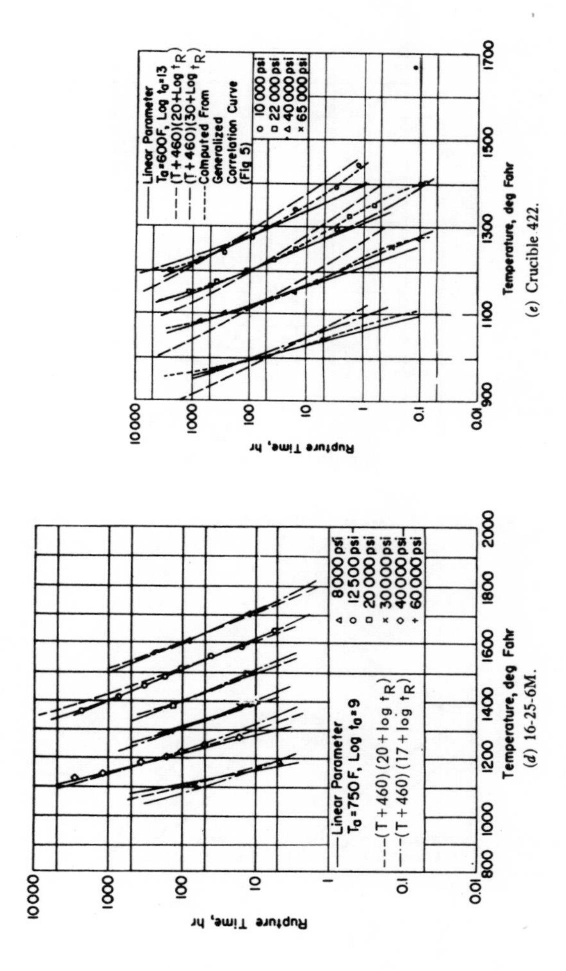

(*d*) 16-25-6M.

(*e*) Crucible 422.

Figure 9-32 — Constant stress data compared to isotherms based on various parameter correlations(50).

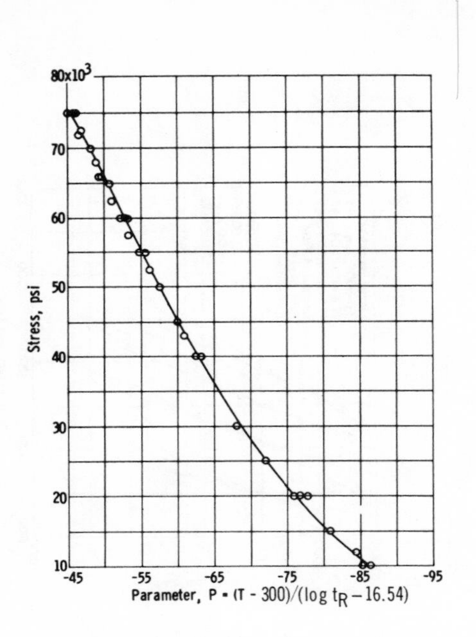

Figure 9-33 – Manson-Haferd master-rupture plot for steel K(57).

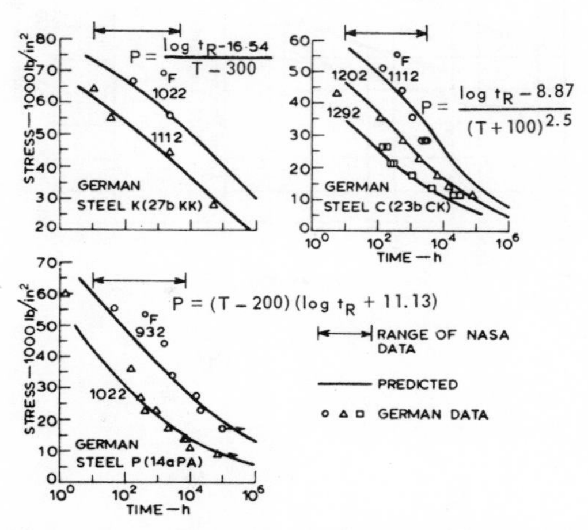

Figure 9-34 – Comparison of German test data with computed results based on NASA data(56).

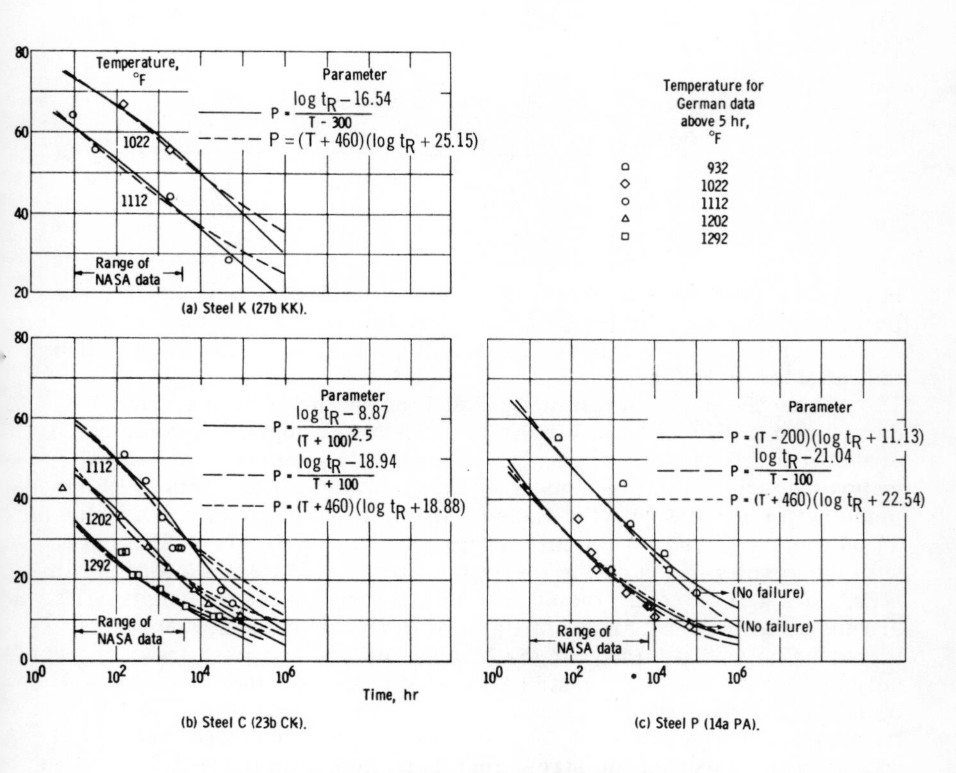

Figure 9-35 – Analysis of German steel data in terms of various parameters[57].

parameters, it is clear that the general parameter leads to the most effective results for all materials considered as a group. If any one of the special cases of this parameter is to be chosen, the linear parameter would be preferred.

An evaluation of the effectiveness of the Larson-Miller, Dorn and Manson-Haferd parameters was also provided in a study of the data for arc-cast molybdenum, tungsten and tungsten-25 rhenium[41] (see Figures 2-10, 3-4 and 4-22). Calculated values for the standard deviation were as follows:

	Standard deviation based on log t_R		
Material	L-M	D	M-H
Mo	0.136	0.155	0.146
W	0.123	0.184	0.098
W-25Re	0.115	0.162	0.070

In general, the Dorn parameter was the least effective with the Manson-Haferd parameter providing the best results. Only in the case of molybdenum did the Larson-Miller approach appear to be slightly better than that of Manson-Haferd.

Noting the poor correlation of the Timken 25-20 stainless steel data shown in Figure 2-32 for the Larson-Miller approach, some re-evaluation of these data seemed in order. Using the optimization procedures described in previous chapters, Conway and Mullikin[41] obtained much better results with the Larson-Miller parameter when a C value of 14.03 was employed. This correlation is shown in Figure 9-36 along with the results based on the use of the Dorn and Manson-Haferd parameters. As will be noted, the standard deviations (based on long time) are identical for the Larson-Miller and Dorn approaches; a slightly higher value was obtained for the Manson-Haferd approach in which only the one form of the linear parameter was evaluated. For this set of data then, the three parameters seem to have about the same effectiveness. In these analyses, however, only a second degree polynomial was used to represent the stress function. Improved correlations might evolve from the use of additional terms.

In a study of the data for 18-8 stainless steel,[41] a Larson-Miller analysis was employed to evaluate the effect of the number of points included in the analysis. A summary of these results is as follows:

Data points	C Value	Standard Deviation
$<$ 100 hours	16.66	0.174
1 to 100 hours	14.13	0.153
all points	15.79	0.156

Optimization procedures were employed to yield the Larson-Miller constant and to position the master-rupture curve. The data points used in

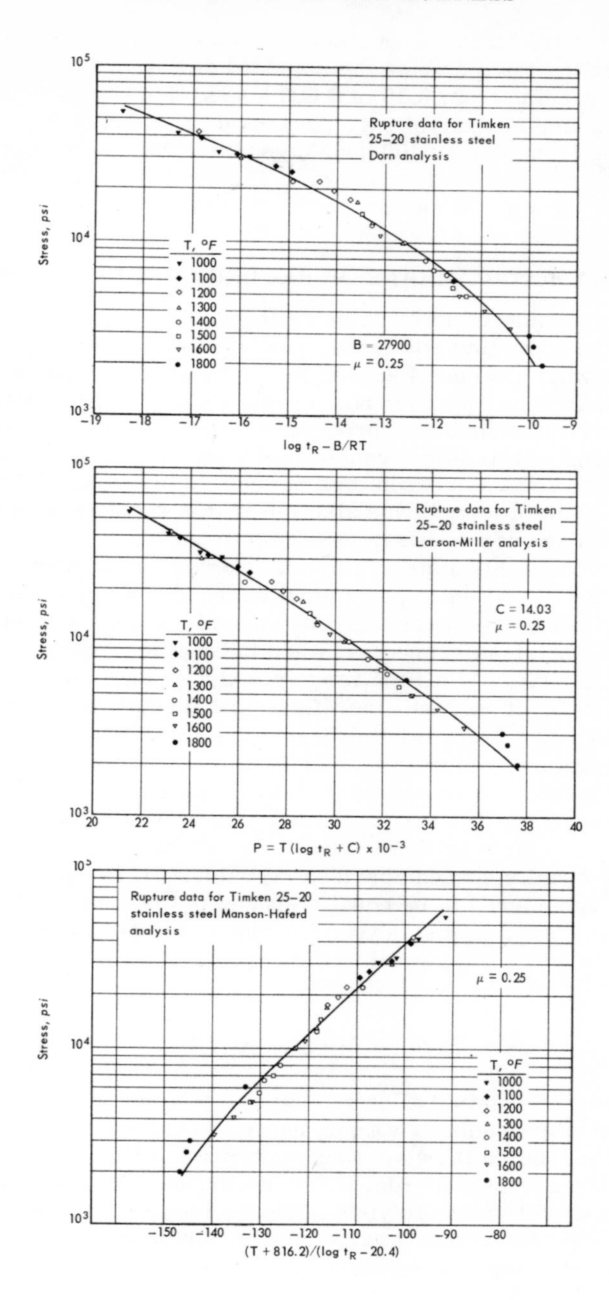

Figure 9-36—Re-evaluation of Timken 25-20 data in terms of Larson-Miller, Dorn and Manson-Haferd parameters.[41]

each analysis are indicated in column 1 (above) with the C value in column 2; in the third column the standard deviation is based on all data points ranging from 0.15 to 8,000 hours. Isotherms constructed from the parameter analysis are presented in Figure 9-37. For the data ranging from 0.15 to 100 hours, good predictions of rupture life to 1,000 hours is obtained as shown in Figure 9-37. At 1500°F the predicted results are somewhat high but at the other temperatures the extrapolations are excellent.

EXTRAPOLATION BY MEANS OF RECURRENCE RELATIONS

Having considered in some depth the extrapolation procedures associated with parametric approaches, it is particularly pertinent to now review what has been found to be a very effective mathematical extrapolation. This approach has no relationship to parameters themselves. It is a mathematical procedure which allows for very accurate extrapolations and its effectiveness has been compared to that of various parameters. For this reason then, a detailed discussion of this approach was felt to be in order. It was also felt that it should correctly be made a part of this chapter on parameter effectiveness.

In developing this approach to data extrapolation, Mendelson and Manson[66] noted that when polynomial expressions are employed to represent a set of data over a given range of x values a good representation can be obtained. However, when these same expressions are used to extrapolate beyond the range of existing data, serious error can be involved. It was felt, therefore, that if improved extrapolations are to be obtained a somewhat different approach must be adopted. These authors, therefore, resorted to a finite difference recurrence relation and used a least squares approach to the identification of the constants in these recurrence relations. Specifically, it was considered that a linear relation exists between successive ordinate (y) values corresponding to equally spaced abscissa (x) values. If in Figure 9-38 the x values are considered to be equally spaced in the range of the data, then, a point y_i at a point x_i just beyond the range of the data (spacing between x_i and x_{i-1} is, of course, equal to the spacing of all x values) can be calculated as:

$$y_i = A_1 y_{i-1} + A_2 y_{i-2} \dots + A_q y_{i-q} \quad (9\text{-}7)$$

This recurrence relation allows a value of y to be calculated based on a knowledge of preceding y values; hence, no values of x are employed except as they define the equi-spaced stations along the abscissa. Also, q is considered to be the order of the recurrence relation and a value 2, 3 or 4 is usually found to yield adequate results. In other words, if q is chosen equal to 3, then, a value of y is calculated based on the 3 previous y values. Based on equation (9-7) and Figure 9-38 it follows that:

$$y_i = A_1 y_{i-1} + A_2 y_{i-2} + A_3 y_{i-3} \quad (9\text{-}8)$$

where, as mentioned above, y_i is an extrapolated value of y located at x_i just beyond the range of the experimental data. Once y_i is calculated it can then serve as a data point to calculate the next y value located at y_{i+1} and corresponding to x_{i+1} ; thus:

$$y_{i+1} = A_1 y_i + A_2 y_{i-1} + A_3 y_{i-2} \tag{9-9}$$

As observed the order is still equal to 3 and the same constants used in equation (9-8) are applicable. This procedure can be repeated until any extent of extrapolation is accomplished. Of course, only those y values corresponding to equi-spaced x values are calculated in this procedure.

It was further assumed by Mendelson and Manson that a family of curves could be described and extrapolated by the recurrence relation shown in equation (9-7). If, for example, the family of curves shown in Figure 9-39 is considered, then it is assumed that recurrence relations can be written for each curve. In this plot, all the data have been calculated using the equation indicated in Figure 9-39. A range of experimental data has been arbitrarily selected ($\log t_R > 3$) so that predicted data stemming from a recurrence analysis of the so-called experimental data could be compared with known or what might be called true values.

A least squares approach was chosen to calculate the constants in all the recurrence relations for the family of curves in Figure 9-39. As a first step it is necessary to fair a smooth curve through the data points at each temperature. Then, n equally spaced stations are chosen along the abscissa for each family (these equi-spaced stations need not be chosen at the same abscissa values for all the curves even though the increment must be constant for all values. For each member of the family of curves:

$$\begin{aligned}
y_k^{(1)} &= A_1 y_{k-1}^{(1)} + A_2 y_{k-2}^{(1)} + A_3 y_{k-3}^{(1)} + \cdots + A_q y_{k-q}^{(1)} \\
y_k^{(2)} &= A_1 y_{k-1}^{(2)} + A_2 y_{k-2}^{(2)} + A_3 y_{k-3}^{(2)} + \cdots + A_q y_{k-q}^{(2)} \\
&\;\;\vdots \\
y_k^{(m)} &= A_1 y_{k-1}^{(m)} + A_2 y_{k-2}^{(m)} + A_3 y_{k-3}^{(m)} + \cdots + A_q y_{k-q}^{(m)}
\end{aligned} \tag{9-10}$$

where $y_k^{(p)}$ represents the value of the dependent variable at the end of the k-th interval and the superscript represents the member of the family under consideration. Obviously, q cannot be greater than the number of intervals chosen.

Values for the constants A_1, A_2, etc., are obtained by applying the usual least squares considerations. An expression for the sum, S, of the squares of the residuals is first written as:

$$S = \sum_{p=1}^{m} \sum_{k=q+1}^{n} \left(y_k^{(p)} - A_1 y_{k-1}^{(p)} - A_2 y_{k-2}^{(p)} - A_q y_{k-q}^{(p)}\right)^2 \tag{9-11}$$

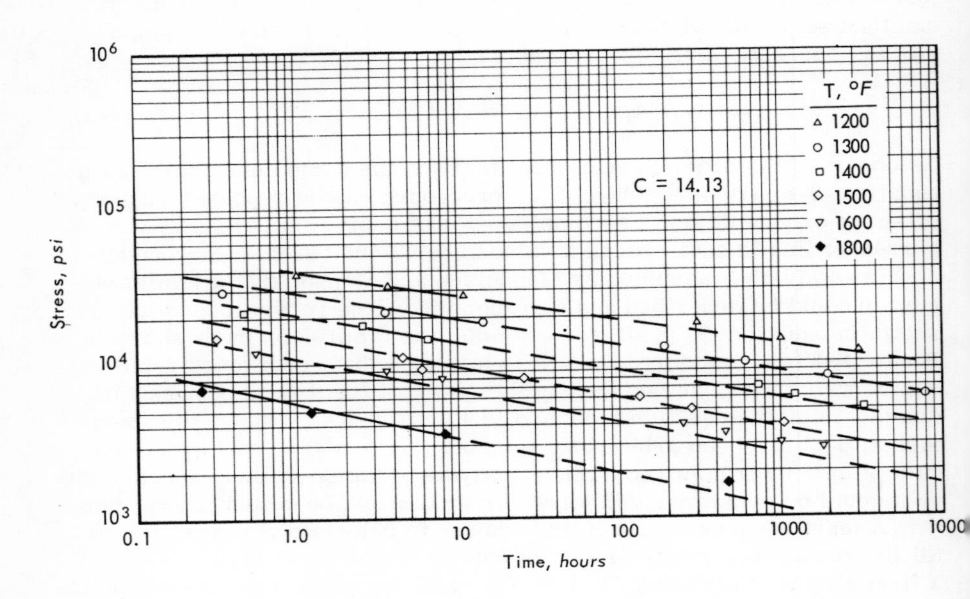
10⁶
10⁵
10⁴
10³
Stress, psi
0.1
1.0
10
100
1000
1000
Time, hours
C = 14.13
T, °F
1200
1300
1400
1500
1600
1800

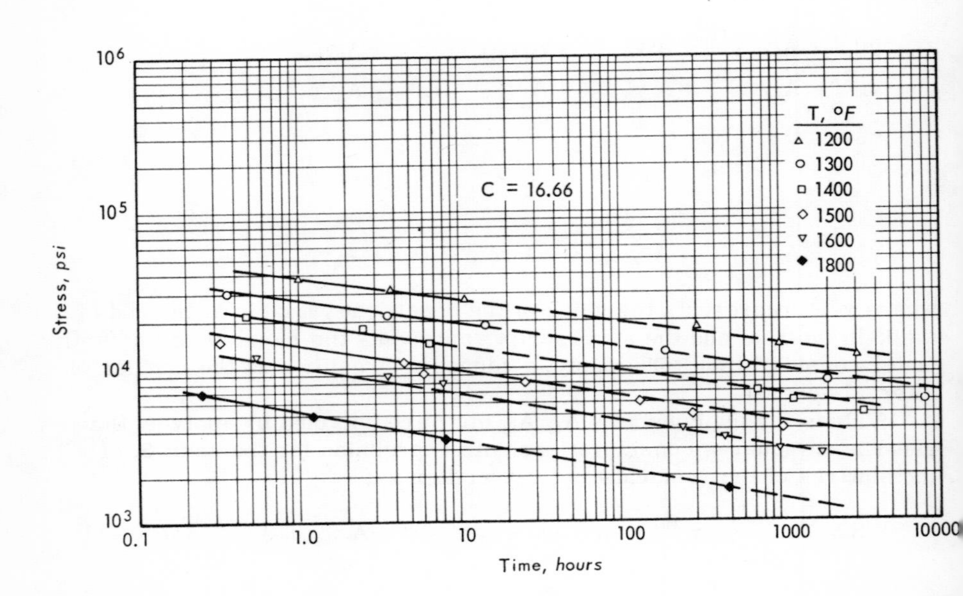
10⁶
10⁵
10⁴
10³
Stress, psi
0.1
1.0
10
100
1000
10000
Time, hours
C = 16.66
T, °F
1200
1300
1400
1500
1600
1800

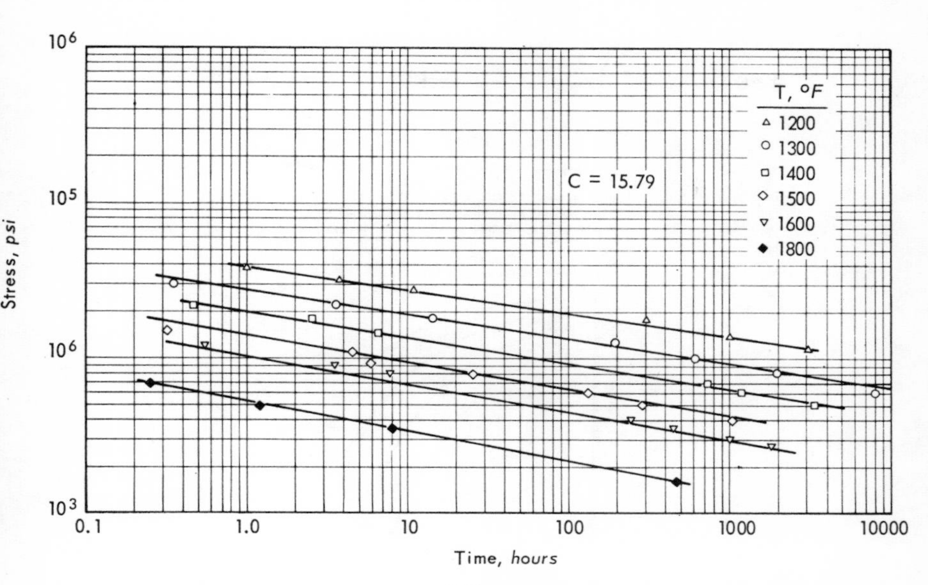

Figure 9-37 – Larson-Miller analysis[41] of 18-8 stainless steel data; effect of number of points included in the analysis is indicated.

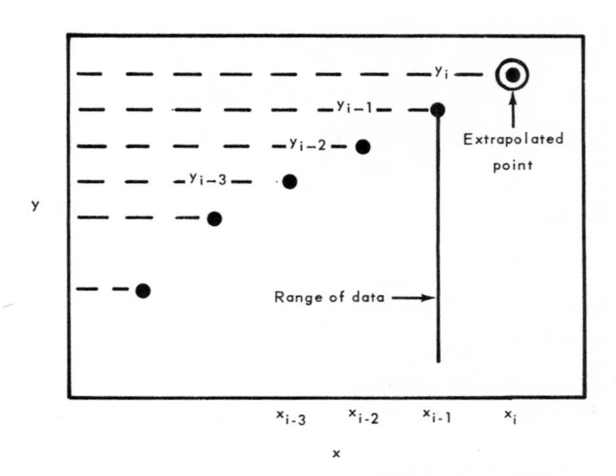

Fig. 9-38 – x-y plot illustrating Mendelson-Manson[66] method.

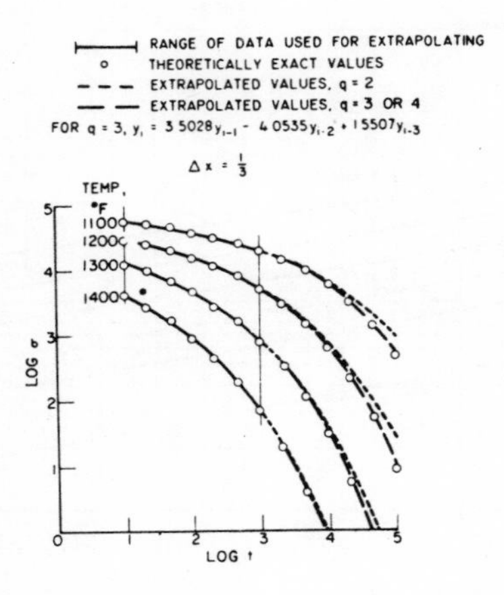

Figure 9-39 – Stress-rupture curves[66] calculated from

$$\log \sigma = 5.131 - \left[\frac{T - 600}{81.8\,(9.5 - \log t_R)}\right]^{2.9326}$$

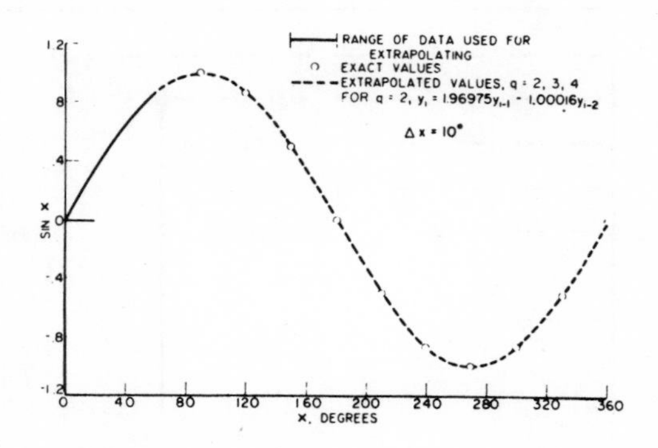

Figure 9-40 – Extrapolation of y = sin x curve[66].

Differentiating with respect to each A value and setting these derivatives equal to zero yields:

$$\left.\begin{array}{l} r_{11}A_1 + A_{12}A_2 + \cdots + r_{1q}A_q = r_{10} \\ r_{21}A_1 + r_{22}A_2 + \cdots + r_{2q}A_q = r_{20} \\ \quad \cdot \qquad \cdot \qquad \cdot \qquad \cdot \\ \quad \cdot \qquad \cdot \qquad \cdot \qquad \cdot \\ \quad \cdot \qquad \cdot \qquad \cdot \qquad \cdot \\ r_{q1}A_1 + r_{q2}A_2 + \cdots + r_{qq}A_q = r_{q0} \end{array}\right\} \qquad (9\text{-}12)$$

where the coefficients r_{ij} are given as:

$$r_{ij} = \sum_{p=1}^{m} \sum_{k=q+1}^{n} y_{k-1}^{(p)} \, y_{k-j}^{(p)} = r_{ji} \qquad (9\text{-}13)$$

Using equation (9-12) all the A values can be calculated and then extrapolations can be made for each member of the family of curves.

An illustration of the above procedure was provided by Mendelson and Manson in an analysis of the simple sine curve shown in Figure 9-40. The range of data is shown as the solid curve and the experimental data (actually calculated from the sine function) available were:

$y_1 = \sin 0° = 0$ $\qquad$ $y_5 = \sin 40° = 0.6428$

$y_2 = \sin 10° = 0.1736$ $\qquad$ $y_6 = \sin 50° = 0.7660$

$y_3 = \sin 20° = 0.3420$ $\qquad$ $y_7 = \sin 60° = 0.8660$

$y_4 = \sin 30° = 0.5000$

It was assumed that the form of the functional relationship was unknown and that extrapolated values were to be calculated. Assuming $q = 2$, equation (9-7) was then employed as:

$$y_i = A_1 y_{i-1} + A_2 y_{i-2} \qquad (9\text{-}14)$$

Then from the considerations given in equation (9-13):

$$r_{11} = \sum_{k=3}^{7} y_{k-1}^2 = y_2^2 + y_3^2 + y_4^2 + y_5^2 + y_6^2$$

$$r_{12} = r_{21} = \sum_{k=3}^{7} y_{k-1}\, y_{k-2} = y_2y_1 + y_3y_2 + y_4y_3 + y_5y_4 + y_6y_5$$

$$r_{22} = \sum_{k=3}^{7} y_{k-2}^2 = y_1^2 + y_2^2 + y_3^2 + y_4^2 + y_5^2$$

$$r_{10} = \sum_{k=3}^{7} y_{k-1}\, y_k = y_2y_3 + y_3y_4 + y_4y_5 + y_5y_6 + y_6y_7$$

and $$r_{20} = \sum_{k=3}^{7} y_{k-2}\, y_k = y_1y_3 + y_2y_4 + y_3y_5 + y_4y_6 + y_5y_7$$

Using the above values of y_1 through y_7:

$$r_{11} = 1.3970488$$

$$r_{12} = r_{21} = 1.0441560$$

$$r_{22} = 0.81029280$$

$$r_{10} = 1.7075120$$

$$r_{20} = 1.2463024$$

Substituting into equation (9-12) and solving simultaneously yields:

$$A_1 = 1.96975$$

$$A_2 = -1.00016$$

Hence:

$$y_i = 1.96975\, y_{i-1} - 1.00016\, y_{i-2}$$

and the extrapolated value at 70° is:

$$\begin{aligned} y_8 &= 1.96975\, y_7 - 1.00016\, y_6 \\ &= 1.96975\,(0.8660) - 1.00016\,(0.7660) \\ &= 0.9397 \end{aligned}$$

Similar calculations led to the comparison shown in Table 9-13 and the dashed curve shown in Figure 9-40. A very impressive agreement is observed between calculated and actual values.

As a second example, Mendelson and Manson considered the extrapolation of the family of curves presented in Figure 9-39. Again, a value of n = 7 was chosen and seven equally spaced stations were chosen along the abscissa between log t_R = 1 and log t_R = 3. Values of y_i were computed from the equation shown in Figure 9-39 and the data (see Table 9-14) were viewed as the experimental data which were to be extrapolated. In this evaluation m was, of course, equal to 4 and q was chosen equal to 2. Then using equation (9-13) the r_{ij} values were computed but now a double summation is required. Thus:

$$\begin{aligned} r_{12} = {} & y_2^{(1)} y_1^{(1)} + y_3^{(1)} y_2^{(1)} + y_4^{(1)} y_3^{(1)} + y_5^{(1)} y_4^{(1)} + y_6^{(1)} y_5^{(1)} \\ & + y_2^{(2)} y_1^{(2)} + y_3^{(2)} y_2^{(2)} + y_4^{(2)} y_3^{(2)} + y_5^{(2)} y_4^{(2)} + y_6^{(2)} y_5^{(2)} \\ & + y_2^{(3)} y_1^{(3)} + y_3^{(3)} y_2^{(3)} + y_4^{(3)} y_3^{(3)} + y_5^{(3)} y_4^{(3)} + y_6^{(3)} y_5^{(3)} \\ & + y_2^{(4)} y_1^{(4)} + y_3^{(4)} y_2^{(4)} + y_4^{(4)} y_3^{(4)} + y_5^{(4)} y_4^{(4)} + y_6^{(4)} y_5^{(4)} \end{aligned}$$

With the r_{ij} values identified, equation (9-12) is then employed to calculate the A values. Then the following recurrence relations:

Table 9-13. Comparison[66] of Extrapolated and Actual Values of Sin x

x, degrees	sin x, extrapolated	sin x, actual
0		0
10		0.1736
20		0.3420
30		0.5000
40		0.6428
50		0.7660
60		0.8660
70	0.9397	0.9397
80	0.9848	0.9848
90	1.0000	1.000
100	0.9848	0.9848
110	0.9396	0.9397
120	0.8658	0.8660
130	0.7657	0.7660
140	0.6423	0.6428
150	0.4993	0.5000
160	0.3411	0.3420
170	0.1725	0.1736
180	-0.0014	0
200	-0.3439	-0.3420
220	-0.6451	-0.6428
240	-0.8685	-0.8660
260	-0.9871	-0.9848
280	-0.9864	-0.9848
300	-0.8666	-0.8660
320	-0.6421	-0.6428
340	-0.3401	-0.3420
360	0.0031	0

Table 9-14. Values[66] of $\log \sigma = 5.131 - \left[\frac{T - 600}{81.8(9.5 - \log t_R)}\right]^{2.9326}$

T, °F / $\log t_R$	1100°	1200°	1300°	1400°
1.0	4.751	4.482	4.111	3.622
1.333	4.703	4.401	3.984	3.434
1.667	4.648	4.306	3.835	3.214
2.000	4.582	4.194	3.659	2.953
2.333	4.504	4.061	3.449	2.642
2.667	4.410	3.900	3.197	2.269
3.000	4.296	3.706	2.891	1.817

$$y_i^{(1)} = A_1 y_{i-1}^{(1)} + A_2 y_{i-2}^{(1)}$$
$$y_i^{(2)} = A_1 y_{i-1}^{(2)} + A_2 y_{i-2}^{(2)}$$
$$y_i^{(3)} = A_1 y_{i-1}^{(3)} + A_2 y_{i-2}^{(3)}$$
and
$$y_i^{(4)} = A_1 y_{i-1}^{(4)} + A_2 y_{i-2}^{(4)}$$

are employed to perform the extrapolation. In this case it was found that $A_1 = 2.2052$ and $A_2 = -1.2048$. Using these values the dashed portions shown in Figure 9-39 were positioned to reveal excellent agreement with the actual data points beyond the experimental range. Also shown is the increased effectiveness when q values of 3 and 4 were employed.

An indication of the generality of the above method was presented by Mendelson and Manson in terms of some stress-rupture data. Data corresponding exactly to the Manson-Haferd parameter were chosen with the calculated data points shown in Figure 9-41. The Larson-Miller parameter would not be expected to apply in this instance so the results obtained if this parameter were used (C value calculated to be 18) are indicated. A rather poor set of extrapolated data results. However, if the recurrence relations are applied to the data below $\log t_R = 3$ and q is chosen equal to 3, the results shown as the dashed curves in Figure 9-41 are obtained. Obviously, this agreement is excellent to emphasize the effectiveness of this approach.

A second calculation was then made using the reverse procedure. A set of data exactly satisfying the Larson-Miller parameter was generated by the equation:

$$(\log t_R + 18)(T + 460) = 33{,}500(5.13 - \log \sigma)0.126 \qquad (9\text{-}15)$$

The data obtained by this equation are very close to those obtained from the equation in Table 9-14 in the range between 10 and 1,000 hours. These data were used to obtain the best values of the constants for the Manson-Haferd parameter and to construct a master curve which was then used to extrapolate the original isothermals. The results are shown in Figure 9-42 and, as expected, the extrapolation using the Manson-Haferd parameter for this case was not very good. However, the extrapolation obtained by the recurrence relation, using the same data, is excellent.

In the previous examples the values of the ordinates required to calculate the r_{ij} by equation (9-13) were precisely known, since they were obtained from exact mathematical expressions such as equation (9-15). It might be expected, therefore, that these input data would reflect implicitly the shape of the curves even at a distance relatively far from the initial range of the data used. In practice, however, the data are given experimentally, and the input data for equation (9-7) are, therefore, much cruder than in the examples given. The extrapolation in this case, therefore, might not be quite as good as previously indicated, particularly if the curves have a large amount of curvature in the extrapolated range.

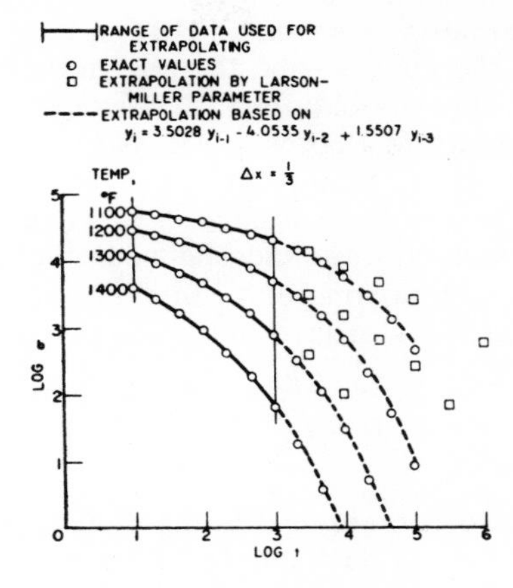

Figure 9-41 – Comparison of extrapolated Manson-Haferd data based on Larson-Miller approach and recurrence relations(66).

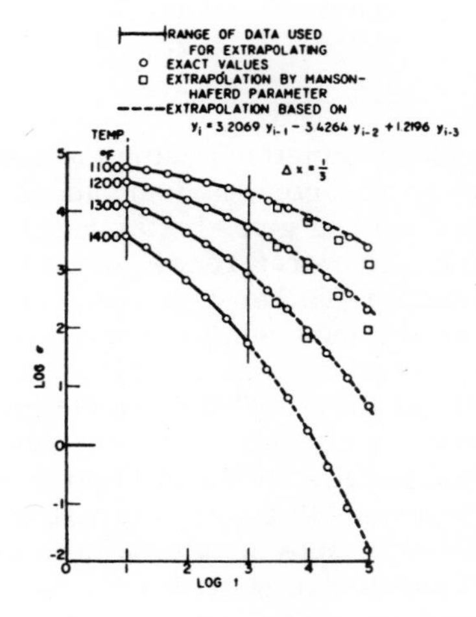

Figure 9-42 – Comparison of extrapolated Larson-Miller data based on Manson-Haferd approach and recurrence relations(66).

The method was, therefore, employed using the actual creep-rupture data for six different materials. The actual data were plotted in the range to be used for extrapolating, and curves drawn by eye through these data. The values of the ordinates at seven equally spaced values of the abscissa were then read from the curves, and the coefficients of the finite difference recurrence relations obtained. These curves were extrapolated and the results are shown in Figure 9-43. It is seen that good extrapolation is obtained for all six materials.

The first three materials in Figure 9-43 were analyzed by Goldhoff[43] where a comparison was made between the Larson-Miller, Manson-Haferd and Dorn parameters. In evaluating the various parameters use was made of the standard deviation defined by:

$$D = \sqrt{\frac{1}{N} \Sigma d^2}$$

where D is the standard deviation, d is the deviation of each data point, and N is the total number of data points. Part of the results comparing the various parameters are reproduced in Table 9-15.

Table 9-15. Standard Deviations

Material	Larson-Miller	Dorn	Manson-Haferd	Recurrence Relation
S-590	0.351	0.430	0.324	0.133
Nimonic 80A	0.385	0.235	0.091	0.045
A-286	0.207	0.172	0.134	0.148

In addition, the standard deviations using the method presented herein for extrapolation were also computed and added to the table. It is seen that the present method gives better results than any of the parameters shown. (NOTE: Some reference should be made to Table 9-9 in view of the re-evaluation that has been made of the data; while the effectiveness of the recurrence relations cannot be disputed, the relative effectiveness of the parameters is slightly changed; as a matter of fact, the Dorn parameter for the S-590 data yields better results than those obtained by the recurrence relations but the reason for this might follow directly from the results shown in Figures 9-41 and -42.)

Inspection of Figure 9-43 shows that this method generally gives good results. However, a note of caution is in order. To use this method a sufficient quantity of short term data is needed for adequate definition of the basic curves to permit proper fairing. If such data are not available then the present method cannot be used. It should also be noted that the value of q, or the number of terms appearing in the recurrence relation, should not be made too large since it has been found that the larger the number of simultaneous equations to be

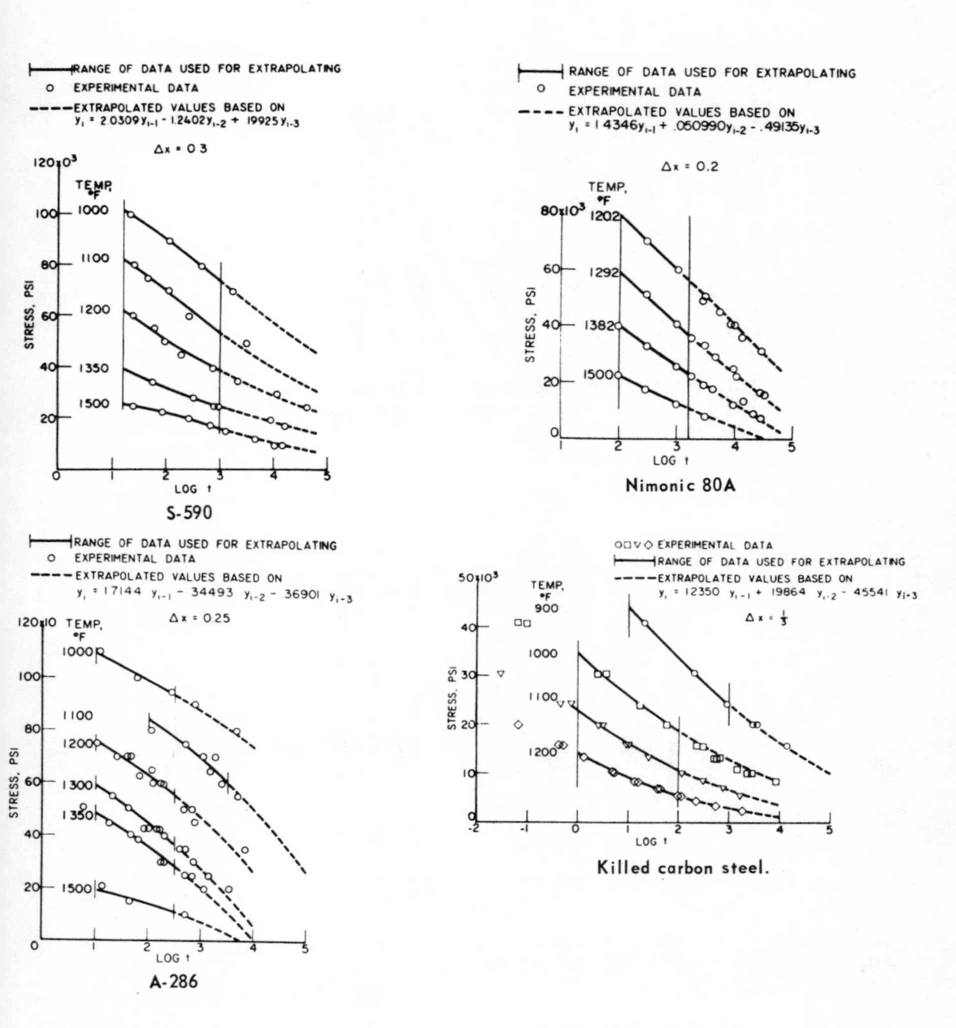

Figure 9-43 – Extrapolation of various data using recurrence relations[66].

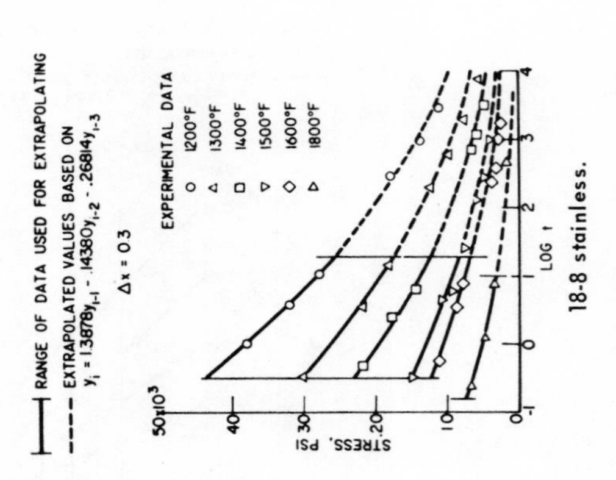

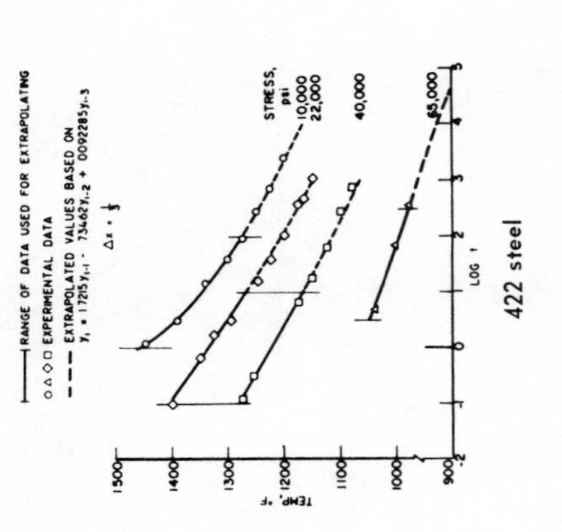

Figure 9-43 (continued)

solved the greater is the loss in significant figures in carrying out the calculations. However, the results for the examples and the materials shown indicate that, in general, a value of q equal to 3 is adequate and that very little can be gained by going to higher values of q.

CHAPTER 10

FUNDAMENTALS OF LEAST SQUARES ANALYSIS PROCEDURES

In many data analysis programs it is necessary to develop a mathematical expression relating two or more variables. A good example of this is provided by the familiar stress-rupture plot relating rupture time, t_R, to applied stress, σ. In general, a plot of log stress (ordinate) versus log rupture time (abscissa) is linear and an equation of the type:

$$\log \sigma = a + b \log t_R \tag{10-1}$$

is indicated. In most cases, a straight edge is placed on such a plot and positioned to allow an equal distribution of the points above and below the line. In this way some form of average representation is obtained and slope and intercept calculations will lead to the identification of the constants in equation (10-1).

While this approach is fairly straightforward and easy to apply it does not lead to a unique solution since a certain amount of individual interpretation is involved. In other words, not every individual analyzing the same data will position the average line in exactly the same place and, hence, slope and intercept calculations will lead to slightly different values for the equation constants. For best results a more rigorous approach is required and one which will lead to a completely unique solution for the equation constants. In this way any individual performing the analysis of the same set of data will obtain the same values for the equation constants. Such an approach is provided by the Principle of Least Squares (see Reference 35 for more advanced treatment).

The Principle of Least Squares has its origin in probability considerations. Simply stated it says that "for a series of repeated measurements the value which is most probably the true value is that value for which the sum of the squares of the residuals is a minimum." In this consideration a residual is the difference between the "most probable value" and a measured or experimental value. If two measured values are considered as follows:

	Measured value	Residual	Residual squared
	3	+1	1
	5	-1	1
arithmetic mean =	4		2 = sum of the squares of the residuals

then the arithmetic mean, which will be considered to be the most probable value, will be seen to be equal to 4. Residuals for the two measured values will be +1 and -1, respectively. Also the sum of the squares of the residuals will obviously be equal to 2. It can be shown from probability considerations that the arithmetic mean is really a least squares value for no other mean or average value will result in the sum of the squares of the residuals having a value smaller than 2.0. In other words, the arithmetic mean is the value for which the sum of the squares of the residuals is at a minimum. It truly then is a least squares value. If the mean were selected as 3.5, it can be easily shown that the sum of the squres of the residuals will be greater than 2.0.

Applying the Principle of Least Squares to the data points shown in Figure 10-1, the same consideration is applied. If line A is to be positioned by the Principle of Least Squares, it must be so placed that the sum of the squares of the residuals, R, will be at a minimum. Hence, since the equation is to be:

$$y = a + bx \tag{10-2}$$

it is seen that the slope, b, of the line is to be adjusted and the vertical position of the line adjusted through the intercept "a" until the condition is reached that the sum of the squares of the residuals is at its lowest value. Mathematically this is written as:

$$\Sigma R^2 = \text{a minimum} \tag{10-3}$$

Now it will be clear from Figure 10-1 that a residual, R, can be written as:

$$R = y_e - (a + bx) \tag{10-4}$$

$$= y_e - a - bx \tag{10-5}$$

where y_e represents the experimental y value at each point and $(a + bx)$ represents the y value calculated from equation (10-2) at the corresponding value of x. In this way a residual can be calculated for each experimental point. Of course, this is only possible when a and b are known. Implicit in this analysis is the assumption that all error can be attributed to measurements of y and that x is known exactly. It is also assumed that the error in measuring y is random and of the same magnitude throughout the range of observation.

It is possible to write mathematical expressions to allow calculation of the least squares values of the constants in equation (10-2) by making use of the condition in equation (10-3). In order to minimize the sum of the squares of the residuals, equation (10-5) is substituted into equation (10-3) and then the summation equation is differentiated with respect to a and then with respect to b and these equations set equal to zero to define the minimum condition. Thus:

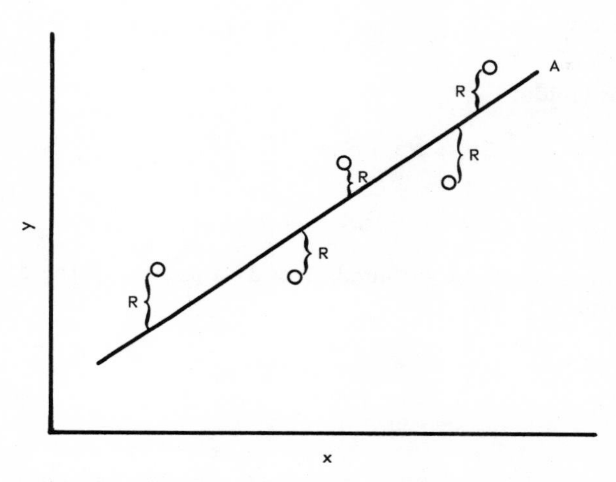

Figure 10-1 – Data points to be analyzed in terms of the Principle of Least Squares.

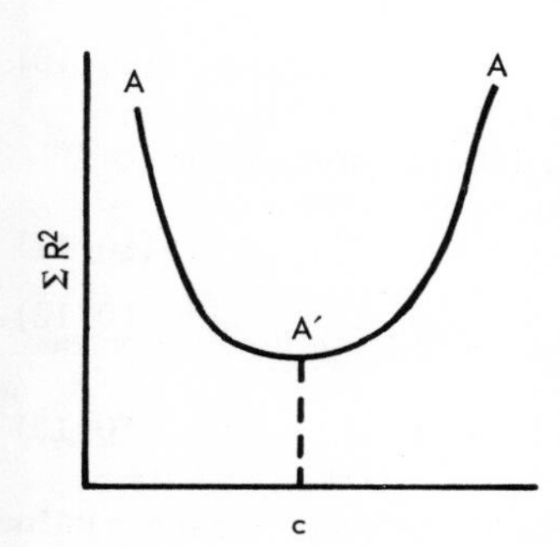

Figure 10-2 – Values of ΣR^2 versus c for calculation of constants in equation (10-15).

$$\frac{\partial \Sigma (y_e - a - bx)^2}{\partial a} = 2\Sigma[(y_e - a - bx)(-1)] = 0 \qquad (10\text{-}6)$$

and

$$\frac{\partial \Sigma (y_e - a - bx)^2}{\partial b} = 2\Sigma[(y_e - a - bx)(-x)] = 0 \qquad (10\text{-}7)$$

Rearranging yields:

$$\Sigma y_e = Na + b\Sigma x \qquad (10\text{-}8)$$

and

$$\Sigma(xy_e) = a\Sigma x + b\Sigma(x)^2 \qquad (10\text{-}9)$$

where N represents the total number of data points. If the data are listed as below:

y_e	x	xy_e	x^2
—	—	—	—
—	—	—	—
—	—	—	—
—	—	—	—
—	—	—	—
Σy_e	Σx	$\Sigma(xy_e)$	$\Sigma(x^2)$

and the xy_e and x^2 terms calculated, then, simple column summations will lead to all the information necessary to the solution of equations (10-8) and (10-9). Simultaneous solution of these two equations will yield the least squares values for the constants "a" and "b."

Similar solutions can be identified for equations which are more complicated than equation (10-2). For example, if a second degree polynomial is considered in the form:

$$y = a + bx + cx^2 \qquad (10\text{-}10)$$

an application of equations similar to (10-6), (10-7), etc., leads to:

$$\Sigma y_e = Na + b\Sigma x + c\Sigma(x^2) \qquad (10\text{-}11)$$

$$\Sigma(xy_e) = a\Sigma x + b\Sigma(x^2) + c\Sigma(x^3). \qquad (10\text{-}12)$$

and

$$\Sigma(x^2y_e) = a\Sigma(x^2) + b\Sigma(x^3) + c\Sigma(x^4) \qquad (10\text{-}13)$$

Simultaneous solution of these equations leads to the least squares values for the constants a, b, and c.

A direct solution for the least squares values of the equation constant is possible only when the equation being analyzed is linear in the constant themselves. This property, of course, is possessed by both equations (10-

and (10-10). When, however, the equation is not linear with respect to the constants, a somewhat more involved solution procedure is required. If, for example, the following equations are considered:

$$y = a + \frac{b}{c + x} \qquad (10\text{-}14)$$

$$y = a + bx^{c} \qquad (10\text{-}15)$$

a non-linearity in the constant "c" is observed. Hence, the identification of the least squares values of the constants is not direct. Applying equation (10-3) to equation (10-15) leads to:

$$\Sigma R^2 = \Sigma(y_e - a - bx^c)^2 = \text{a minimum}, \qquad (10\text{-}16)$$

and differentiation with respect to "a" and "b" gives, on setting these derivatives equal to zero:

$$\Sigma y_e = Na + b\Sigma(x^c) \qquad (10\text{-}17)$$

$$\Sigma(y_e x^c) = a\Sigma(x^c) + b\Sigma(x^{2c}) \qquad (10\text{-}18)$$

and

$$\Sigma(yx^c \ln x) = a\Sigma(x^c \ln x) + b\Sigma(x^{2c} \ln x) \qquad (10\text{-}18A)$$

No algebraic solution of these expressions for c is possible since they are implicit in this constant. However, a trial and error solution is suggested. A value of "c" is assumed and then equations (10-17) and (10-18) are evaluated and solved simultaneously for a and b. Then, the ΣR^2 term in equation (10-16) can be evaluated using the calculated values of a and b along with the assumed values of "c." This procedure is repeated for other assumed values of "c" until the minimum value of ΣR^2 in equation (10-1€) is identified. At this point corresponding a, b and c values are the least squares values for these constants. A schematic of the type of solution just described is shown in Figure 10-2. Each point on the summation curve has values of a and b corresponding to c. When the $\Sigma(R)^2$ value reaches its minimum at point A' the desired least squares solution is obtained. A similar type of solution can, of course, be described for equation (10-14).

A somewhat more complicated solution procedure has been described[74] for use with the deLacombe[62] creep equation. This equation represents a relation between strain and time in the form:

$$\epsilon = \epsilon_0 + at^m + bt^n \qquad (10\text{-}19)$$

where ϵ_0, a, b, m and n are constants (in this case $0 < m < 1.0$ and $n > 1.0$). Applying the procedures described above:

$$\Sigma R^2 = \Sigma(\epsilon_e - \epsilon_0 - at^m - bt^n)^2 \qquad (10\text{-}20)$$

Differentiating with repsect to ϵ_0, a and b and setting these equal to zero yields:

$$\Sigma \epsilon_e = N\epsilon_0 + a\Sigma(t^m) + b\Sigma(t^n) \tag{10-21}$$

$$\Sigma(\epsilon_e t^m) = \epsilon_0\Sigma(t^m) + a\Sigma(t^{2m}) + b\Sigma(t^{m+n}) \tag{10-22}$$

and

$$\Sigma(\epsilon_e t^n) = \epsilon_0\Sigma(t^n) + a\Sigma(t^{m+n}) + b\Sigma(t^{2n}) \tag{10-23}$$

Non-linearity in m and n is seen in equation (10-20) hence some approximate solution must be adopted. Employing a trial and error approach, a value of m between 0.01 and 0.99 is selected and for various values of the constant n ranging from 1.0 to n equations (10-21), (10-22) and (10-23) are evaluated and solved simultaneously for ϵ_0, a and b. Then the summation term in equation (10-20) is evaluated. This solution procedure is repeated at a given value of "m" until the minimum in ΣR^2 is observed and the value of "n" is noted. (A plot for use in this evaluation is shown in Figure 10-3). The above process is repeated for other values of "m" and a minimum ΣR^2 value obtained in each case. When the range of m from 0.01 to 0.99 is covered, a plot is made similar to that shown in Figure 10-4. In this instance, the minimum value of ΣR^2 for each value of "m" is plotted. The minimum in this curve locates the proper "m" and hence "n" values; also, the simultaneous solution of equations (10-21), (10-22), and (10-23) will yield for these "m" and "n" values the proper least squares values of ϵ_0, "a" and "b." In this way, all the necessary equation constants are identified and, of course, represent the condition for which the sum of the squares of the residuals is a minimum. As in all least squares determinations, these constants will provide the best fit of the experimental points for this particular equation type.

NON-LINEAR REGRESSION ANALYSIS*

Linear regression analysis is the term applied to a least squares evaluation when the equation being considered is linear in all the unknown constants. Examples of this type have already been considered in equations (10-2) and (10-10). When a given equation is not linear in all the constants which must be calculated, then a non-linear regression analysis must be employed. One such procedure has already been described in which a trial and error solution was adopted. Iterative procedures can also be incorporated in non-linear regression analyses to allow for more direct solutions of the working equations given by (10-21), (10-22) and (10-23). For example, consider the equation:

$$y = ax^b \tag{10-24}$$

*The suggestion to use non-linear regression procedures in the present study is due to Lars H. Sjodahl who also wrote all the computer programs for this study.

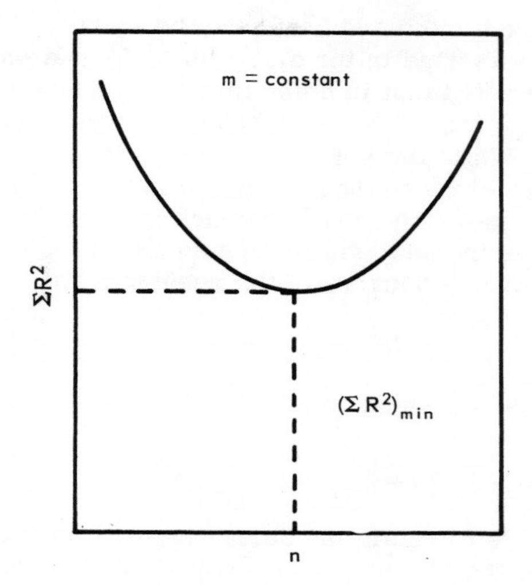

Figure 10-3 – Plot of ΣR^2 versus n.

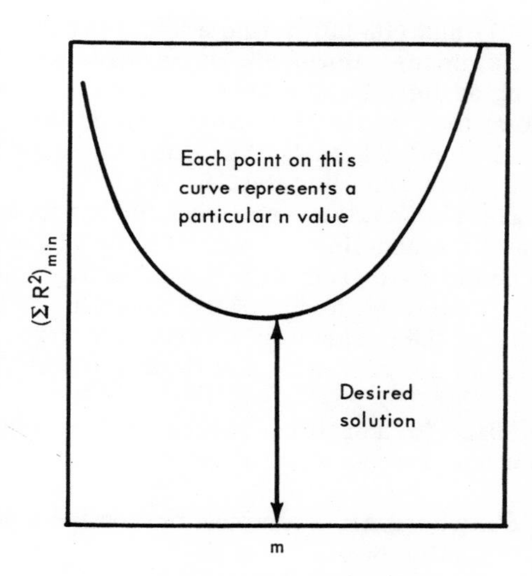

Figure 10-4 – Plot of $(\Sigma R^2)_{min}$ versus m.

It will be noticed that taking logarithms lead to:

$$\log y = \log a + b \log x \tag{10-25}$$

which is linear in log a and b and hence can be solved by linear regression procedures as was done in the discussion of equation (10-1). However, it will also be noted that in doing this the residuals will be given by $\log y_e - \log y_{calc.} = \log (y_e/y_{calc.})$ instead of by differences in the y values themselves. While the solution in the form of equation (10-25) yields constants very close to those obtained in the analysis in terms of residuals in y the more rigorous approach is to be preferred.

In the above case the analysis in terms of y and x^b can be made by expressing the sum of the squares of the residuals as:

$$\Sigma R^2 = \Sigma(y - ax^b)^2 \tag{10-26}$$

Setting the derivative with respect to a equal to zero gives:

$$\Sigma(yx^b) = a\Sigma(x^b \cdot x^b) = a\Sigma(x^{2b}) \tag{10-27}$$

It is also possible to obtain the derivative with respect to b which should be zero when the optimum value of b is used. This derivative is:

$$\frac{\partial \Sigma R^2}{\partial b} = 2\Sigma[(y - ax^b)(-ax \ln x)] \tag{10-28}$$

which, when set equal to zero, yields:

$$\Sigma(yx^b \ln x) = a\Sigma(x^{2b} \ln x) \tag{10-29}$$

Equations (10-27) and (10-29) define a and b but they are not solvable by algebraic means. However, an iterative solution can be effected by assuming an initial value for the constant b. A least squares approach (see below) then yields an improved value for this constant. Repeating this calculation leads to further improvements in the b value and eventually a minimum value for the ΣR^2 term.

Non-linear regression analyses are initiated by using an approximation to the value of the non-linear term (b in this case). These initial values may be obtained from experience with previous similar analyses, by solving simplified forms of the equation, by knowledge of the physical meaning of the parameter, or trial and error if necessary. However, this choice is not generally a serious problem in creep or rupture analysis.

One procedure used for a problem represented by equation (10-24) is to solve, by least squares, an equation of the form:

$$y = ax^b + \left(\frac{\partial y}{\partial b}\right)\Delta b, \text{ where } \Delta b \text{ is a correction on the assumed value of b} \tag{10-30}$$

$$y = ax^b + a\Delta b x^b \ln x \qquad (10\text{-}31)$$

or

$$y = ax^b + cx^b \ln x \qquad (10\text{-}32)$$

where the first term (i.e., ax^b) is viewed as an approximate value of y for an assumed value of the constant, b; the second term, with c/a representing the change in b, provides a correction term to yield a closer approach to the true y value. Using equation (10-32) the residual equation (10-26) becomes:

$$\Sigma R^2 = \Sigma(y - ax^b - cx^b \ln x)^2 \qquad (10\text{-}33)$$

and differentiating with respect to a and c and setting to zero yields:

$$\Sigma(yx^b) = a\Sigma(x^{2b}) + c\Sigma(x^{2b}\ln x) \qquad (10\text{-}34)$$

and

$$\Sigma(yx^b \ln x) = a\Sigma(x^{2b}\ln x) + c\Sigma(x^b \ln x)^2 \qquad (10\text{-}35)$$

A value of b can now be assumed to allow all the terms in equations (10-34) and (10-35) to be evaluated. Simultaneous solution of these equations leads to values for a and c. A new improved value for the constant b is then obtained by adding (with, of course, proper regard for sign) c/a to the previous value of b.* Iterating in this manner leads to continually improved values for the constant b until the value of c is either zero or so small that its effect on b can be neglected. At this point the iterative solution is complete and the proper values for a and b are obtained. Convergence for this type of equation is usually obtained after three or four iterations.

A solution of an equation of this type can be illustrated in terms of some constant temperature strain rate versus stress data for which preliminary logarithmic plotting suggested a form $y = ax^b$ with b close to 3.0. These data are as follows:

$\dot{\epsilon}_s$, min^{-1}	σ, psi
1.75×10^{-5}	150
4.62	200
9.7	250
1.75×10^{-4}	300
3.0	350
4.65	400
6.8	450
9.9	500
1.35×10^{-3}	550
1.8	600
3.0	700
4.7	800

*Best results and more rapid convergence are obtained when the initial value of b is taken somewhat higher than the true value of this constant.

Applying the approach just described, an initial value of b equal to 4.0 was assumed. This selection led to the results presented below where the value for Δb and the sum of the squares of the residuals are given for each iteration step.

Iteration Step	b value	Δb	ΣR^2
1	4.0	-0.12525	3.23×10^{-7}
2	3.87475	-0.12009	2.2×10^{-7}
3	3.75466	-0.1130	1.38×10^{-7}
4	3.6417	-0.1029	7.62×10^{-8}
5	3.5388	-0.0879	3.48×10^{-8}
6	3.4509	-0.0662	1.17×10^{-8}
7	3.3847	-0.0374	2.43×10^{-9}
8	3.3473	-0.0110	4.4×10^{-10}
9	3.3363	-0.0009	3.138×10^{-10}
10	3.3354		3.132×10^{-10}

In the first calculation Δb was found to be -0.12525 which corrected b to 3.87475 for a ΣR^2 value of 2.2×10^{-7}. After step 8, the value of b was known to three significant figures. In step 9, Δb was found to be negligible and the iteration was stopped. In this manner the following equation was obtained:

$$\dot{\epsilon}_s = 9.7456 \times 10^{-13}\, \sigma^{3.3354}$$

For comparison, the same data were analyzed in the form $\ln y = \ln a + b \ln x$. The sum of the squares of the residuals by this method was 3.563×10^{-10} for the equation:

$$\dot{\epsilon}_s = 9.4835 \times 10^{-13}\, \sigma^{3.33967}$$

Even though this expression provides an excellent representation of the data the sum of the squares of the residuals is some 15 percent greater than that for the more rigorous solution.

If an equation of the type:

$$y = ax^b + f \tag{10-36}$$

is considered, no direct solution is available when logarithms are employed. However, the above approach is applicable for again only non-linearity in b is present. It can easily be shown that the approach used in identifying equations (10-34) and (10-35) leads to:

$$\Sigma(yx^b) = a\Sigma(x^{2b}) + f\Sigma(x^b) + c\Sigma(x^{2b}\ln x) \tag{10-37}$$

$$\Sigma y = a\Sigma(x^b) + Nf + c\Sigma(x^b \ln x) \tag{10-38}$$

and

$$\Sigma(yx^b \ln x) = a\Sigma(x^{2b}\ln x) + f\Sigma(x^b \ln x) + c\Sigma(x^b \ln x)^2 \tag{10-39}$$

where N is the total number of data points. As before, improved values of b are obtained by adding c/a to the previous value of b until c is either zero or negligible.

For the case of:

$$y = ae^{bx} \tag{10-40}$$

the solution for b can be made in terms of the equations:

$$\Sigma(ye^{bx}) = a\Sigma(e^{2bx}) + c\Sigma(xe^{2bx}) \tag{10-41}$$

and

$$\Sigma(yxe^{bx}) = a\Sigma(xe^{2bx}) + c\Sigma(xe^{bx})^2 \tag{10-42}$$

A slightly more involved approach must be employed when two terms contain non-linearities. For example, in the de Lacombe equation:

$$y = a + bx^m + dx^n \tag{10-43}$$

non-linearity in both m and n is noted. In this case an improved value of y is given by:

$$y = a + bx^m + cx^m \ln x + dx^n + fx^n \ln x \tag{10-44}$$

where $x^m \ln x$ and $x^n \ln x$ are the derivatives with respect to the exponents m and n, respectively. An expression for the sum of the squares of the residuals is then:

$$\Sigma R^2 = \Sigma(y - a - bx^m - cx^m \ln x - dx^n - fx^n \ln x)^2 \tag{10-45}$$

Differentiating with respect to a, b, c, d and f and setting equal to zero yields:

$$\Sigma y = Na + b\Sigma(x^m) + c\Sigma(x^m \ln x) + d\Sigma(x^n) + f\Sigma(x^n \ln x) \tag{10-46}$$

$$\Sigma(yx^m) = a\Sigma(x^m) + b\Sigma(x^{2m}) + c\Sigma(x^{2m} \ln x) + d\Sigma(x^{m+n}) + f\Sigma(x^{m+n} \ln x) \tag{10-47}$$

$$\Sigma(yx^m \ln x) = a\Sigma(x^m \ln x) + b\Sigma(x^{2m} \ln x) + c\Sigma(x^m \ln x)^2 + d\Sigma(x^{m+n} \ln x) + f\Sigma[x^{m+n}(\ln x)^2] \tag{10-48}$$

$$\Sigma(yx^n) = a\Sigma(x^n) + b\Sigma(x^{m+n}) + c\Sigma(x^{m+n} \ln x) + d\Sigma(x^{2n}) + f\Sigma(x^{2n} \ln x) \tag{10-49}$$

and

$$\Sigma(yx^n \ln x) = a\Sigma(x^n \ln x) + b\Sigma(x^{m+n} \ln x) + c\Sigma[x^{m+n}(\ln x)^2] + d\Sigma(x^{2n} \ln x) + f\Sigma[(x^n \ln x)^2] \tag{10-50}$$

Values for m and n are assumed and the above equations evaluated to yield values for a, b, c, d and f. Improved values for m and n are then obtained by adding c/b and f/d to the previous m and n values, respectively. Iteration is continued, as before, until c and f become zero or negligible. At this point all the constants are identified for use in equation (10-43).

Reference to the Manson-Haferd parameter equation given by equation (4-50) reveals a non-linearity due to the T_a term. Writing this expression in terms of $\log t_R$ gives:

$$\log t_R = \log t_a + a_0(T - T_a) + a_1 x(T - T_a) + a_2 x^2 (T - T_a) \quad (10\text{-}51)$$

for a second degree polynomial in x where $x = \log \sigma$. A solution of this equation cannot be obtained directly because of the non-linearity in T_a. However, an iterative approach is possible based on previous considerations. First of all, though, it should be observed that in equation (10-51) the non-linearity occurs in more than one term and hence involves more than one of the other unknown constants. This, of course, is an added complication and to some extent is similar to the de Lacombe equation where two non-linearities were encountered.

If equation (10-51) is employed and an approximate value fo T_a is selected, an improved value for $\log t_R$ follows as:

$$\log t_R = \log t_a + a_0(T - T_a) + a_1 x(T - T_a) + a_2 x^2 (T - T_a) + a_3(-a_0 - a_1 x - a_2 x^2) \quad (10\text{-}52)$$

where the term in parenthesis following the a_3 coefficient represents F_t', the derivative of the right-hand side of equation (10-51) with respect to T_a, and a_3 is an incremental change in T_a. The final term in equation (10-52) is seen to represent a correction on the $\log t_R$ value. Because of the non-linearity involving other terms, similar corrections for the $\log t_a$, a_0, a_1 and a_2 constants must be written. These are:

c_1 (actually $\Delta \log t_a$)

$(T - T_a)a_0'$ (where a_0' is Δa_0)

$(T - T_a)xa_1'$ (where a_1' is Δa_1)

$(T - T_a)x^2 a_2'$ (where a_2' is Δa_2)

It is now possible to rewrite equation (10-52) for the case where corrections on all unknown constants are included. This leads to:

$$\log t_R = (\log t_a + c_1) + (a_0 + a_0')(T - T_a) + (a_1 + a_1')(T - T_a)x + (a_2 + a_2')(T - T_a)x^2 + a_3(-a_0 - a_1 x - a_2 x^2) \quad (10\text{-}53)$$

A residual will now be given by experimental $\log t_R$ values minus the $\log t_R$ value calculated using equation (10-53). Furthermore, the sum of the squares of the residuals will follow as:

$$\Sigma R^2 = \Sigma[\log t_R - (\log t_a + c_1) - (a_0 + a_0')(T - T_a) - (a_1 + a_1')(T - T_a)x - (a_2 + a_2')(T - T_a)x^2 - a_3(-a_0 - a_1 x - a_2 x^2)]^2 \quad (10\text{-}54)$$

Letting:

$$\log t_R' = \log t_R - \log t_a - a_0(T - T_a) - a_1(T - T_a)x - a_2(T - T_a)x^2 \quad (10\text{-}55)$$

equation (10-54) yields:

$$\Sigma R^2 = \Sigma[\log t_R' - c_1 - a_0'(T - T_a) - a_1'(T - T_a)x - a_2'(T - T_a)x^2 - a_3(-a_0 - a_1 x - a_2 x^2)]^2 \quad (10\text{-}56)$$

Differentiating now with respect to c_1, a_0', a_1', a_2' and a_3 and setting these derivatives equal to zero leads to:

$$\Sigma \log t_R' = Nc_1 + a_0'\Sigma(T - T_a) + a_1'\Sigma[(T - T_a)x] + a_2'\Sigma[(T - T_a)x^2] + a_3\Sigma F_t' \quad (10\text{-}57)$$

$$\Sigma[(T - T_a)\log t_R'] = c_1\Sigma(T - T_a) + a_0'\Sigma[(T - T_a)^2] + a_1'\Sigma[(T - T_a)^2 x] + a_2'\Sigma[(T - T_a)^2 x^2] + a_3\Sigma[(T - T_a)F_t'] \quad (10\text{-}58)$$

$$\Sigma[x(T - T_a)\log t_R'] = c_1\Sigma[(T - T_a)x] + a_0'\Sigma[(T - T_a)^2 x] + a_1'\Sigma[(T - T_a)^2 x^2] + a_2'\Sigma[(T - T_a)^2 x^3] + a_3\Sigma[(T - T_a)xF_t'] \quad (10\text{-}59)$$

$$\Sigma[x^2(T - T_a)\log t_R'] = c_1\Sigma[(T - T_a)x^2] + a_0'\Sigma[(T - T_a)^2 x^2] + a_1'\Sigma[(T - T_a)^2 x^3] + a_2'\Sigma[(T - T_a)^2 x^4] + a_3\Sigma[(T - T_a)x^2 F_t'] \quad (10\text{-}60)$$

and

$$\Sigma[F_t' \log t_R'] = c_1\Sigma F_t' + a_0'\Sigma[F_t'(T - T_a)] + a_1'\Sigma[F_t'(T - T_a)x] + a_2'\Sigma[F_t'(T - T_a)x^2] + a_3\Sigma[F_t'^2] \quad (10\text{-}61)$$

A solution is initiated by assuming values for T_a, $\log t_a$, a_0, a_1 and a_2. It has been found that, in general, these starting values are not critical and in the solutions effected in previous chapters these values were all set at 0.1 initially. Using these assumed values equation (10-55) can be employed to yield $\log t_R'$ values. Then, equations (10-57) through (10-61) can be solved simultaneously for c_1, a_0', a_1', a_2' and a_3. Corrected values for the constants in equation (10-52) follow from:

$$\left.\begin{aligned} &\text{new } \log t_a = \text{old } \log t_a + c_1 \\ &\text{new } a_0 = \text{old } a_0 + a_0' \\ &\text{etc., to} \\ &\text{new } T_a = \text{old } T_a + a_3 \end{aligned}\right\} \qquad (10\text{-}62)$$

With the new values for the constants, equation (10-55) is re-evaluated to yield new log t_R' values and the above procedure repeated. Eventually, and usually after only three or four iterations, the correction terms become zero or negligible and the desired solution is obtained. Good precision is obtainable by this approach and equation (10-51) is completely evaluated.

An illustration of the above calculation procedure was obtained in the analysis of the stress-rupture data for S-590.[43] Initially, as input to the computer, the value of 0.1 was assigned to the constants T_a, log t_a, a_0, a_1 and a_2. This allowed evaluation of the log t_R' term using equation (10-55). Also, this selection allowed values for c_1, a_0', a_1', a_2' and a_3. These values were then used to obtain improved values for the constants by means of equation (10-62). Continued iterations led to convergence to the proper solution as shown in the following table:

$a_3 = \Delta T_a$	T_a	$c_1 = \Delta \log t_a$	$\log t_a$	ΣR^2 *
2.70332	2.80332	23.7919	23.8919	1622.9
-513.234	-510.431	-1.3582	22.5337	0.579080
11.3947	-499.036	-0.1214	22.4123	0.491375
-6.53542	-505.571	+0.0710	22.4833	0.491369
	-0.0357	0.0157	-0.00228	
	a_0	a_1	a_2	

*The sum of the squares of the residuals is calculated without using the last (derivative) term in equation (10-54) in order to assess the efficiency of the current set of constants T_a, t_a, a_o, a_1, and a_2.

As will be noted the first calculation step led to a_3 = 2.70332 and c_1 = 23.7919 which yielded improved values of T_a = 0.1 + 2.70332 = 2.80919 and log t_a = 0.1 + 23.7919 = 23.8919. Each additional step led to improved values of these constants and, except for the first iteration, smaller value for the sum of the squares of the residuals. After only four iterations the ΣR^2 term had reached a minimum value and the correction terms to all th constants were essentially negligible. At this point the values of a_0, a_1 and a_2 had attained the values shown for use in connection with equation (10-51).

BIBLIOGRAPHY

1. F. R. Larson and J. Miller, "Time-Temperature Relationship for Rupture and Creep Stresses," T. ASME, 74, 765, 1952.
2. J. H. Hollomon and L. D. Jaffe, "Time-Temperature Relations in Tempering Steel," T. AIME, Iron and Steel Division, 162, 223, 1945.
3. A. E. Nehrenberg, "Master Curves Simplify Stainless Tempering," Steel, 127, 72, Oct. 23, 1950.
4. J. Miller, "Aid for the High-Temperature Designer," General Electric Review, November 1952, p. 51.
5. S. S. Manson and A. Mendelson, "Optimization of Parametric Constants for Creep-Rupture Data by Means of Least Squares," NASA Memo 3-10-59E, 1959.
6. P. N. Flagella, General Electric Company, Nuclear Materials and Propulsion Operation, Cincinnati, Ohio, Private Communication, 1966.
7. W. V. Green, M. C. Smith and D. M. Olson, "Short-Time Creep-Rupture Behavior of Molybdenum at High Temperatures," T. AIME, 215, 1061, 1959.
8. W. V. Green, "Short-Time Creep-Rupture Behavior of Tungsten at 2250°C to 2800°C," T. AIME, 215, 1057, 1959.
9. H. G. Sell, G. H. Keith, R. C. Koo, R. H. Schnitzel and R. Corth, "Physical Metallurgy of Tungsten and Tungsten Base Alloys," WADD-TR-60-37, Part II, 1961.
10. J. W. Pugh, "Tensile and Creep Properties of Tungsten at Elevated Temperatures," Proc. ASTM, 57, 906, 1957.
11. D. C. Drennen, M. E. Langston, C. J. Slunder and J. G. Dunleavy, "High Temperature Mechanical Properties of Tantalum," BMI Report 1326, W-7405-eng-92, 1959.
12. F. F. Schmidt, "Tantalum and Tantalum Alloys," DMIC-133, OTS PB151091, 1960.
13. Published data from National Research Corporation, Chem. Eng. News, 37 (42), 52, 1959.
14. A. Donlevy, and J. K. Y. Hum, "Some Stress-Rupture Properties of Columbium, Molybdenum, Tantalum and Tungsten Metals and Alloys Between 2400-5000°F," 1961 SAE National Aeronautic Meeting, New York; see also Machine Design, 33, 244, May 11, 1961.
15. P. N. Flagella, W. L. McCullough, and J. H. Foster, Nuclear Materials and Propulsion Operation of General Electric Company, Cincinnati, Ohio, Unpublished Notes, 1965.
16. J. W. Pugh, "The Tensile Properties of Molybdenum at Elevated Temperatures, "Trans. ASM, 47, 984, 1955.
17. J. W. Pugh, "The Tensile and Stress-Rupture Properties of Chromium," Trans. ASM, 50, 1072, 1958.

18. F. F. Schmidt, W. D. Klopp, W. M. Albrecht, F. C. Holden, and H. R. Ogden, "Investigation of the Properties of Tantalum and its Alloys," WADD Technical Report 59-13, 1960.
19. J. H. Bechtold, E. T. Wessel and L. L. France, "Refractory Metals and Alloys," Edited by M. Semchyshen and J. J. Harwood, Interscience Publishers, 1961.
20. F. J. Clauss, "An Examination of High-Temperature Stress-Rupture Correlating Parameters," Proc. ASTM, 60, 905, 1960.
21. J. B. Conway, "Some Correlation Procedures Based on the Larson-Miller Parameter and Their Application to Refractory Metal Data," Trans. Met. Soc. AIME, 236, 1486, 1966.
22. F. Garofalo, "Fundamentals of Creep and Creep-Rupture in Metals," Macmillan Company, New York, 1965.
23. H. J. Tapsell, "Creep of Metals," Oxford University Press, London, 1931.
24. I. S. Servi and N. J. Grant, "Creep and Stress Rupture Behavior of Aluminum as a Function of Purity," T. AIME, 191, 909, 1951.
25. F. C. Monkman and N. J. Grant, "An Empirical Relationship Between Rupture Life and Minimum Creep Rate in Creep-Rupture Tests," Proc. ASTM, 56, 593, 1956.
26. P. Feltham and J. D. Meakin, "Creep in Face-Centered Cubic Metals with Special Reference to Copper," Acta Met., 7, 614, 1959.
27. F. Garofalo, R. W. Whitmore, W. F. Domis and F. vonGemmingen, "Creep and Creep-Rupture Relationships in an Austentic Stainless Steel," T. AIME 221, 310, 1961.
28. P. Brozzo, "A Method for the Extrapolation of Creep and Stress-Rupture Data of Complex Alloys," Joint Int'l. Conf. on Creep, 1963, Book 4, Paper No. 67, p. 6-77.
29. H. Conrad, "Correlation of High Temperature Creep and Rupture Data," J. Basic Engrg., Series D, 81, 617, 1959.
30. E. C. Larke and N. P. Inglis, "A Critical Examination of Some Methods of Analyzing and Extrapolating Stress-Rupture Data," Joint International Conference on Creep, 1963, Book 4, paper No. 50, p. 6-33.
31. G. Murry, "Extrapolation of the Results of Creep Tests by Means of Parametric Formulae," Joint International Conference on Creep, 1963, Book 4, Paper No. 73, p. 6-87.
32. R. L. Orr, O. D. Sherby and J. E. Dorn, "Correlations of Rupture Data for Metals at Elevated Temperatures," T. ASM, 46, 113, 1954.
33. F. Garofalo, "An Empirical Relation Defining the Stress Dependence of Minimum Creep Rate in Metals," Trans. Met. Soc. AIME, 227, 351, 1963.
34. F. Garofalo, C. Richmond, W. F. Domis and F. vonGemmingen, "Strain-Time, Rate-Stress and Rate-Temperature Relations During Large Deformations in Creep," Joint International Conference on Creep, 1963, Book I, Paper 30, p. 1-31.
35. J. B. Scarborough, "Numerical Mathematical Analysis," The Johns Hopkins Press, Third Edition, 1955.
36. S. S. Manson and A. M. Haferd, "A Linear Time-Temperature

Relation for Extrapolation of Creep and Stress-Rupture Data," NACA TN 2890, March 1953.
37. N. J. Grant, "Creep and Fracture of Metals at High Temperatures," 1956, 317 (HMSO, London).
38. N. J. Grant and A. G. Bucklin, "On the Extrapolation of Short-Time Stress-Rupture Data," Trans. ASM 42, 720, 1950.
39. W. Betteridge, "The Nimonic Alloys," E. Arnold Std., London, 1959.
40. J. B. Conway, General Electric Company, Nuclear Materials and Propulsion Operation, Cincinnati, Ohio, unpublished notes.
41. J. B. Conway and M. J. Mullikin, General Electric Company, Nuclear Materials and Propulsion Operation, Cincinnati, Ohio unpublished notes.
42. A. W. Mullendore, J. M. Dhosi, R. Widmer, and N. J. Grant, "Study of Parameter Techniques for Extrapolation of Creep-Rupture Properties," Joint International Conference on Creep, 1963, Book 4, Paper No. 9, p. 6-15.
43. R. M. Goldhoff, "Comparison of Parameter Methods for Extrapolating High Temperature Data," Trans. ASME, 81, 629, 1959.
44. D. S. Wood and J. B. Wade, "Creep and Stress-Rupture Properties of Pressure Vessel Steels," Joint International Conference on Creep, 1963, Book 4, Paper No. 76, p. 5-105.
45. E. S. Machlin and A. S. Nowick, "Stress-Rupture of Heat-Resisting Alloys as a Rate Process," Trans. AIME, 172, 386, 1947.
46. S. S. Manson and G. Succop, "Stress-Rupture Properties of Inconel 700 and Correlation on the Basis of Several Time-Temperature Parameters," ASTM, STP No. 174, Symposium on Metallic Materials for Service at Temperatures Above 1600°F, 1956.
47. W. Betteridge, "The Extrapolation of the Stress-Rupture Properties of the Nimonic Alloys," Inst. of Metals, 86, 232, 1957-58.
48. Digest of Steels for High Temperature Service, 5th Edition, Timken Roller Bearing Co., Steel and Tube Division, Canton, Ohio, 1946.
49. R. M. Goldhoff and R. F. Gill, Written Discussion to Manson, Succop and Brown Article in Trans. ASM 51, 926, 1959.
50. S. S. Manson and W. F. Brown, Jr., "Time-Temperature-Stress Relations for the Correlation and Extrapolation of Stress-Rupture Data," Proc. ASTM, 53, 693, 1953.
51. J. D. Murray and R. J. Truman, "The High Temperature Properties of Cr-Ni-Nb and Cr-Ni-Mo Austenitic Steels," Joint International Conference on Creep, 1963, Book 4, Paper No. 61, p. 5-55.
52. S. S. Manson, G. Succop and W. F. Brown, Jr., "The Application of Time-Temperature Parameters to Accelerated Creep-Rupture Testing," Trans. ASM, 51, 911, 1959.
53. J. W. Pugh, "The Tensile Properties of Molybdenum at Elevated Temperatures," Trans. ASM, 47, 984, 1955.
54. J. P. Smith, General Electric Company, NMPO, Cincinnati, Ohio, private communication, 1967.
55. I. S. Servi and N. J. Grant, "Creep and Stress-Rupture as Rate Process," J. Inst. Metals, 80, 33, 1951-52.

56. S. S. Manson, "Design Considerations for Long Life at Elevated Temperatures," James Clayton Lecture, NASA Lewis TP 1-63, 1963.
57. A. Mendelson, E. Roberts, Jr. and S. S. Manson, "Optimization of Time-Temperature Parameters for Creep and Stress-Rupture With Application to Data From German Cooperative Long-Time Creep Program," NASA-TN-D-2975, 1965.
58. C. R. Barrett, A. J. Ardell and O. D. Sherby, "Influence of Modulus on the Temperature Dependence of the Activation Energy for Creep at High Temperatures," Trans. Met. Soc. AIME, 230, 200, 1964.
59. O. D. Sherby, "Factors Affecting the High Temperature Strength of Polycrystalline Solids," Acta Met. 10, 135, 1962.
60. C. Zener and J. H. Hollomon, "Plastic Flow and Rupture of Metals," Trans. ASM, 33, 163, 1944.
61. S. S. Manson, Discussion in Joint International Conference on Creep, Volume II-Discussion, Institution of Mechanical Engineers, London, England, 1965.
62. J. deLacombe, "A Method of Representing Creep Curves," Rev. Metal, 36, 178, 1939.
63. A. Chitty and D. Duval, "The Creep-Rupture Properties of Tubes for High Temperature Steam Power Plant," Joint International Conference on Creep, 1963, Book 3, Paper No. 2, p. 4-1.
64. T. R. Running, "Empirical Formulas," John Wiley and Sons, Inc., New York, N. Y., 1917.
65. G. von Bandel and H. Gravenhorst, "Behavior of High Temperature Steels During Creep Testing at Temperatures of 500° to 700°C," Arch. Eisenhüttenw. 28, 253, 1957. British I.S. Inst. Translation Service, 1958, No. 587.
66. A. Mendelson and S. S. Manson, "The Extrapolation of Families of Curves by Recurrence Relations With Application to Creep-Rupture Data," J. Basic Engg. 82, 839, 1960.
67. A. Graham and K.F.A. Walles, "Relationships Between Long and Short Time Creep and Tensile Properties of a Commercial Alloy," J. Iron and Steel Inst. 179, 105, 1955.
68. A. Graham, "Numerical Regularities in Uniaxial Deformation," IX Congress International de Mechanique Applique, 8, 227, 1957.
69. K.F.A. Walles and A. Graham, "On the Extrpolation and Scatter of Creep Data," A.R.C., C.P. No. 680, 1963.
70. P. G. Nutting, "A New General Law of Deformation," J. Franklin Inst., 191, 679, 1921.
71. K.F.A. Walles, "The Extrapolation of Creep Rupture Data," A.R.C. 21, 253, October, 1957.
72. A. Graham and K.F.A [illegible]les, "Regularities in Creep and Hot-Fatigue Data," Part I, A.R.C., [illegible] 379, December, 1956.
73. K.F. A. Walles and A. Graham, "Regularities in Creep and Hot-Fatigue Data," Part II, A.R.C.C.P. 380, December, 1956.
74. J. B. Conway, "Properties of Some Refractory Metals, V. Numerical Methods for Creep and Rupture Analyses," GEMP-397, Nuclear Materials and Propulsion Operation, General Electric Company, Cincinnati, Ohio, January 31, 1966.

75. G. P. Tilly, "Fracture Behavior of Two Creep-Resistant Materials Subjected to Cyclic Loading at Elevated Temperature," Proc. Instn. Mech. Engrs., 180, 1, No. 46, 1045, 1965-66.
76. K.F.A. Walles, National Gas Turbine Establishment, Pyestock, Farnborough, Hants, private communication, May, 1967.

APPENDIX A

PARAMETER NOMOGRAPHS

Nomographs are presented for the (1) Larson-Miller, (2) Dorn, and (3) Manson-Haferd parameters. These have been constructed to cover only narrow ranges of the variables. Nomographs for increased ranges would have to be made larger if accurate results are to be assured. Alternately, several nomographs could be constructed each covering specific data ranges.

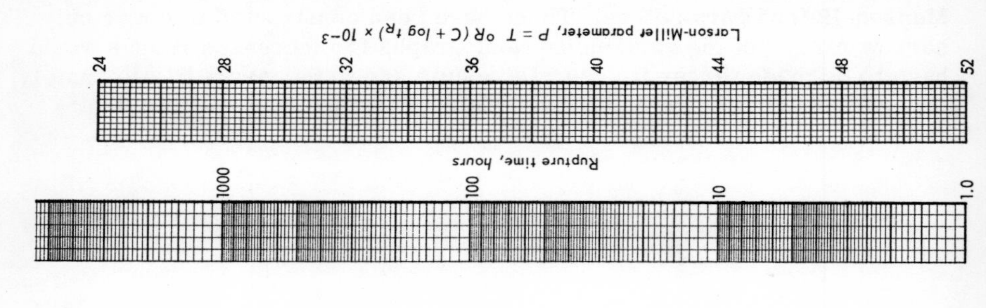

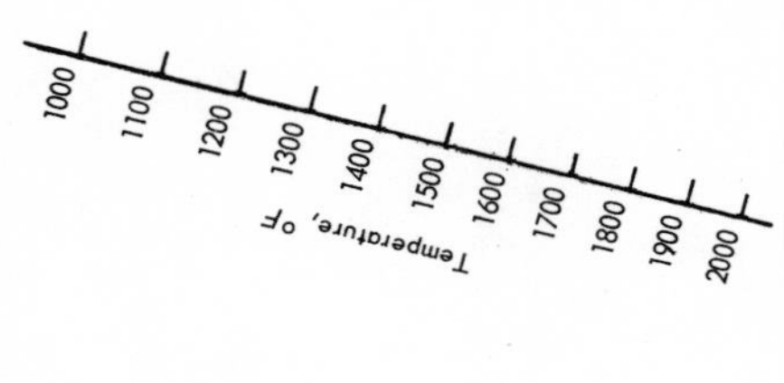

Key:
$P-T-\alpha$
$C-\alpha-t_R$

α scale

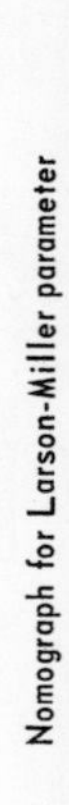
Nomograph for Larson-Miller parameter

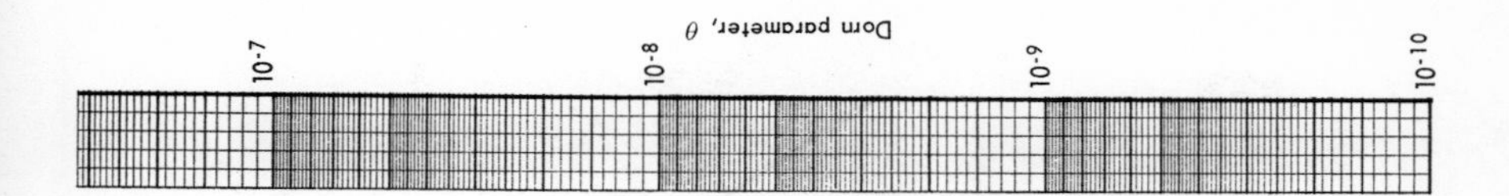

Key:
$\Delta H - T - A$
$A - t_R - \theta$

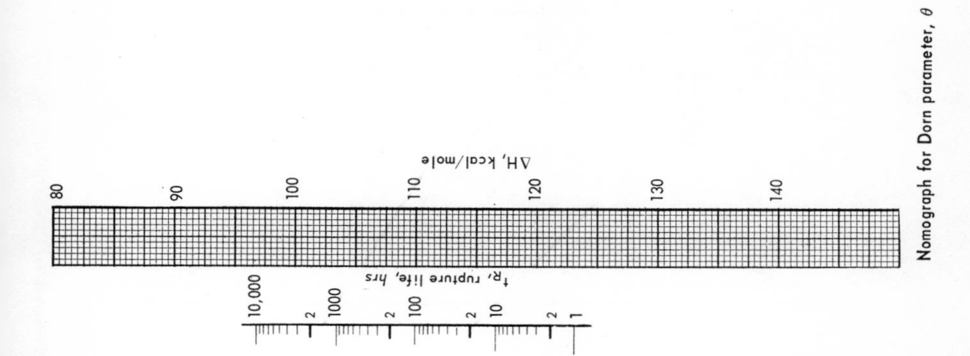

Nomograph for Dorn parameter, θ

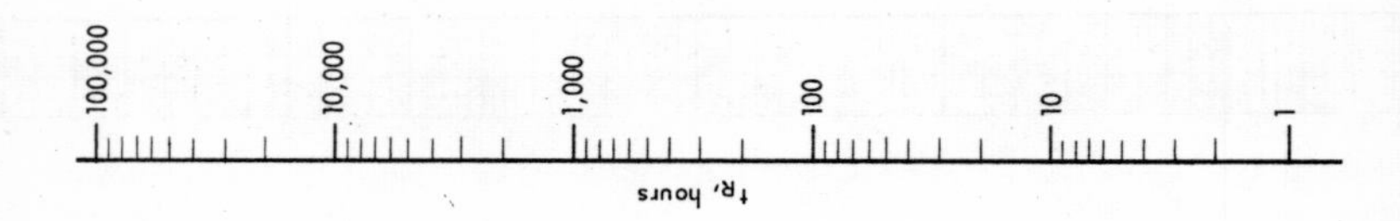

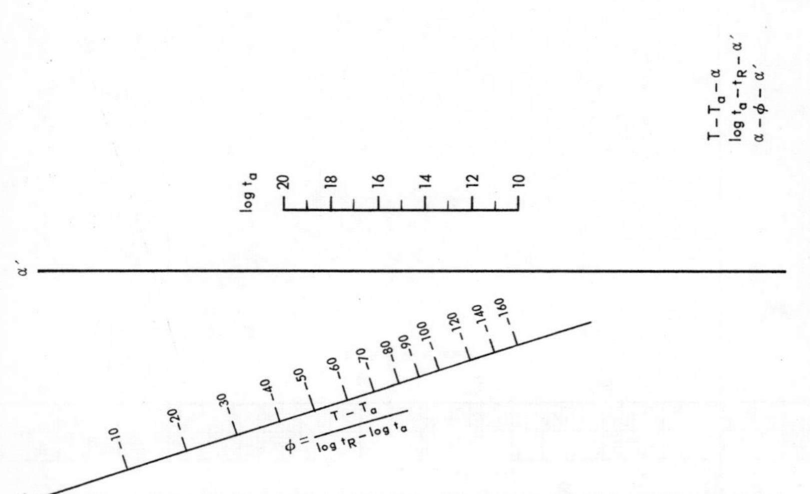

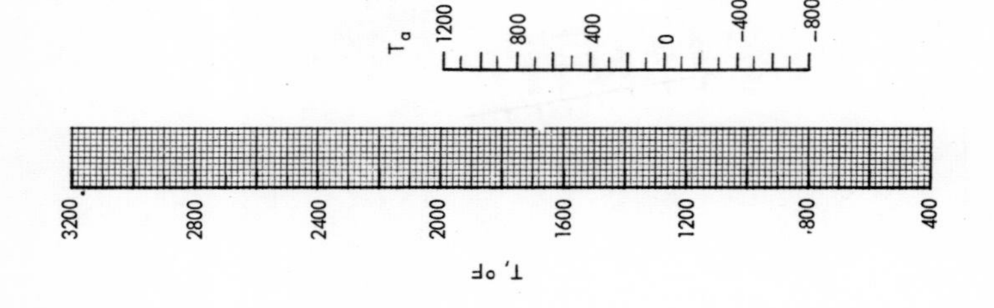

Nomograph for Manson-Haferd parameter

APPENDIX B

TYPICAL STRESS-RUPTURE DATA

A few sets of stress-rupture data have been selected from the literature and are included in this section. These are not provided for use as design data but only for convenience should the reader desire to apply a certain analysis procedure to a specific set of experimental results.

Data are presented for:

347 SS
316 SS
18-8 SS

Inconel 700

S-816
S-590
A-286
"17-22-A"S

Low Cr, Mo, V Steel

Nimonic 80A
Nimonic 90
Silicon Killed Steel

W
W-25Re
Mo

347 Stainless Steel[51]

Temp., °C	Stress, tons/in^2	Rupture Life, hours
600	20.0	320
	19.0	345
	17.0	784
	16.0	1,138
	15.0	3,010
	13.0	3,949
	11.0	7,197
	9.0	18,302
	7.0	37,604
650	18.0	40
	16.0	105
	15.0	297
	12.5	455

347 Stainless Steel[51] (Cont'd)

Temp., °C	Stress, tons/in^2	Rupture Life, hours
	10.0	1,590
	8.5	3,900
	7.0	10,970
	6.0	14,923
	5.0	27,095
	4.0	60,260
700	14.0	28
	12.0	154
	10.0	317
	8.0	1,157
	6.0	2,364
	5.0	4,517
	4.0	9,014
	3.0	37,958
	2.0	57,213
750	7.0	167
	6.0	463
	5.0	593
	4.0	1,336
	3.0	3,550
	2.0	10,269
	1.0	34,798
800	5.0	95
	4.0	137
	3.0	677
	2.0	2,748
	1.0	16,629
850	3.0	69
	2.0	468
	1.0	3,731

316 Stainless Steel[51]

Temp., °C	Stress tons/in^2	Rupture Life, hours
600	17.0	96
	16.0	141
	15.0	512
	14.0	1,105
	13.0	2,344
	12.0	5,670

316 Stainless Steel[51] (Cont'd)

Temp., °C	Stress, tons/in²	Rupture Life, hours
	11.0	20,437
	10.0	29,910
625	12.0	1,437
	11.0	3,004
	10.0	7,980
	8.5	20,582
	7.0	28,180
650	11.5	407
	11.0	453
	10.0	1,059
	8.5	3,561
	7.0	13,953
	6.0	24,305
675	10.0	193
	8.5	1,743
	7.0	3,941
700	10.0	88
	8.5	205
	8.0	233
	7.0	1,010
	6.0	2,857
	5.0	10,698
	4.0	20,140

18-8 Stainless Steel[48]

Temp., °F	Stress, psi	Rupture Life, hours
1200	38,000	1
	32,000	3.759
	28,000	10.97
	18,000	302
	14,000	1000
	11,500	3091
1300	30,000	0.35
	22,000	3.548
	18,500	14.45
	12,500	190.5
	10,000	616.6
	8,000	1995
	6,000	7943

18-8 Stainless Steel[48] (Cont'd.)

Temp., °F	Stress, psi	Rupture Life, hours
1400	22,000	0.47
	18,000	2.512
	14,600	6.456
	7,000	724.4
	6,000	1202
	5,000	3311
1500	15,000	0.32
	11,000	4.571
	9,400	5.888
	8,000	25.7
	6,000	131.8
	5,000	281.8
	4,000	1047
1600	12,000	0.55
	9,000	3.548
	8,000	7.943
	4,000	245.5
	3,500	457.1
	3,000	1000
	2,760	1820
1800	7,000	0.25
	5,000	1.202
	3,550	8.128
	1,650	478.6

Inconel 700[46]

Temp., °F	Stress, psi	Rupture Life, hours
1010	130,000	1596
1035	130,000	634
1060	130,000	376
1090	130,000	147
1120	130,000	33
1120	130,000	38
1150	130,000	16
1160	100,000	829
1180	130,000	7.3
1180	130,000	5.3
1200	100,000	272
1240	100,000	70
1240	130,000	0.5
1280	100,000	17.7

Inconel 700[46] (Cont'd.)

Temp., °F	Stress, psi	Rupture Life, hours
1300	100,000	7.7
1320	70,000	187
1340	70,000	159
1340	100,000	2.2
1370	70,000	69.7
1380	100,000	0.75
1400	70,000	22.7
1400	70,000	19.2
1420	100,000	0.3
1440	70,000	7.2
1440	40,000	1819
1460	40,000	943
1460	70,000	4.7
1490	40,000	327
1500	70,000	1.4
1510	40,000	179
1530	40,000	90.5
1540	70,000	0.6
1560	40,000	40.8
1590	40,000	13.6
1590	40,000	12.1
1615	15,000	2269
1620	20,000	467
1630	20,000	413
1640	40,000	2.9
1660	20,000	131
1660	15,000	587
1670	20,000	99.8
1680	40,000	0.55
1700	40,000	0.4
1700	20,000	27.2
1700	20,000	31.6
1700	15,000	103
1720	20,000	17
1740	20,000	7.2
1740	15,000	20.9
1760	20,000	2.7
1770	15,000	6.8
1780	20,000	2.0
1790	15,000	4.1
1795	15,000	3.1
1800	5,000	123
1820	5,000	122
1860	5,000	20.6

Inconel 700[46] (Cont'd.)

Temp., °F	Stress, psi	Rupture Life, hours
1900	5,000	6.9
1940	5,000	5.6
1980	5,000	0.9
2020	5,000	0.7

S-816[38]

Temp., °F	Stress, psi	Rupture Life, hours
1200	120,000	0.001
	100,000	2.1
	90,000	3.0
	80,000	20.9
	56,000	652.0
1350	90,000	0.092
	90,000	0.01
	80,000	0.12
	75,000	0.43
	70,000	1.0
	60,000	5.9
	50,000	13.0
	50,000	9.3
	40,000	249.0
	40,000	140.0
	35,000	363.0
	30,000	2019.0
1500	85,000	0.0016
	80,000	0.0055
	75,000	0.0061
	70,000	0.02
	60,000	0.061
	45,000	0.37
	40,000	2.23
	34,000	7.9
	30,000	24.8
	25,000	112.0

S-590[38]

Temp., °F	Stress, psi	Rupture Life, hours	Temp., °F	Stress, psi	Rupture Life, hours
1200	100,000	0.0003-0.001*	1600	55,000	0.0028
	90,000	0.043		50,000	0.008
	85,000	0.088		35,000	0.202*
	80,000	0.67		30,000	1.0
	70,000	6.81*		20,000	22.1
	60,000	29.9		15,000	42.3*
	45,000	510.5		15,000	100.5
	43,000	485.0		13,000	223.0*
	39,000	4019.0			
			1700	45,000	0.0025*
1350	80,000	0.0014		40,000	0.007
	75,000	0.016		30,000	0.086
	70,000	0.02		20,000	1.33
	60,000	0.22		15,000	7.90
	50,000	1.88*		10,000	132.6
	43,000	6.75		7,000	550.0
	40,000	9.90			
	30,000	127.5	1900	30,000	0.0015
	23,000	6323.0†		30,000	0.0013
				25,000	0.006
1500	70,000	0.0008		20,000	0.033
	65,000	0.0014		12,500	0.33
	60,000	0.0033*		10,000	1.40
	50,000	0.029		9,900	1.24
	40,000	0.19		4,600	35.5
	30,000	3.3		3,750	81.3
	17,000	1112.0		2,500	228.7*

*Broke at or out of gage marks.
† Test discontinued.

A-286[43]

Temp., °F	Stress, psi	Rupture Life, hours	Temp., °F	Stress, psi	Rupture Life, hours
1000	80,000	4554	1100	75,000	517
	90,000	710		80,000	123
	95,000	294			
	100,000	62	1200	35,000	7131
	110,000	12		45,000	983
				50,000	481
1100	55,000	5244		50,000	711
	60,000	2550		50,000	469
	65,000	1501		50,000	483
	70,000	1861		60,000	196
	70,000	1081		60,000	118

A-286[43] (Cont'd.)

Temp., °F	Stress, psi	Rupture Life, hours	Temp., °F	Stress, psi	Rupture Life, hours
	60,000	176		50,000	44
	62,500	74		55,000	22
	65,000	120	1350	20,000	1232
	70,000	46		25,000	726
	70,000	24		25,000	548
	70,000	45		30,000	187
	75,000	11		30,000	204
	80,000	6		38,000	70
1300	20,000	3538		40,000	50
	25,000	1435		45,000	19
	30,000	764		50,000	6
	35,000	530	1500	10,000	546
	35,000	439		10,000	349
	40,000	213		15,000	46
	42,500	151		20,000	13
	42,500	167			
	42,500	109			
	42,500	93			

"17-22-A"S[50]

Temp., °F	Stress, psi	Rupture Life, hours	Temp., °F	Stress, psi	Rupture Life, hours
1370	10,000	2.8	1285	40,000	0.075
1370		3.7	1260		0.37
1350		4.5	1210		1.35
1315		12.5	1210		1.90
1270		48.5	1175		6.60
1270		51.3	1150		13.6
1235		129.8	1120		39.5
1210		228.7	1100		83.0
1160		1301	1075		205.7
1400	20,000	0.1	1140	80,000	0.033
1375		0.12	1070		1.5
1320		1.0	1045		2.5
1270		3.9	1030		5.7
1230		13.3	1000		15
1190		48.0	985		82
1170		102.7	970		109.2
1140		242.1	970		433
1100		987			

Low Alloy Cr, Mo, V Steel[49]

Temp., °F	Stress, psi	Rupture Life, hours	Temp., °F	Stress, psi	Rupture Life, hours
900	90,000	37	1100	70,000	1
	82,000	975		60,500	18
	78,000	3,581		50,000	167
	70,000	9,878		40,000	615
1000	80,000	7		29,000	2,220
	75,000	17		22,000	6,637
	68,000	213	1200	40,000	19
	60,000	1,493		30,000	102
	56,000	2,491		25,000	125
	49,000	5,108		20,000	331
	43,000	7,390	1350	20,000	3.7
	38,000	10,447		15,000	8.9
				10,000	31.8

Nimonic 80A[47]

Temp., °C	Stress, tons/in^2	Rupture Life, hours
650	30	274
	28	481
	26	898
	24	1,292
	22	2,655
	20	5,270
	18	8,171
	16	13,386
700	23	208
	21	443
	19	683
	16	1,735
	13	4,836
	10	10,896
	7	34,053
750	17	138
	16	230
	14	419
	12	852
	10	1,857
	8	4,450
	6	13,089
	4	22,657

Nimonic 90[47]

Temp., °C	Stress, tons/in^2	Rupture Life, hours
650	35	106
	32	347
	30	850
	28	2,268
	26	4,111
	24	6,443
	23	5,375
	20	15,294
700	28	108
	25	328
	22	1,007
	19	2,545
	13	12,094
	12.5	20,399
750	22	120
	19	273
	17	590
	14	1,299
	12	2,547
	10	7,593
	7	22,159
815	13	132
	11	263
	9	587
	7	1,315
	5.5	3,342
	4	6,830
870	7	125
	5	528
	3	1,920
	2*	16,292

*Doubtful result because of interruption during test.

Silicon-killed Steel[44]

Temp., °C	Stress, tons/in^2	Rupture Life, hours
475	14	23
	12	108
	11	411
	10	803
450	16	27
	14	151
	12	800
	11	1,782
	10	4,116
425	18	75
	16	402
	14	1,461
	12	8,117
	11	17,793
400	22	24
	20	80
	18	720
	18	875
	16	1,400
	14	23,180
375	22	390
	20	2,905
	18	12,290

Tungsten[15]

Temp., °C	Stress, psi	Rupture Life, hours	Temp., °C	Stress, psi	Rupture Life, hours
1600	4,800	160	2400	650	146
	6,000	30.9		800	61.4
	7,000	14.7		1,000	17.5
	8,000	6.45		1,200	9.25
1800	3,000	150		1,500	3.09
	4,000	28.4	2600	400	123
	4,800	7.6		500	43.4
2000	1,500	256		650	15
	2,000	63.1		800	4.77
	2,500	17.6		1,200	0.78
	3,000	6.7	2800	250	144
2200	1,000	237		300	51.9
	1,200	119		400	14
	1,500	40.7		500	4.3
	2,000	7.72	3000	300	2.8

Tungsten-25 Rhenium[15]

Temp., °C	Stress, psi	Rupture Life, hours
1600	10,000	24
	8,000	62.1
	7,000	119
	6,000	195
	4,800	513
2000	5,000	2.4
	3,000	21.9
	2,000	107
	1,500	266
2200	800	252
2400	1,000	7.3
	800	27.7
	650	33.1
	500	82
2600	500	7.04

Molybdenum[15]

Temp., °C	Stress, psi	Rupture Life, hours
1200	16,000	0.08
	12,500	0.52
	12,500	0.52
	12,250	0.75
	11,750	0.83
	12,000	1.51
	11,000	2.21
	10,500	3.03
	10,000	4.36
	9,000	12.0
1600	3,500	0.52
	3,000	2.34
	3,000	2.61
	2,500	5.54
	2,000	24.9
1800	2,000	0.58
	1,800	1.94
	1,600	2.78
	1,600	2.89
	1,500	4.22
	1,350	5.28
	1,250	9.8
2000	1,100	1.4
	850	5
	650	17.3
	500	44.1
2200	850	0.34
	750	0.53
	700	0.58
	600	1.28
	500	2.53
	450	2.72
	445	4.51
	450	5.72
	400	6.47
	200	99.6
	200	133
2400	400	0.31
	400	0.4
	300	1.65
	300	1.7
	225	5.03
	225	5.5